Principles and Applications in Aquatic Microbiology

Proceedings of
Rudolfs Research Conference
Rutgers—The State University
New Brunswick, New Jersey

Principles and Applications in Aquatic Microbiology

edited by
H. HEUKELEKIAN, *Chairman*
and NORMAN C. DONDERO, *Professor*
Department of Environmental Science
Rutgers—The State University

John Wiley & Sons, Inc.   *New York • London • Sydney*

Library of Congress Catalog Card Number: 64-15423

Printed in the United States of America

CHAIRMEN OF THE SESSIONS

CLAUDE E. ZOBELL
Scripps Institution of Oceanography
University of California, La Jolla, California

DAVID PRAMER
Department of Agricultural Microbiology
Rutgers - The State University

FRANK H. JOHNSON
Department of Biology
Princeton University, Princeton, N.J.

HARRY W. SEELEY
Division of Bacteriology,
Department of Dairy and Food Science
Cornell University, Ithaca, New York

H. HEUKELEKIAN
Department of Environmental Science
Rutgers - The State University

HENRY J. VOGEL
Institute of Microbiology
Rutgers - The State University

This conference was supported, in part,

by the

WILLEM RUDOLFS MEMORIAL FUND

and by the funds from the

UNITED STATES PUBLIC HEALTH SERVICE

GRANT, WP-78

Preface

The first of the Rudolfs Research Conferences, which was held in 1960, was devoted to the topic The Principles of Colloidal Behavior and Their Application to Water Sanitation. The second conference, in 1961, dealt with the subject Public Health Hazards of Microbial Pollution of Water. We chose for this year the theme of Principles and Applications in Aquatic Microbiology as another of the many facets in the science and technology of water.

The term "aquatic" is used in its broadest connotation and embraces microbial phenomena, be they in lakes, reservoirs, streams, estuaries, oceans, or in sewage treatment processes. The differences in these various environments are merely quantitative with respect to organic and inorganic nutrients. A major objective is to get a comprehension of the organisms and their activities in these environments.

Work of this nature has been relatively meager in the past and it is hoped that this conference will, in some measure, foster research in this area. A disproportionate amount of work in aquatic microbiology, especially on fresh waters, has been concerned with enteric microorganisms in general, and with coliforms as an index of pollution in particular. Important as the public health phases are, we all recognize that there is a great number of other types of microorganisms which are of concern, some perhaps native to water, others entering from the soil and air, and still others introduced by man-made pollution. These organisms play an important role in the transformations of organic and inorganic materials; under natural conditions at a rather slow pace, but under artificial conditions, at an accelerated rate.

In addition to selecting topics dealing specifically with some of the microorganisms and their activities which we consider to play an important role in the aquatic environment, we also "crossed disciplinary lines" to include subjects of indirect interest, because the techniques and insights available from these areas (rumen microbiology, for example) can contribute greatly to the solution of our problems in aquatic microbiology. Accordingly, we went somewhat afield in securing our speakers. Many other significant topics could have been included had time permitted. We were, indeed, fortunate in obtaining the experts and cannot adequately express the appreciation they deserve for the efforts they have exerted.

Some time after the plans for the program of this conference had been formulated, a paper was prepared for the
conference, Global Aspects of Applied Microbiology, held
in Stockholm, Sweden, in July 1963. The paper, Trends
and Needs of Research in Aquatic Microbiology, embodied
some of the views which were the basis for the formulation
of the program of this Rudolfs Research Conference. Although
the paper was not presented at the Rudolfs Conference, it is
included with some modification, as the last paper of the
proceedings, not as a summary but as an apologia in extenso,
as it were.

Acknowledgments

The undertaking of a conference of this kind required the cooperation of many persons. The contributions made by the speakers and of the chairmen were conspicuously noteworthy and deserving of appreciation. The efforts put forth by a number of others were, in general, less conspicuous, but also essential for the execution of arrangements and the handling of the myriad burdensome, and often troublesome, details which accompany an endeavor of this sort. While the Proceedings themselves will attest to the contributions of the speakers, we wish to acknowledge with gratitude the generous participation of others in the arrangements which supported the conference and the publication of the Proceedings. Without their contribution there is no doubt that the conference would have been more difficult to carry out, if not impossible, and less pleasant for the participants.

It is usual to acknowledge the services, willing or unwilling, of the departmental graduate students in an affair of this kind in a collective fashion. We shall depart from custom to list, as follows, the graduate students of the Department of Environmental Science who contributed generously of their time with industry and initiative: Osman M. Aly, Ronald D. Barbaro, Jeanette Chemasko, Emil J. Genetelli, Edward F. Gilardi, Constantine J. Gregory, Frederick C. Lorentz, David T. Lordi, Martin C. Manger, Harold Okrend, T. B. S. Prakasam, Frank P. Terraglio, Richard F. Unz, and Antra Zarins.

A not inconsiderable contribution to the conference was made by Miss Elizabeth M. Crenner and Miss Mary F. Hayden, who cheerfully and efficiently handled many of the preliminary arrangements and much of the correspondence.

The aid of the Rutgers University Extension Division in the persons of Mr. Joseph Czapp and Mr. Edmund Jenusaitis and their assistants was indispensable for arrangements pertaining to living, dining, and the auditorium, as well as for the printing of programs and announcements.

The discussions following the presented papers were expertly recorded and transcribed by Mr. George A. Sakson.

The refreshments for a pleasant evening social hour were provided through the courtesy of the New Brunswick Scientific Company.

In the preparation of the Proceedings of the conference for

publication, sincere appreciation is due to Mrs. John A. Cushing and Miss Ethel Orlick of our department for their forbearance and diligence.

To the entire staff of the Department of Environmental Science, we owe gratitude for their comments and criticism during the development of the program and for their invaluable aid and cooperation during the conference itself.

H. Heukelekian
N.C. Dondero, Editors
Department of Environmental Science
Rutgers University
New Brunswick, N.J.

Contents

CONTENTS

Principles and Applications in Aquatic Microbiology

1

HYDROCARBON STRUCTURE: ITS EFFECT
ON BACTERIAL UTILIZATION OF ALKANES

Eva J. McKenna and R. E. Kallio
Department of Microbiology
University of Iowa

Utilization of various aliphatic hydrocarbons by bacteria and other microorganisms has been a recognized phenomenon for about 70 years. From earlier studies, largely conducted with impure hydrocarbon substrates and frank mixtures of hydrocarbons, little information could be gleaned regarding the specificities of diverse organisms and the alkane substrates they were capable of utilizing for growth. In recent years, with the advent of more sophisticated preparative and analytical tools, the avalability of pure hydrocarbons has become more general. Additionally, increased interest in the general area of microbial hydrocarbon oxidation has increased and through recent studies many early notions have been radically revised.

We began in our laboratories some years ago, a study directed at the mechanisms involved in microbial paraffin oxidations. As an ancillary part of the investigation, we have been gathering a fairly extensive array of hydrocarbons in an attempt to establish, if possible, the parameters of alkane structures amenable to microbial attack. This report outlines some of our results in the area. Studies on enzymatic mechanisms are still going on but do not seem to fit the framework of this conference.

In the beginning, we were concerned with tests involving organisms isolated from hydrocarbon enrichments because of our preoccupation with the older literature. Gradually, it became evident to us (and to those few others in the field) that the literature had let us astray -- hydrocarbon utilizing

organisms are not rare and specialized types which are
isolatable only from conventional enrichments. What developed as our screening progressed was, in fact, the feeling
that hydrocarbon utilization is a character widespread in the
microbial world. These comments deserve substantiation.
We chose, as an important parameter of microbial alkane-
utilization, the ability of an organism to grow at the expense
of hydrocarbon in an otherwise mineral medium. That this
measure of utilization may be less than ideal will be dealt
with later.

It is now clear to us that many organisms chosen at
random may well be more diversified with respect to ability
to degrade alkanes than microorganisms selectively chosen
from enrichments. A very large number of bacteria, yeasts,
and fungi from culture collections were tested for the characteristic, of which from 6 to 20 per cent of the many groups
of organisms tested showed the capacity to degrade alkanes.
Similar results have been found by Kester (1) at the University of Texas.

A more pertinent and interesting part of our general
investigations was directed at utilization in terms of molecular configuration -- an attempt to determine the ground rules
of microbial enzyme specificities. It is, of course, evident
that in the longer chain alkanes, say 12 to 16 carbon atoms,
the possibilities for isomerization are very great.

In what follows, much data will be presented as the best
averages of results we could objectively arrive at in as-
sembling the findings. Figure 1, for example, compares
growth of a "hydrocarbon" bacterium with Nocardia corallina
(one of many Nocardia species tested). It is evident that
Nocardia generally are more versatile with respect to growth
at the expense of hexadecane isomers. With these notions
in mind, we chose to study some 19 test organisms com-
prising five species of Micrococcus, four species of Mycobacterium, five species of Pseudomonas, and five species of
Nocardia - a total of only six organisms in the test group were
isolated from hydrocarbon enrichments. Organisms were
tested in mineral media with the appropriate hydrocarbon
added and, in questionable cases, incubation was for four weeks.

Results from studies with hexadecane isomers raised
several interesting questions: (1) what is the effect of more
than one methyl substituent on a normal alkane chain, and
(2) what is the effect of larger hydrocarbon substitutions on

Effect of isomerization on biological availability

Compound	Micrococcus cerificans	Nocardia corallina
n̲-Hexadecane	+	+
2-Methylpentadecane	+	+
3-Methylpentadecane	+	+
4-Methylpentadecane	+	+
5-Methylpentadecane	+	+
6-Methylpentadecane	+	+
7-Methylpentadecane	+	+
8-Methylpentadecane	+	+
3-Ethyltetradecane	+	+
4-Propyltridecane	0	+
6-Propyltridecane	0	+
7-Propyltridecane	0	+
5-Butyldodecane	0	+
6-Pentylundecane	0	+

Fig. 1: Growth = + , no growth = 0

an alkane chain? Figure 2 shows average data obtained with a few multiply methyl-branched hydrocarbons. Pristane (2, 6, 10, 14-tetramethyl pentadecane) occurs in nature, as does the methyl branch pattern of this hydrocarbon; pristane occurs in basking shark liver and in other natural locales. Thus, the utilization of this material might well have been predicted; the more so since a similar pattern of methyl branches occurs in rubber, squalene, portions of carotenes, and in the plant alcohol, phytol.

When more than one methyl group appears on a carbon atom, particularly if the carbon atom is the penultimate carbon, the resulting hydrocarbon is extremely resistant to microbial degradation (Fig. 3). Perhaps even more significant is the finding that these (and other hydrocarbons possessing neopentyl groups) yield no growth in enrichment cultures. Even in those cases where the dimethyl carbon

Branching vs. Availability

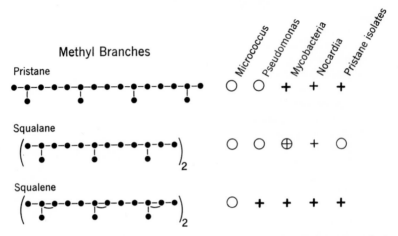

Fig. 2—Growth = + (the relative weight of the symbol indicates relative amounts of growth), no growth = 0, questionable growth = ⊕.

atom appears well inside the alkane chain, the quaternary carbon exerts a considerable effect on the microbial availability of hydrocarbons. In the case, for example, of a series of 1-phenyl alkanes the following was noted (Fig. 4): All seventeen of these test organisms grew profusely at the expense of 1-phenyl decane but it is clear that the insertion of even one methyl group (1-phenyl-4-methyl decane) renders the hydrocarbon unavailable to many organisms; a quaternary carbon atom at the 4 position makes the hydrocarbon highly refractory to bacterial oxidation, as measured by growth.

Groups larger than methyl, i. e., propyl or phenyl likewise appear to prevent utilization. For instance, a limited series of propyl-branched alkanes were available to many nocardia and mycobacteria so long as only one propyl branch was present. Two propyl branches appear to make the molecule unavailable to these bacteria. The situation with respect to phenyl substituted alkanes is somewhat more complex and

Branching vs. Availability

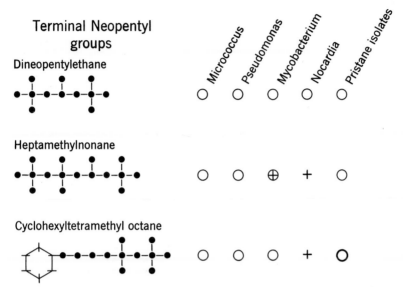

Fig. 3—Growth = + (the relative weight of the symbol indicates relative amounts of growth), no growth = 0, questionable growth = ⊕.

will have to be approached along with other factors involved in the structures of hydrocarbons tested for microbial growth sustaining properties. A small digression or two here may be of some interest. First, it is known that some microorganisms attack alkanes diterminally to yield dioic acids. Presumably, a phenyl group at one end of an alkane will prevent omega-oxidation and essentially "force" the oxidations to take place on the alkyl portion of phenyl alkanes. Detergents of the alkyl benzene sulfonate type may contain hydrocarbon moieties similar to the structures discussed here and it may be possible to extrapolate these data to the problem of de - tergent "hardness". No claim is made for any degree of such extrapolation although it seems significant that current consensus in the detergent industry indicates alkyl benzene sulfonate degradation begins at the alkyl portion of the molecule.

In any case, a number of phenyl alkanes were assayed for their ability to support growth of a variety of organisms. An intriguing preliminary finding was the fact that, even in a

Effect of Branching

	1-Phenyldecane	1-Phenyl-4-methyldecane	1-Phenyl-4,4-dimethyldecane
Micrococcus cerificans HO1-N	+	O	O
Micrococcus cerificans HO3	+	O	O
Micrococcus cerificans HO4	+	O	O
Micrococcus cerificans S18.2	+	O	O
Micrococcus cerificans S14.1	+	O	O
Pseudomonas aeruginosa 119JWF	+	O	O
Pseudomonas aeruginosa 191JWF	+	O	O
Pseudomonas aeruginosa SOL20JS	+	O	O
Mycobacterium phlei No. 451	+	+	O
Mycobacterium fortuitum No. 389	+	+	O
Mycobacterium smegmatis No. 422	+	+	⊕
Mycobacterium rhodochrous No. 382	+	+	O
Nocardia opaca	+	+	+
Nocardia rubra	+	+	+
Nocardia erythropolis	+	+	⊕
Nocardia polychromogenes	+	+	+
Nocardia corallina	+	+	+

Fig. 4—Growth = + (the relative weight of the symbol indicates relative amounts of growth), no growth = 0, questionable growth = ⊕.

group of similar organisms, considerable variation existed with respect to the utilization of these materials. Six strains of alkane-utilizing micrococci were tested for their ability to grow at the expense of a series of phenyl alkanes. Whereas all six strains grew at the expense of 1-phenyl decane, two, remarkably, did not utilize 1-phenyl undecane or 1-phenyl dodecane. Moving the phenyl group along the carbon chain of the alkyl moiety exerts considerable effect -- 6-phenyl alkanes are used as carbon sources by only a few of the strains tested; and even this "utilization" is of a very questionable nature, i.e., very slight (apparent) increase in the number of cells inoculated. Figure 5 illustrates results from a large series of tests -- hydrocarbons have been arranged into groups determined by the length of the alkyl chain.

Effect of Degree and
Position of Substituents

	Micrococcus	Pseudomonas	Mycobacterium	Nocardia
Phenyldecanes				
1-ϕ-Decane	+	+	+	+
1-ϕ-4-Methyldecane	O	O	+	+
1-ϕ-4, 4-Dimethyldecane	O	O	O	+
Phenylundecanes				
1-ϕ-Undecane	+	⊕	+	+
2-ϕ-Undecane	O	O	+	+
2-ϕ-2-Methyldecane	O	O	+	+
6-ϕ-Undecane	O	O	⊕	+
Phenyldodecanes				
1-ϕ-Dodecane	+	+	+	+
2-ϕ-Dodecane	O	O	+	+
3-ϕ-Dodecane	O	O	+	+
6-ϕ-Dodecane	O	O	+	+

Fig. 5—Growth = + (the relative weight of the symbol indicates relative amounts of growth), no growth = 0, questionable growth = ⊖.

Effects of degree of substitution and position of substituents is very clear, especially with respect to the phenyl placement along the alkane chain; thus all test organisms utilize 1-phenyl dodecane -- utilization of the phenyl alkane decreases as the phenyl is moved along the skeleton to the C_6 position. Figure 6 illustrates utilization of phenyl alkanes and the data (and structures) have been arranged in terms of the length of free alkyl chain. Definite indications of an "odd-even" effect are noticeable here -- an effect which appeared to substantiate data obtained some years ago by Webley and co-workers (1955). A careful scrutiny of the test organisms in the hydro-carbon survey with phenyl fatty acids from benzoic to 11-phenyl undecanoic acid, however, revealed no such odd-even effect except in the case of a few Nocardia. That the length of the total alkyl chain is not the sole criterion of availability

Ø-Alkane Structure vs. Availability

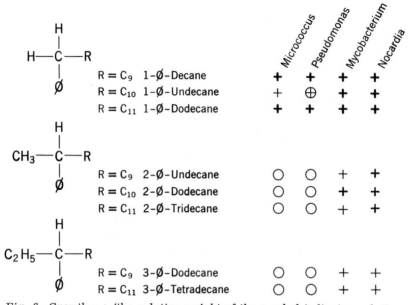

Fig. 6—Growth = + (the relative weight of the symbol indicates relative amounts of growth), no growth = 0, questionable growth = ⊖.

is shown in Fig. 7 where the data and structural formulae have again been rearranged - - this time in such a way as to compare hydrocarbons with equal lengths of "free alklyl" chain. It is immediately clear that compounds with equivalent alkyl chains are not equally available to the test organisms. The Figure 8 is a summary tabulation and shows:

(1) effect of placement of the substituent groups of the alkane skeleton,
(2) effect of substituent size,
(3) effect of "total" chain length of the alkane skeleton.

The choice of growth as a parameter of hydrocarbon utilization was made because it seemed clear-cut results might ordinarily obtain, i. e., growth or no growth on a given hydrocarbon substrate in an otherwise defined medium. Manometric analysis of hydrocarbon oxidation poses some intriguing questions which should be raised here even if they

Ø-Alkane structure vs. Availability

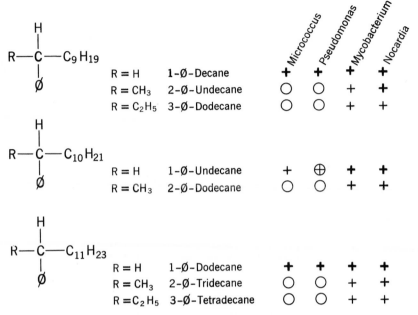

Fig. 7—Growth = (the relative weight of the symbol indicates relative amounts of growth), no growth = 0, questionable growth = ⊖.

cannot be answered. Kester and Foster, and Leadbetter and Foster (3, 4, 5) have shown that a number of alkanes are oxidized by organisms for which the alkanes may not serve as carbon sources. How widespread this phenomenon is, among the many classes and types of hydrocarbons and microorganisms, is not known. In any event, if "utilization" is defined as oxidation without concomitant growth then, clearly, the two methods may yield quite different utilization patterns.

There appears to be a problem with certain hydrocarbons (and perhaps other substances) which may, in some way, increase the endogenous respiration of the test organisms without being oxidized. If a manometric experiment is clean-cut and the experimental oxygen consumption is well in excess of a low auto-respiratory rate then the conventional technique of subtracting the latter from the former may be valid. On the other hand, if oxygen is consumed by an organism in the presence of hydrocarbon (which does not support growth) at

Substituent size

Structure	R	Hydrocarbon	Micrococcus	Pseudomonas	Mycobacterium	Nocardia
C_{11} chain $CH_3-\overset{H}{\underset{R}{C}}-C_9H_{19}$	$C_5H_{11}^-$	6-Methylpentadecane	+	+	+	+
	$\emptyset-$	2-$\emptyset$-Undecane	O	O	$\oplus$	+
$CH_3-\overset{\emptyset}{\underset{CH_3}{C}}-C_9H_{19}$		2-$\emptyset$- 2-Methylundecane	O	O	$\oplus$	$\oplus$
$C_5H_{11}-\overset{H}{\underset{R}{C}}-C_5H_{11}$	$C_5H_{11}^-$	6-Pentylundecane	O	O	+	+
	$\emptyset-$	6-$\emptyset$-Undecane	O	O	$\oplus$	$\oplus$
C_{12} chain $CH_3-\overset{H}{\underset{R}{C}}-C_{10}H_{11}$	$C_4H_9^-$	5-Methylpentadecane	+	+	+	+
	$\emptyset-$	2-$\emptyset$- Dodecane	O	O	+	+
C_{13} chain $CH_3-\overset{H}{\underset{R}{C}}-C_{11}H_{23}$	$C_3H_7^-$	4-Methylpentadecane	+	+	+	+
	$\emptyset-$	2-$\emptyset$-Tridecane	O	O	$\oplus$	+
$C_3H_7-\overset{H}{\underset{C_3H_7}{C}}-C_9H_{19}$		4-Propyltridecane	O	O	+	+
C_{14} chain $C_2H_5-\overset{H}{\underset{R}{C}}-C_{11}H_{23}$	CH_3^-	3-Methylpentadecane	+	+	+	+
	$C_2H_5^-$	3-Ethyltetradecane	O	O	$\oplus$	+
	$\emptyset-$	3-$\emptyset$-Tetradecane	O	O	$\oplus$	$\oplus$

Fig. 8—Growth = +, no growth = 0, questionable growth = $\oplus$.

a level only slightly, but definitely, above the endogenous, the question of true oxidation versus stimulation of auto-respiration may be properly raised and would require clarification. Unhappily, to make a choice between the two possibilities requires more sophisticated techniques and may not lend itself to routine assaying. It should, however, be worked out in selected cases to ascertain the occurrence of the phenomenon.

LITERATURE CITED

1.   Kester, A.S. 1961. Studies on the oxidation of hydro-carbons by microorganisms. Ph. D. Thesis, University of Texas.

2.   Webley, D.M., R. B. Duff, and V. C. Farmer. 1955. Beta-oxidation of fatty acids by Nocardia opaca. J. Gen. Microbiol. 13:361-369.

3.   Kester, A. S., and J. W. Foster. 1963. Diterminal oxidation of long-chain alkanes by bacteria. J. Bacteriol. 85:859-869.

4.   Leadbetter, E. R., and J. W. Foster. 1960. Bacterial oxidation of gaseous alkanes. Arch. Mikrobiol. 35:92-104.

DISCUSSION

Dr. Melvin A. Benarde (Rutgers Univ.): Do the designations heavy, medium, and light growth represent growth after one month of incubation, and, after adaptation in the various experiments, are you able to reduce this incubation period?

Dr. Kallio: Under our conditions, when there was utilization, it usually occurred reasonably rapidly; that is, within a week we could make our notations and then hold everything for a month, and there were very few instances of getting reasonable growth at the end of a month that we had not seen by the end of a week. When I say profuse growth, I mean it would compare very favorably to growth in a defined medium with 2.0 per cent glucose constituting the carbon source.

Dr. Benarde: Then the growth takes place rapidly in the beginning?

Dr. Kallio: Yes.

Dr. André R. Brillard (Sun Oil Co.): Dr. Kallio, you
stated that the utilization of alkanes is widespread throughout many groups. However, there is a lack of mention of
organisms of the family Enterobacteriaceae in general. In
your experience, is there utilization of alkanes by any of
these organisms, specifically Escherichia?

Second, have you seen utilization of alkanes by some of
the Clostridium?

Dr. Kallio: We have not tested any of the Escherichia
group. Some Japanese workers have done so and, if I
remember correctly, they found no utilization by this group.
I would quess that there are some groups which do not have
the capacity and this may be one of them.

Regarding the anaerobes, we have done nothing in anaerobic alkane utilization since the experiments of Dr. Hanson
in our laboratory, who essentially showed that we could not
get oxidation of alkanes anaerobically in the presence of
nitrate, with nitrate reducers, and the more recent O^{18}
work, both in our laboratory and in Jackson Foster's laboratory. There appears to be a mechanism by which heptane,
for example, can be anaerobically oxidized to the corresponding heptene by an extract of Pseudomonas, but we have done
nothing on these anaerobic pathways.

Moreover, we are presently involved in some experiments
using the same organisms as Dr. Senez and we find that there
are probably several ways in which heptane can be utilized
by this organism. One of them is through oxygenation; that
is, by a gaseous oxygen-incorporating enzyme system,
very probably, we think, passing through 1-hydroperoxide.

I would quess that there is very little anaerobic decomposition of saturated alkanes. However, we have not done
any surveying in that field.

Dr. Brillard: Would you comment upon the possibility of
utilization of the alkanes by the Enterobacteriaceae?

Dr. Kallio: No.

Professor E. G. Mulder: (Netherlands): Are you quite
sure that your micrococci are real micrococci and not
arthrobacters? We have found many "micrococci" in soil
and they all appeared to be arthrobacters. Now, the fact

that your other strains which are able to decompose these alkanes included mycobacteria and cocci is in agreement, because these organisms are very close to the arthrobacters; they are almost similar morphologically. That is my first question.

The second question is: Is it correct to confine your definition to the breakdown of the alkanes in inorganic media? There is an observation by Jensen that the mycobacteria can decompose other compounds in the presence of proteins or amino acids but not in inorganic media.

Dr. Kallio: In answer to your first question, we are reasonably sure they are micrococci. I appreciate the relationship between the nocardias, the mycobacteria, and the arthrobacters, but there are other groups not related to these which are still good utilizers of hydrocarbons.

The ability of the nocardias and mycobacteria to utilize branched alkanes may not be very surprising in view of the occurrence of various branched fatty acids in these organisms. A great number of those exotic methyl branched compounds that I showed you have been isolated from extracts of mycobacteria.

To your second question, I shall say that, because of stricture of time, I left out the interesting and important notion of co-oxidation. There are a series of observations which indicate that substances may be utilized in complex media or in the presence of other carbon sources. Pseudomonas methanica will oxidize ethane, but will not oxidize ethane in the absence of methane. There are a great number of cases like this. We did not attempt to analyze for these in order to avoid introducing new factors into the assays which multiply the number of observations and of pieces of equipment to the point where they became too unwieldy.

Mr. James E. Zajic (Kerr-McGee Oil Industries): Do you think that, as the chain length decreases, that the number of species of microbes which are able to utilize or oxidize those hydrocarbons for growth is more restricted?

Dr. Kallio: It appears that, as the chain lengths of normal alkanes shorten, there is, in fact, less utilization. There are far fewer cases of profuse growth in enrichments, and the like, under these conditions, and I think that there may be some physical factor involved. In support of this I shall

cite a few experiments which we have done: namely, that
if you decrease the temperature by, for example, 10 degrees,
you observe an increase in the number of alkanes used by an
organism. If the limit, going from hexadecane down to, say,
propane falls at octane, by dropping the temperature 10
degrees the limit can be decreased by a few more carbons.
This also lowers the vapor pressure and has a few other
consequences, but we do not know precisely what determines
specificity or toxicity. I like to think in terms of micelle
formation, possibly in the lipids of the cytoplasmic membrane,
but I have no supporting data.

Dr. A. H. Romano (Univ. of Cincinnati): Where there
are differences in patterns of utilization among organisms
as, for example, among strains of the same species such as
Micrococcus, would you speculate that the differences are
due to the actual differences in the enzyme equipment or due
to something such as permeability?

Dr. Kallio: I do not know. I prefer to think that enzyme
specificity is involved because it would be very difficult for
me to conceive of a permeability mechanism which would
prevent the ingress of nonane but not of octane, which differs
by one carbon atom, or which would permit the ingress of
1-phenyl decane but not 2-phenyl undecane, for example. We
have looked very carefully at the relationships of various
paraffins and built models, and so forth. Some of these compounds look so much alike that there is no way that we can
recognize any significant difference in the models. There is
no complicated folding permitted in one but not permitted in
the other model, so that we cannot make any generalizations
on this basis. Thus, we like to think that utilization must
have something to do with the enzymatic machinery. Perhaps
the movement of the phenyl group along the chain prevents
the evanescent juxtaposition of the substrate and the enzyme.

2

MICROBIOLOGY OF PESTICIDES
AND RELATED HYDROCARBONS

Martin Alexander
Laboratory of Soil Microbiology
Department of Agronomy
Cornell University

Soil microbiologists have been investigating the microbiology of pesticides for some time, but only in very recent
years has the need for these studies become truly urgent.
There is no need to reiterate the cause of this great interest,
but I shall review briefly certain facets of the topic of microbiology of pesticides without going into detail. Time does not
permit an adequate review of the entire field, but certain
general conclusions will be brought out prior to a detailed
discussion of that topic probably of greatest current concern
to the soil and the aquatic microbiologist, namely the microbial decomposition of these compounds and their persistence
in nature.

Three types of chemicals have been examined by microbiologists interested in the interactions between the microflora
and pesticides. These are insecticides, fungicides, and
herbicides. Compounds indentified by abbreviations or common names are listed in an appendix to this paper. Considerable attention has been given to the influence of these com -
pounds on microbial processes in the soil or on the development of specific microorganisms. The chief techniques employed to assess the antimicrobial effects involve comparisons
of CO_2 production, O_2 consumption, number of microorganisms or rate of nitrification in either treated or untreated
soil, or in laboratory cultures. No single procedure is entirely adequate to characterize the influence of the foreign
chemical, but by judicious use of several tests a picture of

the possible alterations of the microflora can be obtained.

Herbicides, the first group of these synthetic materials, are, as a rule, applied in the particular environment at levels of a few parts per million. At such concentrations, the chemicals have a profound influence upon susceptible plants, but microorganisms or microbial transformations seem little affected at the low levels recommended for weed control. Inhibitions are indeed noted, but the quantities of the herbicide required for a significant suppression of the microflora or its activities commonly far exceed those used in practice. The data in Table 1 are merely part of a large accumulation of experimental results, many chapters and verses which indicate the absence of a serious deleterious action upon the prominent microbiological processes in nature.

TABLE 1:   Conc. of herbicides required for toxicity

Reaction	lb/acre 2,4-D	MCPA	2,4,5-T
CO_2 evolution	100	250	250
Nitrification	50	250	250
Ammonification	100	–	–
Total count	200	250	250
Rhizobium spp.	100	100	100

Insecticides are applied at somewhat higher rates than herbicides, and there are many reports of effects of this group of chemicals on the population of soil microorganisms. Partial inhibitions of one or another group, based upon total counts or upon measurement of rates of biochemical change, have been demonstrated in certain soils with many of the insecticides, but these inhibitions are rarely dramatic.

Chemicals selected for use as fungicides, on the other hand, pass through a careful screening process to ensure their antimicrobial usefulness, and they are applied at concentrations sufficiently high to eradicate not only a large segment of the population of pathogens but also a significant proportion of the saprophytic fungi, bacteria, and actino-mycetes as well. Many of the alterations in the composition of the soil microflora induced by fungicides are probably of only limited significance in aquatic environments, and I shall

not, therefore, expand upon these modifications in populations of microrganisms.

The pesticide coin, like most of the coins employed in
the gambling commonly called research, has a second
distinctly different side. The first face of the coin deals
with the influence of the chemical upon microorganisms
and their activities in nature. The second side is concerned
with the effect of microorganisms upon pesticides; that is,
the biological decomposition, modification, or detoxication
of these synthetic substances. It is this topic which will
provide the basis for the remainder of this review. The
subject is of immediate concern because of the potential
accumulation in nature of the applied chemicals or their
toxic residues, the inability of microorganisms to destroy
many of these molecules at significant rates, and because
of the microbial formation from the applied compound of
intermediates, some of which may in turn exhibit toxicity to
certain lower or higher forms of life. Not only are such
investigations of interest to the microbial ecologist, the
naturalist, and the public health worker, but these studies
also offer some fascinating problems to the microbial physiologist foolish enough to select molecules as frighening as
these as possible substrates for his organisms.

The elimination of pesticides from a particular environment may occur by one or more of several different means.
Leaching and the consequent removal of the chemical from
the surface soil layers is one way in which the chemical is
moved out of the reaches of the soil microbiologist and out
of the agronomic realm, but the burden of eventual decomposition is merely shifted to the population of another environment. Chemical reactions or adsorption and inactivation by
colloidal materials may likewise be important in affecting
the duration of toxicity. Certain pesticides are highly volatile,
and those compounds may be dissipated to the atmosphere.
On the other hand, many chemicals are degraded microbiologically, and such compounds appear to serve as nutrient
sources for a small but significant portion of the microbial
flora. The active bacteria, fungi, and actinomycetes have
modified the well-worn dictum, "If you can't beat them, eat
them."

A number of methods have been developed to ascertain
the persistence or decomposition of pesticides. In certain
instances, procedures have been developed which make it

possible to determine quantitatively the amount of the
substance in nature. However, such techniques have their
limitations because of the small quantiti es initially added or
remaining after a time, the interference by other substances,
and the inability of the analytic procedure to differentiate
between structurally related compounds or their derivatives.
Recent developments in gas chromatography, however, have
provided means by which certain pesticides can be detected
directly in concentrations of parts per million or even parts
per billion.

A number of bioassay techniques have also been developed,
procedures in which the response of a sensitive indicator
organism is ascertained at regular intervals after treatment.
When growth of the indicator species in treated samples is
identical to that in the controls, the chemicals or toxic products formed from them are considered to be no longer present (Burger, MacRae, and Alexander, 1962).

Other tests of persistence rely upon some property
peculiar to the individual compound; e. g., the release of
organic chlorine from the chlorinated hydrocarbons as the
free halide (Jensen, 1957), the change in ultraviolet light
absorption resulting from cleavage of the benzene ring of
aromatic pesticides (Whiteside and Alexander, 1960) or the
production of C^{14} - CO_2 following incorporation of
isotopically-labelled pesticides into the soil (Hill et al.,
1955). Care must be exercised in interpreting the results
of such indirect tests since chloride release, aromatic ring
cleavage, or the recovery of tagged CO_2 do not of themselves
necessarily demonstrate loss of toxicity, inasmuch as new
inhibitory products formed from the pesticide may remain.
Moreover, the deleterious effects may be dissipated entirely
without any detectable change in the indirect analyses.

These three procedures -- direct estimation, bioassay,
and indirect measurements -- reflect only a loss in activity
of the applied material, but they do not establish whether the
loss resulted from biological or non-biological agencies.
Typically, the significance of microorganisms in the decomposition or detoxication is assessed by comparison of persistence in sterile versus nonsterile aliquots of the particular
soil or water sample. Alternatively, the rate of inactivation
can be compared in the presence and absence of suitable
microbial inhibitors. The isolation, in culture, of the
microorganisms responsible for the biochemical change

supplies the coup de grace.

Let us now turn to the specific microbiological role in the destruction or inactivation of pesticides. Immediately, it becomes clear to the investigator that a time-honored principle of microbiology must be modified. This is the principle of elective culture, which states, in effect, that microorganisms can be isolated on essentially any organic compound. This may be alternatively considered as the Principle of Microbial Infallibility. The detergent industry has known for some time, as we are learning in these investigations of pesticides, that microorganisms in soil and water are quite fallible, much to our mutual regret. Many pesticides are resistant to microbial action, and either they remain unaltered, even in the presence of a large and active microbial population, or they are metabolized at a disturbingly slow rate. This fact is shown by some randomly selected data presented in Table 2.

The periods of persistence are solely for illustrative purposes, and greater durability of many of these insecticides has been recorded. In view of the extended duration of action, it seems unlikely that microorganisms are of consequence in the detoxication of many of the common insecticides.

Indeed, isolates capable of using such insecticides as carbon sources have yet to be obtained in culture, a necessary step in establishing that the microflora is involved in the decomposition or inactivation. There is yet no explanation for the resistance of insecticides to microbial attack, although such information would be of considerable significance in attempts to synthesize new, biodegradable pesticides.

TABLE 2: Persistence of insecticides in soil

>3 Yr.	>5 Yr.	>11 Yr.
DDT	Parathion	BHC
Dieldrin	Pb Arsenate	Chlordane
Toxaphene		

Some changes in insecticide molecules may, however, take place, and microorganisms may be involved in certain

of these modifications. For example, heptachlor epoxide is
formed in nature from heptachlor, and dieldrin is produced
from aldrin (Lichtenstein and Polivka, 1959; Lichtenstein
and Schulz, 1960). The great resistance to biological degradation of these insecticide molecules or their toxic deriva-
atives has considerable practical importance, a fact that
needs no repetition in view of the current interest and concern
of governmental and other agencies. Microorganisms, so
often taken to task because they do too much in nature, are
now attracting attention because they are not undoing a
problem which man himself has created.

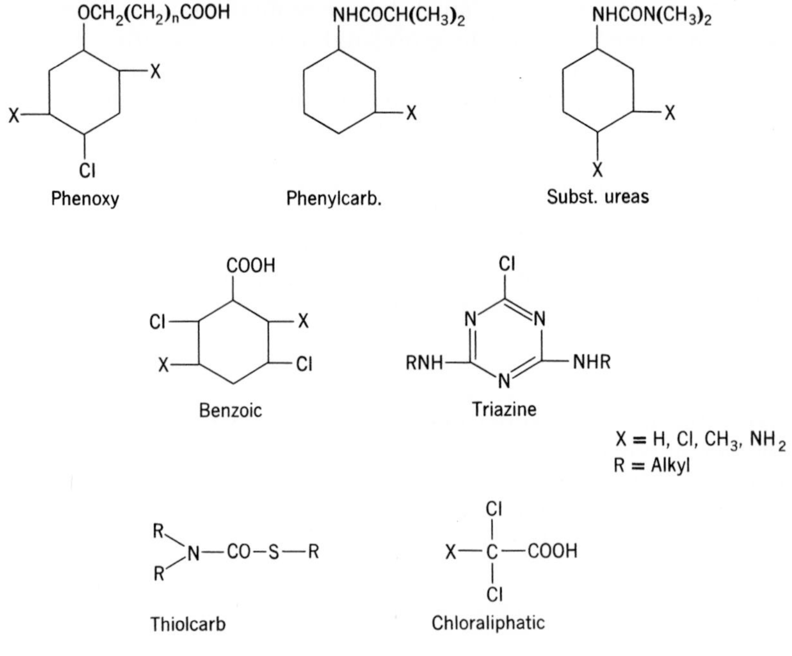

Fig. 1—Pesticide formulae.

Little attention has been given to the degradation and
biological factors concerned with the decomposition of
fungicides. Frequently, the toxicity disappears after a few
days, but often the compound remains active in soil for some
time after application. Many are removed from the zone of
operation of the soil microbiologists through volatilization;
from the biologist's view, however, this is merely passing
the buck, for the offending material may now be an aerial

pollutant. Of the non-volatile fungicides, some persist for
more than two months; others are eliminated from soil by
physicochemical rather than by enzymatic mechanisms,
while microorganisms do appear to participate in the destruction of several of the fungicides (Richardson, 1954;
Munnecke, 1958; Domsch, 1958).

The current state of knowledge is quite advanced with
the herbicides though here, too, the picture is far from
complete. Considerable attention has been given to the
persistence of these compounds, the microorganisms concerned in their destruction, and the metabolic pathways
and intermediates that are concerned in the activity. Moreover, consistent patterns of microbial fallibility are now
beginning to emerge.

First, as a means of introduction to the difficulties of the
pesticide microbiologist, let us view some of the chemicals
that are currently under consideration (Fig. 1). Unfortunately, as one begins to attain some familiarity with the chemistry of one class of materials and the possible intermediates
in metabolism, industry adds additional fuel to the fire of
biological confusion by the introduction of new chemicals.

Herbicides remain active in soil for periods as short as
a week or as long as a year or more (Table 3). The duration of effectiveness depends upon the specific chemical,
the rate and method of application, and specific environmental
conditions. The data presented serve only an illustrative
purpose inasmuch as the persistence is so markedly governed
by environmental conditions following treatment.

TABLE 3: Persistence of herbicides in soil

< 2 Mo.		2-4 Mo.	> 6 Mo.
Amiben	IPC	MCPA	2,4,5-T
Amitrol	Dalapon	TCA	2,3,6-TBA
2,4-D	Neburon	Monuron	Triazines

Some of the compounds whose decomposition is, in whole
or in part, the result of microbial agencies and several of
the active organisms are listed in Table 4.

Various types of herbicides are apparently suitable as
substrates for the microbial flora. Undoubtedly, more

compounds will eventually be added to the list, but too little
data is presently available for a thorough tabulation. Although conclusions are not yet warranted, the fact that a
large proportion of the active species are bacteria and that
few are fungi and actinomycetes may be of some significance.

TABLE 4: Microorganisms concerned in herbicide decomposition

MCPA:	Achromobacter	MH:	Alcaligenes
4-CPA:	Achromobacter	Monuron:	Pseudomonas
TCA:	Trichoderma	DNOC:	Corynebacterium
2,4-D:	Arthrobacter, Flavobacterium, Achromobacter		
	Dalapon: Nocardia, Agrobacterium, Pseudomonas		

One major aspect of these investigations was prompted
initially by the observation that 2, 4-D disappears readily
from treated soil while 2, 4, 5-T, a compound differing from
2, 4-D by only a single chlorine on the aromatic ring, remained active in soil for many months (De Rose and Newman,
1947). Since 2, 4-D is destroyed through microbial action,
it was proposed that the great persistence of 2, 4, 5-T resulted from its resistance to microbial detoxication. In
agreement with this suggestion is the ease of isolating 2, 4-D-
utilizing microorganisms and the difficulty in obtaining
2, 4, 5-T strains; indeed, no such isolate has been found. The
agriculturalist now, with considerable justification, turns to
the microbiologist for answers. What is the influence of
molecular structure upon microbial degradation of such
chemicals, and why should one substance be unyielding to
the pressure of microbial nutrient demands while its
structurally related neighbor quickly meets its doom at the
hands of microbial enzymes?
    Establishing the organisms and biochemical explanations
for the degradation of so diverse a group of compounds is a
task requiring both extensive and intensive investigation.
Clearly, only a few herbicides can be investigated in detail.
We have selected for our studies compounds related to 2, 4-D
and 2, 4, 5-T because of the clear structural influence on
microbial decomposition, although the effect of molecular
structure on biodegradability has been reported for other
pesticides as well (Steenson and Walker,1956; Sheets, 1958;
Webley, Duff, and Farmer, 1958; Hirsch and Alexander, 1960;

Jensen, 1960; Alexander, 1963). Some of the type structures
in the phenol and phenoxy classes of pesticides are shown in
Fig. 2.

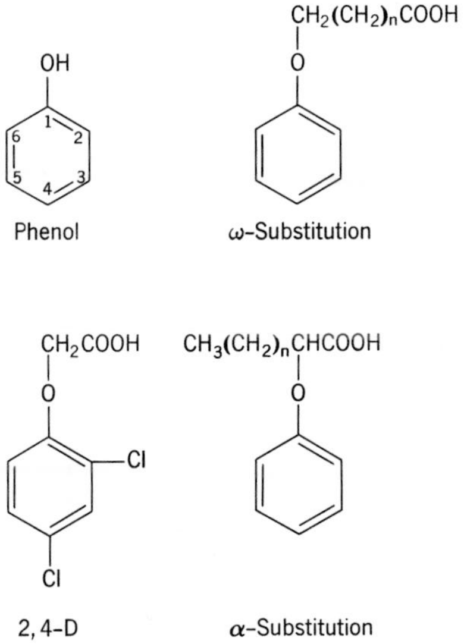

Fig. 2—Type structures of phenol and phenoxy pesticides.

The effect of chemical structure on microbial decomposition of these compounds has been examined in nearly
natural soil environments by a spectrophotometric method
designed to establish the time of aromatic ring cleavage and
by plant bioassay techniques as well as by means of pure
cultures in artificial incubation mixtures (Whiteside and
Alexander, 1960; Alexander and Aleem, 1961; Burger,
MacRae and Alexander, 1962). The spectrophotometric
method relies on the absorption of ultra violet light by
compounds with an aromatic ring. When the substance is
degraded, the characteristic ultra violet absorption disappears, suitable controls being employed to eliminate interference by water-soluble soil constituents.

In Fig. 3 is depicted the activity of a mixed, soil microflora upon three molecules of the 2, 4-D group: the acetate,
butyrate, and the alpha-propionate. The data demonstrate
that the acetate and butyrate were readily decomposed but

that the ring of the propionate remained intact for long
periods. The activity was greater following retreatment
with the acetate and butyrate, as the population had become
enriched by the first application.

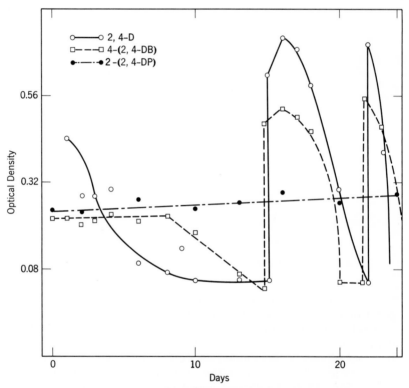

Fig. 3—Action of soil microflora on 2,4-D compounds.

Our surprise at the longevity of the dichlorophenoxy-
propionate was compounded when the spectrophotometric
technique was applied to related molecules of the 2, 4, 5-T
group. In no instance was there evidence (Fig. 4) of
significant ring cleavage in the periods indicated or even
by the end of 6 months with the acetic, 2-propionic, and
4-butyric derivatives of 2, 4, 5-T. These laboratory observations are in agreement with field data under natural
conditions.

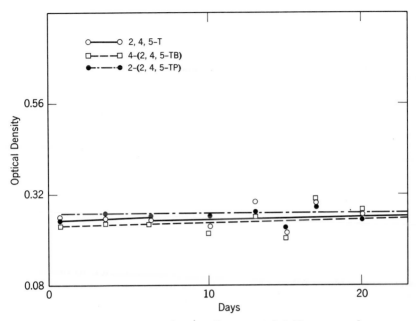

Fig. 4—Action of soil microflora on 2,4,5-T compounds.

As the list of compounds examined by the spectrophotometric technique was extended, more compounds appeared on
the debit side. Even in natural conditions, there is apparently a broad and diverse group of, to use Dr. Kallio's term,
"recalcitrant" molecules. But, as the number of potential
substrates offered to the microflora was increased, a
definite pattern began to emerge.

In Table 5 is summarized a portion of the data obtained
with a large group of phenoxy compounds. The left column
gives the position of the chlorine on the ring, and the values
reflect days for aromatic ring cleavage of phenoxy compounds
with fatty acid side-chains containing 2, 4, or 5 carbons. Two
major conclusions can be drawn from these observations: (1)
no compound having on its aromatic nucleus a chlorine in the
meta position (that is, at positions 3 or 5) is transformed to
an extent sufficient to cause a significant loss in ultra violet
absorption; and (2) the point of linkage of the fatty acid
side-chain (alpha vs. omega linkage) regulates the suscepti-

bility of the aromatic portion of the molecule to microbial attack.

TABLE 5: Phenoxy ring cleavage

| Herbicide | Omega | | | Alpha |
	2C	3C	4C	3/5C
4-Cl	11	11	53	*
2,4-Cl	26	4	11	*
3,4-Cl	> 205	> 81	> 205	*
2,4,5-Cl	> 205	> 81	> 205	*

*> 205 & > 81 days for 3C & 5C

The spectrophotometric method requires that the aromatic ring be cleaved in order for microbial action to be detected. Many other changes in the molecule, including some associated with loss of toxicity, could occur without being detectable by changes in the ultra violet region. However, a bioassay procedure may be employed to assess the effect of molecular structure on microbial degradation as reflected in the time for loss of toxicity to a suitable indicator plant.

TABLE 6: Phenoxy persistence: bioassay

| Herbicide | Omega | | Alpha | |
	2C	4C	3C	4C
4-Cl	27+	27	54	
2,4-Cl	27	54	> 103	>103
3,4-Cl	> 103	>103	> 103	>103
2,4,5-Cl	103	103	> 103	>103

Days of Phytotoxicity

The data (Table 6) presented reinforce the hypothesis advanced earlier on the significance of halogen substitution and aliphatic linkage.

An independent test of the influence of ring substitution on biodegradability can be performed with chlorophenols, molecules unencumbered by aliphatic handles. Moreover, here microbial metabolism is typically reflected by an immediate ring cleavage and concomitant decrease in ultra violet absorption. Table 7 is a summary of a number of experiments, including all the mono- and dichlorophenols as well as several tri- and tetrachlorophenols. The absorption of pentachlorophenol, not listed, persisted for more than 10 weeks. It is readily evident that the only phenols persisting for greater than 10 weeks were those with at least one halogen in positions 3 or 5, both being meta positions.

TABLE 7: Phenol ring cleavage

< 2 wk.		> 10 wk.	
Phenol	4-Br	3-Cl	2,5-Cl
2-Cl	2,4-Cl	3-Br	3,5-Cl
4-Cl	2,6-Cl	2,3-Cl	2,4,5-Cl
2-Br	2,4,6-Cl	3,4-Cl	2,3,4,6-Cl

We have reported other structural effects in connection with benzoic acid herbicides and structurally-related benzoates in a soil-solution mixture (Alexander, 1963) and with cultures of Flavobacterium, Pseudomonas, and Nocardia metabolizing chlorine-containing aromatic compounds and halogenated aliphatic acids (Burger, MacRae, and Alexander, 1962; Hirsch and Alexander, 1963). The major conclusion for microbiologists concerned with either soil or water tainted with these pesticides is that basic principles can be established with respect to the susceptibility or resistance of such molecules to microbial degradation. These structural characteristics may in turn serve as a means of predicting the relative longevity of such toxic compounds in terrestrial or aquatic habitats.

Turning away from the topic of microbial infallibility, a sore point for a microbiologist, I should like finally, to consider some of the problems associated with the decomposition of certain specific compounds upon which the microflora leaves its mark. As a rule, it is assumed that the

microbial transformation of a pesticide entails the conversion
of the initial toxic material through a series of innocuous
intermediates to the final products of breakdown. Such is
not always the case. Three general exceptions can be cited:
(1) the applied chemical is itself not toxic, but it is converted
to inhibitory products; (2) the toxic pesticide is transformed
to an intermediate which is also capable of inhibiting specific
organisms; and (3) the starting chemical is transformed into
stimulatory products. An example of the first exception, the
conversion of an inactive to an active compound, is 2, 4-DES,
which is itself not inhibitory; in soil, however, it is converted microbiologically to 2, 4-dichlorophenoxyethanol,
which in turn is oxidized to the corresponding acetic acid.
The latter, of course, is 2, 4-D (Audus, 1953; Vlitos and
King, 1953). Illustrations of the second exception are the
conversion of 4-(2, 4-DB) to 2, 4-D (Lisk and Alexander, unpublished data) and the breakdown of 2, 4-D itself, which
may yield phytotoxic intermediates (Audus and Symonds,
1955). There is also some evidence that a substance formed
during the decomposition of 2, 4-D enhances development of
at least certain plants (Jensen and Peterson, 1952; Newman,
Thomas, and Walker, 1952).

Yet, despite the obvious importance of an understanding
of the intermediates formed during the metabolism of
pesticides, surprisingly little is known of the mechanism of
the microbial decomposition. In view of the array of com -
pounds and the variety of active organisms, the problem is
indeed vast. The dilemma becomes further compounded as
new chemicals gain prominence, and additional microorganisms are characterized. To avoid greater confusion than
actually exists, only the phenoxy herbicides and related
hydrocarbons will be mentioned in the present discussion,
although some information is beginning to appear for other
pesticides.

Webley, Wain, and their colleagues (Webley, Duff, and
Farmer, 1957; Taylor and Wain, 1962) have demonstrated
quite convincingly that cultures of Nocardia and certain
bacteria initiate the metabolism of phenoxyalkyl carboxylic
acids by beta-oxidation of the aliphatic side-chain; that is,
the organism removes individual 2-carbon fragments from
the fatty acid linked to the chlorophenol moiety. From the
dichlorophenoxybutyrate, the corresponding phenoxyacetate

should be formed. We have recently applied the ultrasensitivity and selectivity of the gas chromatograph to the detection of metabolic pathways operating within soil itself after the application of pesticides at levels of parts per million. In samples of soil receiving these minute quantities of the dichlorophenoxybutyrate, the corresponding acetate has been found. In samples receiving dichlorophenoxyhexanoate, octanoate, and decanoate, the dichlorophenoxybutyrate accumulates. Further, application of such traces of the dichlorophenoxyheptanoate, nonanoate, and undecanoate, the dichlorophenoxyropionate and pentanoate are produced; that is, phenoxy compounds having an even number of carbons in the side-chain are degraded via the butyrate derivative and compounds with an odd number of carbons proceed via the propionate and pentanoate derivatives. Moreover, in the case of the chemical with the 7-carbon fatty acid moiety, the corresponding 5 and 3-C intermediates appear (Lisk and Alexander, unpublished data). Thus, even in nature, a beta-oxidation sequence operates in the destruction of pesticides. The applied implications of these findings become apparent when one considers the differences in toxicities of these substances.

Nature often has more than one means of disposing of its wastes, and the existence of a possible alternative mechanism was suggested by the peculiar behavior (Fig. 5) of a Flavobacterium isolated for its ability to decompose the dichlorophenoxybutyrate known in the jargon of the trade as 4-(2, 4-DB).

Growth upon the phenoxybutyrate results in the induction in the organism of enzymes capable of oxidizing not only 4-(2, 4-DB) but also 2, 4-dichlorophenol. The 2, 4-D molecule, which was expected to be an intermediate on the basis of the beta-oxidation sequence, was not oxidized as measured by O_2 uptake, ring cleavage, or chloride release. Further, although 2, 4-dichlorophenol was metabolized completely, the rate of oxidation of 4-(2, 4-DB) fell sharply when 6 moles of O_2 were consumed per mole of substrate. This is far less than the theoretical value of 10. 5, but it is just sufficient to account for the destruction of the aromatic portion of the molecule.

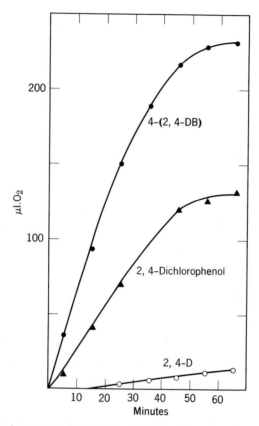

Fig. 5—Simultaneous adaptation experiments with 4-(2,4-DB) grown
flavobacterium cells.

Moreover, the slow rate of oxidation following the initially
rapid phase was identical with the rate of O_2 uptake in the
presence of butyric or other 4-carbon acids. Paper chromatography revealed the presence in the culture filtrates of 4-
chlorocatechol, butyrate, and crotonate.

Gas chromatograms of extracts of the filtrate are shown
by portion A of Fig. 6. These two peaks could be resolved
by fractionation into one peak identical with that for authentic
2,4-dichlorophenol, shown by the arrow in B, and an acid
fraction indicated by C.

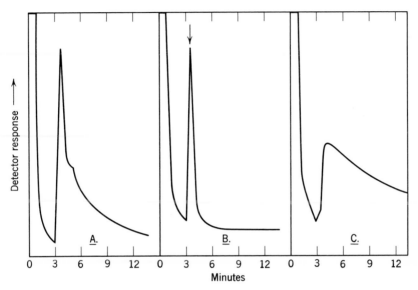

Fig. 6—Chromatograms of flavobacterium culture fractions.
    A. Ether-soluble fraction from a flavobacterium culture metab-
    olizing 4,(2,4-DB)
    B. 2,4- Dichlorophenol
    C. Unidentified Acid and trace of 2,4-Dichlorophenol

Four compounds proposed in Fig. 7 as intermediates
have therefore been characterized; namely, 2, 4-dichloro-
phenol, 4-chlorocatechol, and butyric and crotonic acids;
moreover, the manometric experiments support the pathway
proposed (MacRae, Alexander, and Rovira, 1963).

The oxidation, by Flavobacterium, of some of the acids
in the series 2, 4-dichlorophenoxyacetate to the undecanoate
is shown in Fig. 8.

Only the phenoxy acids having side chains with an even
number of carbon atoms are presented. The number of carbons represents the aliphatic moiety only. For illustrative
purposes, three of the curves have been moved to the right.
With each substrate, the initial rapid rate of metabolism
declined when enough oxygen was consumed to account for
complete dissimilation of the aromatic moieties of the various molecules, as indicated by the arrow. Similar results

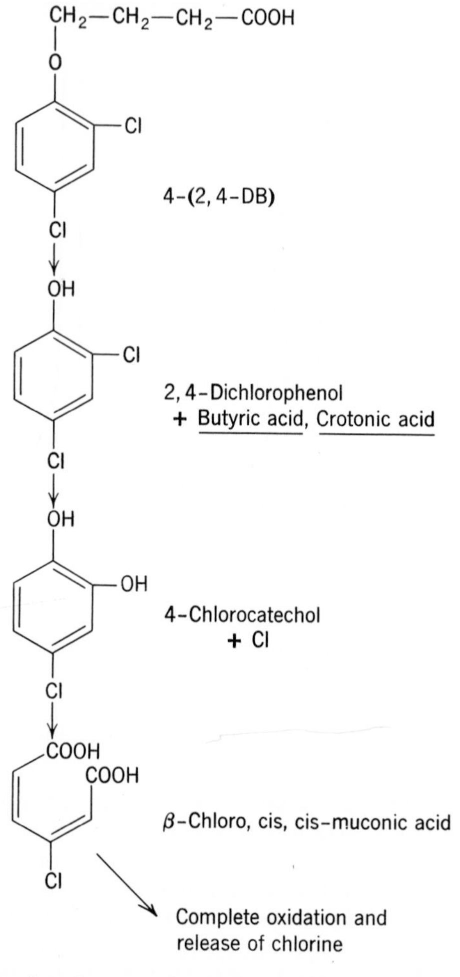

Fig. 7—Proposed pathway in breakdown of 4-(2,4-DB) by flavobacterium Sp.

were obtained with phenoxy acids with odd numbers of carbon atoms. Ultra violet determinations revealed destruction of the aromatic ring as well.

Gas chromatographic analysis of the reaction mixtures revealed more precisely the mechanism of degradation (Fig. 9). The circles represent retention volumes of the authentic fatty acids from propionic to octanoic acids. The plus signs

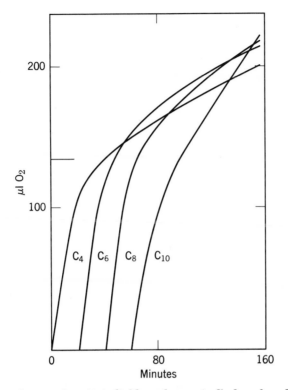

Fig. 8—Oxidation of ω-(2,4-dichlorophenoxy) alkyl carboxylic acids.

designate the retention volumes of unknowns formed from
2, 4-dichlorophenoxy propionic (A), butyric (B), pentanoic
(C), hexanoic (D), heptanoic (E) and octanoic (F) acids.
Thus, the free fatty acid corresponding to the specific side
chain was detected when the Flavobacterium acted upon all
6 of these compounds. These results demonstrate the existence of a new pathway for the metabolism of such substances, a cleavage at the ether linkage to liberate a phenol
and the fatty acid.

A summary of the observations suggesting the existence
of two different mechanisms is presented in Table 8. The
data for Nocardia are from the studies of Taylor and Wain
(1962); data for Flavobacterium are from our own findings
(MacRae and Alexander, unpublished data). These two mechanisms for the metabolism of phenoxyalkanoic acid herbicides

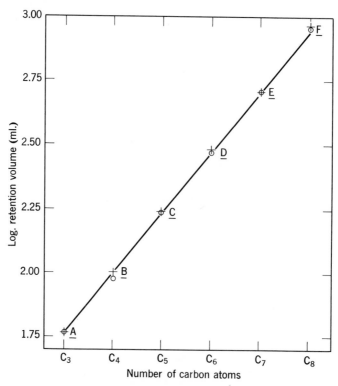

Fig. 9—Retention volumes of C_3 - C_8 fatty acids and of products of phenoxy, alkanaic acid metabolism.

TABLE 8: Metabolism of 2,4-dichlorophenoxy
alkyl carboxylic acids

| Substrate | Products | |
	Nocardia	Flavobacterium
$Cl_2PhO\text{-}C_3$	—	C_3
$Cl_2PhO\text{-}C_4$	$Cl_2PhO\text{-}C_2$	C_4 , Cl_2PhOH
$Cl_2PhO\text{-}C_5$	$Cl_2PhO\text{-}C_3$	C_5
$Cl_2PhO\text{-}C_6$	$Cl_2PhO\text{-}C_4$	C_6
	$Cl_2PhO\text{-}C_2$	
$Cl_2PhO\text{-}C_7$	$Cl_2PhO\text{-}C_3$	C_7 , C_6
$Cl_2PhO\text{-}C_8$	—	C_8 , C_6

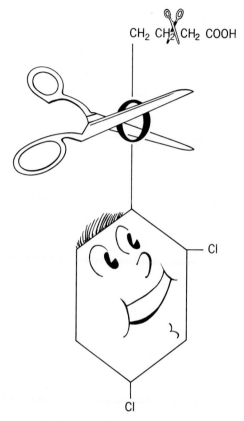

CH₂ CH₂ CH₂ COOH

Cl

Cl

Fig. 10—Metabolism of phenoxy alkanoic acid herbicides.

are depicted graphically in Fig. 10. One mechanism involves beta-oxidation of the aliphatic moiety, a pathway that may yield new phytotoxic products. The second involves cleavage of the ether linkage and an immediate detoxication of the molecule.

Many problems remain unsolved in the realm of the microbiology of pesticides. Three have been touched upon very briefly, the influence of the chemical upon microorganisms, the effect of molecular structure on decomposition, and the physiological mechanisms that result in destruction or inactivation of the pesticide. These synthetic products offer several challenges to the microbiologist, a challenge to his knowledge of ecology, to his knowledge of microbial biochemistry, as well as to his interest in the importance of microorganisms to man's welfare.

LITERATURE CITED

Alexander, M. 1963. A simple method for evaluation of microbial decomposition of benzoic acid herbicides. Soil Microbiol. Methods Newsletter, No. 3, pp. 24-26.

Alexander, M. and M. I. H. Aleem. 1961. Effect of chemical structure on microbial decomposition of aromatic herbi - cides. J. Agr. Food Chem. 9: 44-47.

Audus, L. J. 1953. Fate of sodium 2, 4-dichlorophenoxyethyl sulphate in soil. Nature, 171: 523-524.

Audus, L. J. and K. V. Symonds. 1955. Further studies on the breakdown of 2, 4-dichlorophenoxyacetic acid by a soil bacterium. Ann. Applied Biol. 42: 174-182.

Burger, K., I. C. MacRae, and M. Alexander. 1962. Decomposition of phenoxyalkyl carboxylic acids. Soil Sci. Soc. Am. Proc. 26: 243-246.

De Rose, H. R. and A. S. Newman. 1947. The comparison of the persistence of certain plant growth-regulators when applied to soil. Soil Sci. Soc. Am. Proc. 12: 222-226.

Domsch, K. H. 1958. Die Wirkung von Bodenfungiciden. II. Wirkungsdauer. Z. Pflanzenkrankh. 65: 651-657.

Hill, G. D., J. W. McGahen, H. M. Baker, D. W. Finnerty, and C. W. Bingeman. 1955. The fate of substituted urea herbicides in agricultural soils. Agron. J. 47: 93-104.

Hirsch, P. and M. Alexander. 1960. Microbial decomposition of halogenated propionic and acetic acids. Can. J. Microbiol. 6: 241-249.

Jensen, H. L. 1957. Decomposition of chloro-substituted aliphatic acids by soil bacteria. Can. J. Microbiol. 3: 151-164.

Jensen, H. L. 1960. Decomposition of chloroacetates and chloropropionates by bacteria. Acta Agr. Scand. 10: 83-103.

Jensen, H. L. and H. I. Peterson. 1952. Decomposition of hormone herbicides by bacteria. Acta Agr. Scand. 2:215-231.

Lichtenstein, E. P. and H. B. Polivka. 1959. Persistence of some chlorinated hydrocarbon insecticides in turf soils. J. Econ. Entomol. 52:289-293.

Lichtenstein, E. P. and K. R. Schulz. 1960. Epoxidation of aldrin and heptachlor in soils as influenced by autoclaving, moisture, and soil types. J. Econ. Entomol. 53:192-197.

MacRae, I. C., M. Alexander, and A. D. Rovira. 1963. The decomposition of 4-(2,4-dichlorophenoxy) butyric acid by Flavobacterium sp. J. Gen.Microbiol. in press.

Munnecke, D. E. 1958. The persistence of nonvolatile diffusible fungicides in soil. Phytopathol. 48:581-585.

Newman, A. S., J. R. Thomas, and R. L. Walker. 1952. Disappearance of 2,4-dichlorophenoxyacetic acid and 2,4,5-trichlorophenoxyacetic acid from soil. Soil Sci. Soc. Am. Proc. 16:21-24.

Richardson, L. T. 1954. The persistence of thiram in soil and its relationship to the microbiological balance and damping-off control. Can. J. Botany 32:335-346.

Sheets, T. J. 1958. The comparative toxicities of four phenylurea herbicides in several soil types. Weeds 6:413-424.

Steenson, T. I. and N. Walker. 1956. Observations on the bacterial oxidation of chlorophenoxyacetic acids. Plant and Soil 8:17-32.

Taylor, H. F. and R. L. Wain. 1962. Side chain degradation of certain ω-phenoxyalkane carboxylic acids by Nocardia coeliaca and other microorganisms isolated from soil. Proc. Royal Soc. (London) B156, 172-186.

Vlitos, A. J. and L. J. King. 1953. Fate of sodium 2,4-dichloro-phenoxyethyl-sulphate in soil. Nature 171:523.

Webley, D. M., R. B. Duff, and V. C. Farmer. 1957. Formation of a β-hydroxy acid as an intermediate in the microbial conversion of monochlorophenoxybutyric acids to the corresponding substituted acetic acids. Nature

179:1130-1131.

Webley, D. M., R. B. Duff, and V. C. Farmer. 1958. The influence of chemical structure on β-oxidation by soil nocardias. J. Gen. Microbiol. 18:733-746.

Whiteside, J. S. and M. Alexander. 1960. Measurement of microbiological effects of herbicides. Weeds 8:204-213.

APPENDIX

Index of Compounds

Amiben	3-amino - 2, 5 - dichlorobenzoic acid
Amitrol	3-amino - 1, 2, 4 - triazole
BHC	1, 2, 3, 4, 5, 6 - hexachlorocyclohexane
Dalapon	sodium 2, 2 - dichloropropionate
DDT	dichlorodiphenyltrichloroethane
DNOC	4, 6 - dinitro-o-cresol
IPC	isopropyl N-phenylcarbamate
MH	maleic hydrazide
Monuron	3- (p-chlorophenyl) -1, 1-dimethylurea
MCPA	2 - methyl-4- chlorophenoxyacetic acid
Neburon	1 - n - butyl - 3-(3, 4-dichlorophenyl)-1-methylurea
TCA	trichloroacetic acid
2, 4-D	2, 4-dichlorophenoxyacetic acid
2, 4-DES	2, 4-dichlorophenoxyethyl sulfate
2, 3, 6-TBA	2, 3, 6-trichlorobenzoic acid
2, 4, 5-T	2, 4, 5-trichlorophenoxyacetic acid
2-(2, 4-DP)	2-(2, 4-dichlorophenoxy)propionic acid
2-(2, 4, 5-TP)	2-(2, 4, 5-trichlorophenoxy)propionic acid
4-(2, 4-DB)	4-(2, 4-dichlorophenoxy)butyric acid
4-(2, 4, 5-TB)	4-(2, 4, 5-trichlorophenoxy)butyric acid

DISCUSSION

Mr. J. Zajic (Kerr-McGee Oil Ind.): You pointed out the stability of many of these insecticides and herbicides in soils; would you expect them to be as stable in an aqueous environment?

Dr. Alexander: There is always a possiblity that these compounds can be degraded under other natural environmental conditions; however, the persistence of many of these compounds for periods of twelve years in a variety of circumstances suggests that these molecules are indeed, difficult to eat. We have tried a number of means of isolating organisms and several methods of analysis for detecting decomposition, but have failed to show microbial action on many compounds. There has been little work in aquatic microbiology with these compounds, but the indications are that the same general principles hold. There is one exception with 2, 4, 5-T, but I have yet to see the methods used in this specific exception.

Mr. Zajic: You made a statement about the elective culture method which I would like you to repeat.

Dr. Alexander: Any compound which is synthesized biologically is degraded microbiologically; these pesticides are not synthesized biologically.

Dr. R. Kallio: (Univ. of Iowa) Do you have any information about cleavage of aromatic rings with fluorine substitutions, in view of the close similarity between the carbon-fluorine and the carbon-hydrogen bond?

Dr. Alexander: Not with aromatics. We have done some work with fluoroacetic and fluoropropionic acids. The fluoro compounds are often more resistant than the corresponding chloro, or bromo, or iodine compounds. In some cases, resistance may result from toxicity of the test compound.

Dr. David Pramer (Rutgers Univ.): The figures for toxicity that you presented relate to soil. Would you expect that more or less material would be required to exert comparable toxicity in an aquatic environment?

Also, how do you differentiate between a molecule which is directly toxic and one which is simply not available as a nutrient substrate?

Dr. Alexander: In answer to the first question, I could only hazard a guess on the relative toxicity of some of these compounds in water as compared with soil. I would expect that, because of absorption phenomenona in soil, there might be less toxicity in soil than in water. In some instances, we tested these compounds in culture media in the absence of any colloidal materials, and we noted a similar lack of significant inhibition at practical levels of pesticide application. Others have studied this problem more extensively, however.

As for the second point, the structural relationships in toxicity are entirely independent of the structural effects related to susceptibility to degradation. For example, 2, 4-D and 2, 4, 5-T are both phytotoxic compounds, whereas 2, 4-D is readily degraded while the 2, 4, 5-T is quite resistant. There are other examples.

Dr. Pramer: What about toxicity to microorganisms rather than to plants?

Dr. Alexander: This is a topic with which I am not familiar.

Dr. Benarde (Rutgers Univ.): When you indicate that chlordane, for instance, is found after 12 years in the soil, do you imply that the concentration is the same now as it was 12 years ago, or was there a diminution?

Also, with so many other different types of nutrients available in the soil, would it be necessary for the microorganisms to utilize these compounds?

Dr. Alexander: The chlordane concentration does, indeed, diminish slowly in time. I do not know whether it is because of leaching, volatilization of specific pesticides, microbial activity, or chemical detoxication.

As for the second facet of your question, it is a dictum of soil microbiology that the limiting nutrient in the soil environment is carbon, so that added carbonaceous molecules usually disappear readily because the carbon supply is limiting. There is always the possibility that materials such as chlordane and DDT are degraded very slowly, as is true for the degradation of lignin. I am not suggesting that these pesticides are decomposed microbiologically, only that they are extremely resistant.

Dr. R. S. Wolfe (Univ. of Illinois): Have either you or
Dr. Kallio seriously considered adding CO_2 to your artificial
cultures? It seems to me that the microorganisms may be
able to do something to a molecule, but if they did not have
building blocks to put the electrons on, they could not function.

Dr. Alexander: I doubt that CO_2 would have an effect,
particularly since the molecules persist in a CO_2-rich environment, but we have not investigated this point. Possibly
Dr. Kallio has.

Dr. Kallio: We have not. In relation to some of the data
I presented, I am not sure that CO_2 would have much effect.
The difference, let us say, between 1-phenyl decane and 2-
phenyl undecane is such that I cannot see where CO_2 would
assist.

Mr. Leslie Reed (Chipman Chemical Co.): Would you
expect to find the same microorganisms active in both soil
and water in the breakdown of some of these chemicals you
talked about?

Dr. Alexander: I would expect the same general types.
Organisms which degrade many aromatics are commonly
found in both soil and water, but there has been little work
with the aquatic species.

Dr. George Orgel (Colgate-Palmolive Co.): Both Dr.
Kallio and you indicate that the initial attack occurs on the a
alkane side-chain. I wonder whether this effect represents
experimental expediency, in that you first looked for it, or
is it known whether or not aromatic ring opening occurs
before or simultaneously with side-chain cleavage?

Dr. Alexander: One of the figures (Fig. 8) showed the
bacterium to effect a rapid oxidation, but the oxidation rate
declined after about six moles of oxygen were consumed per
mole of substrate. This suggests an initial ring cleavage
and metabolism of the aromatic portion followed by a subsequent degradation of the aliphatic moiety; that is the flavobacterium metabolizes the aromatic moiety prior to the
aliphatic portion. This fact probably explains why the aliphatic
portions were detected so readily by gas analysis.

Dr. Kallio: We found, in common with the detergent
people, that apparently the attack on phenyl alkanes, for

example, starts at the alkyl end. Many organisms will not
use phenylacetic acid, benzoic acid, and so forth, and these
products will accumulate. Nocardias are notorious in this
regard. Thus, the utilization of phenylalkanes results in
the accumulation of these aromatic acids. The same is true
of a number of our organisms, although we have not identified all of the products. To put it another way, one can see
that the peaks for phenyl absorption in the infra red are among
the last to disappear -- this again in common cause with the
detergent people. You will remember, also, that in alkyl
benzene sulfonate degradation, not only does the aromatic
ring seem to disappear last but the sulfonate appears as
sulfate very late after the phenyl ring goes. All of these
facts together suggest that the alkyl chain is attacked, presumably by beta-oxidation, then the ring is opened, probably
through the making of catechols. Then the sulfonate comes
off rather late or just at the time of ring cleavage. The series
of reactions looks very much like going from, let us say,
benzoate to catechol to muconic acid. My guess would be the
sulfonate comes off before making catechol, but in any case,
late.

3

MICROBIAL TRANSFORMATIONS OF MINERALS

Henry L. Ehrlich
Department of Biology
Rensselaer Polytechnic Institute

This discussion will deal with special biological processes of a few groups of microorganisms which cause transformations of large amounts of mineral matter. These processes stand in contrast to those common to all living cells, which cause transformation of small amounts of mineral matter. The latter small-scale processes often have to do with enzyme function, as in enzyme activation or electron transport. The large-scale processes have to do with functions other than enzyme function and may utilize more than 1,000 times as much mineral matter than the small-scale processes.

Large-scale transformation of inorganic matter by microbes may result, on the one hand, in the genesis of relatively insoluble mineral aggregates from soluble substances, and, on the other hand, in the solubilization of preexistent insoluble mineral aggregates, possibly followed by reprecipitation of the solubilized matter in a different form (Fig. 1). In nature, the first type of process corresponds to sedimentary formation of ore and rock, and the second type of process to weathering and, possibly, mineral metamorphosis or replacement. Of course, similar changes can and do occur in the absence of microbes or other life, but they are likely to be slower, less extensive and perhaps of a different chemistry under the same conditions. This is not to suggest for a moment that all mineral transformations in nature are the result of biological action.

How may microbes interact with mineral matter? In general, one can divide the mechanisms of interaction into

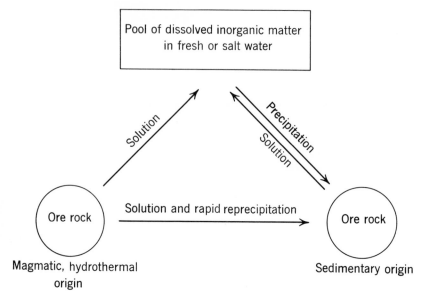

Fig. 1—Patterns of biological mineral transformations.

two categories.   The first is direct enzymic interaction,
and the second is indirect, nonenzymic interaction.   In the
first category belong enzymic oxidations and reductions,
enzymic hydrolysis, and enzymic chelate destruction.   In
the second category belong corrosion of insoluble matter by
metabolically produced acid; precipitation of inorganic ions
by other, metabolically-produced inorganic ions; adsorption
onto cell surfaces; and metal chelate formation.   Organisms
which may participate in these reactions include bacteria,
fungi, algae, protozoa, even a few metazoa, lichens, and
higher plants.   At present, the best understood biological
mineral interactions are those of bacteria.   Metabolic interactions with minerals by the remaining organisms are more
poorly understood.   It is the finished product of the activities
by non-bacterial organisms of which we are most aware, as,
for instance, the siliceous tests of diatoms and radiolaria,
of the calcareous tests of certain algae and foraminifera, the
calcareous accretions of corals, and shells of mollusks.   It
is important to point out that in nonbacterial creatures, large-
scale mineral transformations seem to result in variously
organized mineral accumulations in or on the organism, where
they serve a structural purpose.   In most bacteria, large-

scale mineral transformations have mainly a functional purpose. Let us examine the bacterial problem more closely.

When bacterial mineral transformations are mediated
through enzymes, oxidations and reductions are very frequently involved (1). Oxidations release energy while reductions consume energy. Some bacteria, the chemosynthetic autotrophs, use mineral oxidation as a source of
chemical energy and reducing power for the synthesis of
organic matter from CO_2 and H_2O. Other bacteria, the
photosynthetic autotrophs, use mineral oxidation merely as
a source of reducing power in CO_2 assimilation while depending for a supply of energy on radiation, particularly in
the visible spectrum. In both these processes, relatively
large amounts of mineral are oxidized to accommodate the
large energy or reducing-power requirements. Enzymatic
mineral reductions are not a source of useful energy; indeed,
as pointed out before, they consume energy. Neverthless,
they can be useful to the cell because they are coupled with
energy-yielding oxidations for consumption of excess reducing
power generated by the oxidations. Without this consumption
of excess reducing power, the oxidations could not take place,
and thus energy, vital for protoplasmic synthesis and other
processes, would not be generated. Organisms that carry
out these reductions are usually anaerobes or facultative
organisms. They use large amounts of mineral in these reductions because they generate a lot of reducing power to
meet their energy demands. They usually couple these reductions to oxidations of organic compounds, but not always.
Thiobacillus denitrificans, for instance, couples nitrate
reduction with sulfur oxidation. The foregoing principles of
biological mineral oxidation and reduction are summarized
in Fig. 2.

It is not clear to the author to what extent enzymic hydrolysis of minerals by bacteria occurs in nature. Since the
enzyme, inorganic pyrophosphatase, is present in bacteria
(7), it is not inconceivable that, if pyrophosphate exists in
nature, various bacteria can hydrolyze it to orthophosphate
with such an enzyme. Since pyrophosphate can complex
Mn^{3+} and probably some other mineral ions, destruction of
such complexes by hydrolysis of pyrophosphate could lead
to the precipitation of the ions.

The existence of various organic, metal chelates in

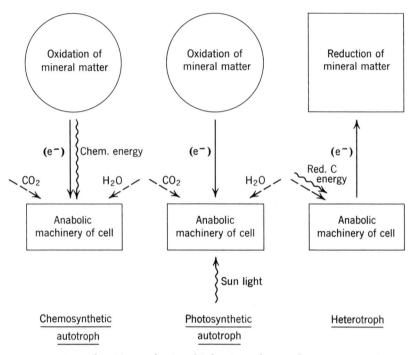

Fig. 2—Major functions of microbial mineral transformations. The anabolic machinery may include conventional energy-releasing reactions which also help to drive it.

nature is generally accepted. The effect of the chelates is to stabilize metal ions under a given set of conditions and prevent them from precipitating. Enzymic breakdown of the chelating agent by bacteria and other microorganisms may result in bringing the metal ions out of solution (38).

Now let us look at nonenzymic interactions of microbes with minerals. In this category, the aforementioned four types of reactions must be considered: acid corrosion, precipitation, adsorption, and chelation. All four are directly dependent on metabolism, or more specifically, on end products of metabolism. In acid corrosion, we have to consider the action of nitric acid, end product of nitrification; sulfuric acid, end product of sulfur oxidation; carbonic acid, end-product of complete and partial organic carbon oxidation; or organic acids, products of partial, organic carbon oxidation (1). These acids can act on acid-soluble minerals. In precipitation, metabolically produced carbonate, sulfate, and sulfide can bring certain cations out of solution under appropriate conditions (3, 4, 32). Some precipitations may be quite extensive with formation of amorphous or crystalline agglomerates. In adsorption, iron and manganese oxides can be picked up by the sheaths of certain bacteria and algae with the formation of relatively heavy encrustations (22, 34). This adsorption can have the effect of concentrating mineral matter, originally in dilute solution. A modification of this adsorption process is exhibited by some foraminifera which accumulate and cement together small carbonate and silicate particles from their environment, agglutinating them to form tests (11). In chelation, a metabolically produced organic compound may complex one or another metal ion, with the result that the metal ion is protected from precipitation, or oxidation, or reduction (2).

Microbial mineral-transforming processes can be expected to occur in two major types of environments, the terrestrial and the aquatic. One important difference between them is, obviously, the relative availability of water. It determines the degree of dispersal of the inorganic and organic food supply and waste accumulations. In a terrestrial environment water may not be abundantly available as a solvent. Hence soluble products may rapidly reach toxic concentrations and inhibit further microbial activity on minerals unless the products can be removed from solution by precipitation or adsorption. In an aqueous environment such a build-up of toxic waste is obviously not a problem because of the possibility of extensive dilution of the product.

A limited supply of water in a terrestrial environment may mean a relatively concentrated food supply and, hence, extensive microbial growth throughout the solution. This is in contrast to an abundant supply of water in an aqueous environment, which may mean a dilute food supply and, hence, limited microbial growth. However, such limited growth in an aqueous environment can be partially overcome through adsorption and thus concentration of food on solid surfaces. Abundant microbial growth on solid surfaces is not an unusual observation in aqueous environments in which dissolved food is very dilute, as, for instance, in marine environments (43). It is important to note that if the adsorbent of food is mineral matter, it could also facilitate close contact with mineral-transforming microorganisms and thus action on mineral matter.

A number of workers have reported direct association of microbes with mineral aggregates (13, 14, 15, 22, 28, 33). The question arises, where in the aggregates may microbes be found? The answer is, in the environment immediately surrounding the aggregates, on the surface of the aggregates, and within them. If microbes are found within aggregates, they must exist in pores, cracks, or fissures to be actively growing. Only such structural features would allow free movement of nutrients to, and waste and excess cell population from the microbial habitat. Otherwise, microbes within mineral aggregates would be expected to be dormant or dead.

We shall now examine two specific cases of microbial interaction with minerals and see how some of the principles which have been outlined are applied. First, let us consider bacterial oxidation of metal sulfides. This activity is an example of mineral break-down in a terrestrial environment. The initial observations of autotrophic bacteria of the Thiobacillus-Ferrobacillus group that oxidize iron disulfides like marcasite, pyrite, and sulfur ball were made by Leathen et al. (25), Temple and Delchamps (41), and Silverman et al. (37). The bacteria were discovered in an attempt to find an explanation for the acid drainage from coal mines in West Virginia and Pennsylvania. The isolated bacteria could be shown to oxidize Fe^{2+} to Fe^{3+} in a completely inorganic medium under aerobic conditons (36, 40). They use a portion of the energy released in this oxidation for the assimilation of CO_2. It is of importance to the bacteria that Fe^{3+} formed by them hydrolyzes extensively to ferric hydroxide, thereby rendering the medium increasingly more acid. The bacteria require an acid pH for growth and survival. Their optimum pH range for iron oxidation is between 2.5 and 4.2 (36). They die at neutral pH (15). One possible mechanism whereby they oxidize iron disulfides is that given by Leathen et al. (26).

(1) $2FeS_2 + 2H_2O + 7O_2 \longrightarrow 2FeSO_4 + 2H_2SO_4$

(2) $4FeSO_4 + 2H_2SO_4 + 2O_2 \longrightarrow 2Fe_2(SO_4)_3 + 2H_2O$

(3) $Fe_2(SO_4)_3 + 2H_2O \longrightarrow 2Fe(OH)SO_4 + H_2SO_4$

Of these three reactions, only the second is considered to be biological. The first is nonbiological and, according to this idea, provides the $FeSO_4$ at the expense of which the bacteria can grow. It is quite likely, however, that the bacteria can oxidize pyrites directly without prior nonbiological release of Fe^{2+}. The enzymatics of iron oxidation by these organisms have been studied by Vernon et al. (42) and by Blaylock and Nason (5, 6).

Bacterial pyrite oxidation illustrates large-scale auto-trophic mineral oxidation in which at least one of the oxidation products, Fe^{3+}, is precipitated as hydroxide, or, more likely, as basic sulfate. The iron in this case may not be transported far from the primary mineral, pyrite, but be extensively redeposited close to the pyrite as a secondary, oxidized mineral accumulation.

Translocation of dissolved products of mineral sulfide oxidation need not always be over restricted distances. In bacterial oxidations of copper sulfides, where copper is released as Cu^{2+}, as from chalcocite (Cu_2S) or covellite (CuS), the copper may stay in solution and be transported over some distance before being precipitated or adsorbed. Bacterial oxidation of natural copper sulfides was first reported by Bryner and coworkers (8, 9, 10).

Other simple sulfides oxidized by the Thiobacillus-Ferro-bacillus group include molybdenite (MoS_2), sphalerite (ZnS), millerite (NiS), and orpiment (As_2S_3) (9, 19, 30, 35). Mixed sulfides, such as tetrahedrite ($Cu_8Sb_2S_7$), bornite (Cu_5FeS_4), and chalcopyrite ($CuFeS_2$), are also known to be attacked by these bacteria (8). The over-all effect of bacterial oxidation of any of these minerals appears to be always the same. Some of the products remain in solution while others are reprecipi-tated upon formation. In all cases an acid pH is maintained and even enhanced because of hydrolysis of many of the products, to the benefit of the bacteria.

The environment in which mineral sulfide oxidation occurs might seem very unfavorable for supporting organisms other than the Thiobacillus-Ferrobacillus group. But this is not so. Lackey (24) reported the presence of various types of protozoa, a few algal types, and a rotifer in acid drainage from coal mines. Razzell and Trussell (35) and Ehrlich (15, 18) have found fungi along with bacteria in the drainage from copper mines and their minerals. Ehrlich (18), moreover, found protozoa in copper mine effluent. His observations showed a direct nutritional dependence of the protozoa on the bacteria

and fungi. Indeed, an ecosystem may exist in this environment, according to him, in which major CO_2 fixation is not
dependent on photosynthesis but on chemosynthesis. In
other words, the primary source of energy for life is not
derived from the sun, in this case, but from oxidation of
inorganic minerals.

Now let us look briefly at another bacterial interaction
with minerals. This is a formation of mineral concretions
in an aqueous environment under microbial aegis. The
mineral to be considered is a ferro-manganese agglomerate,
found at the bottom of most oceans (12, 31). Agglomerates
of a superficially similar compositon but of more porous
texture, lighter density, and different shape have also been
found in fresh water (20). The marine concretions, called
nodules, contain a significant number of bacteria. As many
as 10^4 per g have been detected, and not all of the same kind
(17). At least some of the bacteria seem to facilitate adsorption of Mn^{2+} by these nodules, presumably by oxidizing
the adsorbed manganese to a higher oxidation state, as in
MnO_2. Such oxidized manganese can then adsorb more Mn^{2+}
(17). Although the bacteria responsible for the presumed
oxidation are heterotrophic, they may be able to use the
energy from Mn oxidation for assimilating organic carbon.

Dissolved manganese in the ocean has been assumed to be
derived from terrestrial manganese introduced into the ocean
by rivers and streams, from meteoritic dust, and from submarine vulcanism (12, 21). Pelagic manganese thus exists
in two phases, a dissolved phase and a fixed, solid phase.
Fixed manganese in the ocean appears not only in nodules
but as coatings on a variety of surfaces, including certain
of the bottom muds, various calcareous objects, pumice,
etc. (12). It is usually associated with iron (21).

Two kinds of chemical reaction may return fixed manganese
into solution, a biological one and a nonbiological one. The
biological reaction uses the fixed manganese as an oxidant in
its respiratory activity. The nonbiological one uses Mn^{2+}
as a reductant for manganese of the 4+ valence state, with
the result that Mn^{3+} in a soluble form appears. The biological reaction can be demonstrated by allowing certain bacteria to act on nodular material or on MnO_2 in the presence of
glucose (16, 17). The nonbiological reaction can be demonstrated by allowing Mn^{2+} to react with nodular substances or
MnO_2 in the presence of a high concentration of inorganic

pyrophosphate. Under these conditons a pink to red manganipyrophosphate complex develops with time (Fig. 3). The reaction is faster with nodular material than with MnO_2. It is readily shown that the complex is not formed with Mn^{2+}, nodular material, or MnO_2 alone. The reaction may be described by the following set of equations:

(1) $Mn^{2+} + MnO_2 + 4H^+ \longrightarrow 2Mn^{3+} + 2H_2O$

(2) $Mn^{3+} +$ pyrophosphate $\longrightarrow$ manganipyrophosphate.

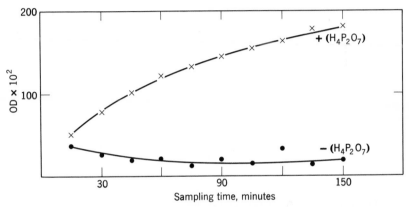

Fig. 3—Rate of manganipyrophosphate formation from the interaction between Mn^{2+} and oxides of manganese in nodules. Content of reaction vessel (+$H_4P_2O_7$): 1.0g crushed nodule, particle size of 62μ; 10 ml natural sea water; 10 ml sat. $Na_4P_2O_7$ (pH 6.8); 1.0 ml 0.2 M $MnSO_4$. Content of reaction vessel (-$H_4P_2O_7$): 1.0 g crushed nodule, particle size of 62μ; 10 ml natural sea water; 10 ml distilled water; 1.0 ml 0.2 M $MnSO_4$. Sampled at appropriate times by transferring 1.0 ml aliquots of supernatants to 1.0 ml sat. $Na_4P_2O_7$ (pH 6.8) and centrifuging. Color read in spectrophotometer at 535 mu. OD = optical density.

Interestingly, nonbiological release of manganese by Mn^{2+}
in the absence of pyrophosphate from a few nodules and
from manganiferous marine muds can occur but the chemistry of this reaction is still obscure (Fig. 4).

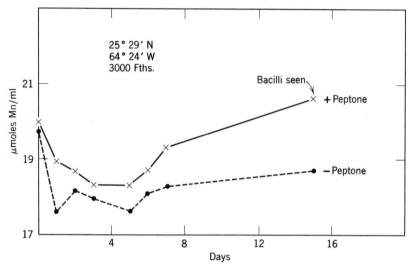

Fig. 4—Mn adsorption by marine mud. Reaction vessels were set up and
assayed as described in (17), except that 2.0 g marine mud were used
as adsorbent instead of crushed nodule.

The processes of manganese release from fixed manganese
make it clear that visulization of the ocean as a sump in
which all manganese ends up permanently as insoluble oxide
is untenable. A very complicated manganese cycle must
exist in the ocean, with occasional, locally high concentrations of Mn^{2+}. The average concentration of soluble manganese has been given as 0.001 to 0.01 ppm (39).

The presence of iron in manganese nodules must be of
greater significance than mere chance association through
simultaneous adsorption with Mn^{2+}, as suggested by Goldberg
(21). This is reflected by experiments on manganese adsorption of 80 per cent pure MnO_2, roasted in a crucible
over a bunsen flame for 1 hour. With such a preparation as
an adsorber of Mn^{2+}, Arthrobacter of nodular origin causes
temporary addition of $\overline{Mn^{2+}}$ to the MnO_2, but the process is

reversed in due time (Fig. 5). In the absence of Arthrobacter, the MnO_2 adsorbs less Mn^{2+} and releases it sooner.
The same effect is obtained with 99.9 per cent pure, un-
calcined MnO_2. The cause of manganese release in these
experiments may be similar to the dismutation reaction previously described, although it proceeds in the absence of
pyrophosphate in this instance. While these observations
strongly suggest that the iron in nodules is partly or wholly
responsible for the stability of adsorbed manganese, direct
evidence to support this view remains to be worked out.

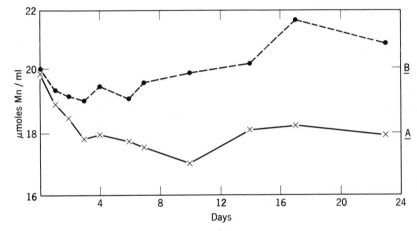

Fig. 5—Bacterial acceleration of Mn^{2+} adsorption by MnO_2. Reaction
vessel A contained 0.5 g of 80 percent pure MnO_2, roasted for 1 hr,
and sterilized by autoclaving under 20 ml distilled water. After
sterilization, the distilled water was replaced with 17 ml sterile sea
water, 2.0 ml of sterile 0.2 M $MnSO_4$ with 1 per cent peptone, and
1.0 ml Arthrobacter suspension (4.8×10^9 orgs.) Reaction vessel B
was similarly set up, except that it contained 18 ml sterile sea water and no cells. The supernatants of vessels A and B were assayed
as described in (17).

    The observations of a manganese cycle in the sea seem
to mirror previously made observations of such cycles in
soil and fresh water. Mann and Quastel (29) presented clear
evidence for microbial manganese oxidation and reduction
in soil. Leeper (27) has lucidly described the transformation
of manganese in soil on the basis of his own observations

and those of others. Ingols and Wilroy (23), have presented
striking evidence for sudden rapid deposition of manganese
oxides from fresh water on surfaces. They have also observed occasional translocation of MnO_2 by dismutation
similar to the process described in this discussion, except
that tannins were implicated as the complexing agents instead
of pyrophosphate.

The importance of microbial mineral transformation to
water pollution and purification must be apparent. A fuller
understanding of the details of various microbial mineral
transformations should do much to help control pollution and
purification problems.

ACKNOWLEDGMENTS

Original work in this paper was supported by grants from
the Medical Sciences Research Foundation, Stanford University, Calif., and from the Geschickter Fund for Medical
Research, Inc., Washington, D. C. The author was ably
assisted in his work by Alice R. Ellett.

LITERATURE CITED

1. Alexander, M. 1961. Introduction to soil microbiology.
New York, John Wiley and Sons, Inc.
2. Bear, F. E. (editor). 1955. Chemistry of the soil. New
York, Reinholt Publ. Corp.
3. Barghoorn, E.S. and R. C. Nichols. 1961. Sulfate reducing bacteria and pyritic sediments in Antarctica. Science
134:190.
4. Bavendamm, W. 1932. Die mikrobiologische Kalkfaellung
in der tropischen See; Bericht ueber die mikrobiologischen
Ergebnisse einer im Jahr 1930 von den Universitaeten
Princeton and Rutgers (USA) unternommenen Forschungsreise
nach den Bahama Inseln. Archiv. Mikrobiol. 3:205-276.
5. Blaylock, Barbara A. and A. Nason. 1961. Electron
transport studied in the chemoautotroph Ferrobacillus
ferrooxidans. Fed. Proc. 20:46.
6. Blaylock, Barbara A. and A. Nason. 1962. Iron oxidation
by extracts of the chemoautotroph Ferrobacillus ferrooxidans.
Fed. Proc. 21:49.
7. Blumenthal, B. I., M. K. Johnson, and E. J. Johnson.
1962. Distribution of the heat-labile and heat-stabile inorganic
pyrophosphatases amongst the bacteria. Bacteriol. Proc.
p. 104.

8. Bryner, L. C., J. V. Beck, D. B. Davis, and D. G. Wilson, 1954. Microorganisms in leaching sulfide minerals. Ind. Eng. Chem. 46:2587-2592.
9. Bryner, L. C. and R. Anderson. 1957. Microorganisms in leaching sulfide minerals. Ind. Eng. Chem. 49:1721-1724.
10. Bryner, L. C. and A. K. Jameson. 1958. Microorganisms in leaching sulfide minerals. Appl. Microbiol. 6: 281-287.
11. Cushman, J. A. 1940. Foraminifera. Their classification and economic use. 3rd ed. Cambridge, Mass. Harvard Univ. Press.
12. Dietz, R. S. 1955. Manganese deposits on the northeast Pacific sea floor. Calif. J. Mines Geol. 51:209-220.
13. Dombrowski, H. J. 1960. Balneobiologische Untersuchungen der Nauheimer Quellen. II. Mitteilung: Pseudomonas halocrenaea (nova species). Zentralbl. Bakt. Parasitenk. 178:83-90.
14. Ehrlich, H. L. 1961. Bacterial ecology of certain minerals. Bacteriol. Proc. p. 54.
15. Ehrlich, H. L. 1962. in Biogeochemistry of sulfur isotopes. M. L. Jensen, (ed) National Science Foundation Symposium. Yale University, New Haven, Conn. pp. 153-168.
16. Ehrlich, H. L. 1963. unpublished data.
17. Ehrlich, H. L. 1963. Bacteriology of manganese nodules. I. Bacterial action on manganese on nodule enrichments. Appl. Microbiol. 11:15-19.
18. Ehrlich, H. L. 1963. Microorganisms in acid drainage from a copper mine. J. Bacteriol. 86:350-352.
19. Ehrlich, H. L. 1963. Bacterial action on orpiment. Econ. Geol. 58:991-994.
20. Gillette, N. J. 1961. Oneida Lake pancakes. The N. Y. State Conservationist, April-May, p. 19.
21. Goldberg, E. D. 1954. Marine geochemistry. 1. Chemical scavengers of the sea. J. Geol. 62:249-265.
22. Harder, E. C. 1919. Iron depositing bacteria and their geologic relations. U.S. Geol. Survey, Prof. P. 113, pp. 1-89.
23. Ingols, R. S. and R. D. Wilroy. 1962. Observations on manganese in Georgia waters. J. Am. Water Works Assoc. 54:203-207.

24. Lackey, J. B. 1938. The flora and fauna of surface waters polluted by acid mine drainage. Publ. Health Reports 53:1499-1507.
25. Leathen, W. W., S. A. Braley, Sr., and Lois D. Mc Intyre. 1953. The role of bacteria in the formation of acid from certain sulfuritic constituents associated with bituminous coal. II. Ferrous iron oxidizing bacteria. Appl. Microbiol. 1:65-68.
26. Leathen, W. W., S. A. Braley, Sr., and Lois D. Mc Intyre. 1953. The role of bacteria in the formation of acid from certain sulfuritic constituents associated with bituminous coal. I. Thiobacillus thiooxidans. Appl. Microbiol. 1:61-64.
27. Leeper, G. W. 1947. The forms and reactions of manganese in the soil. Soil Sci. 63:79-94.
28. Lipman, C. B. 1932. Living organisms in ancient rocks. Fuel 11:164-170.
29. Mann, P. J. G. and J. H. Quastel. 1946. Manganese metabolism in soils. Nature 158:154-156.
30. Malouf, E. E. and J. D. Prater. 1961. Role of bacteria in alteration of sulfide minerals. J. Metals 13:353-356.
31. Mero, J. L. 1962. Ocean -floor manganese nodules. Econ. Geol. 57:747-767.
32. Nadson, G. A. 1928. Beitrag zur Kenntniss der bakteriogenen Kalkablagerung. Arch. Hydrobiol. 19:154-164.
33. Paine, S. G., F. V. Lingood, Freda Schimmer, and T. C. Thrupp. 1933. IV. The relationship of micro-organisms to the decay of stone. Roy. Soc. (London) Phil. Trans. 222B:97-127.
34. Pringsheim, E.G. 1949. The filamentous bacteria Sphaerotilus, Leptothrix, Cladothrix, and their relation to iron and manganese. Trans. Roy. Soc. (London) 233B: 453-482.
35. Razzell, W. E. and P. C. Trussell. 1963. Microbial leaching of metallic sulfides. Appl. Microbiol. 11:105-110.
36. Silverman, M. P. and D. G. Lundgren. 1959. Studies on the chemoautotrophic iron bacterium Ferrobacillus ferrooxidans. II. Manometric studies. J. Bacteriol. 78: 326-331.
37. Silverman, M.P., M. H. Rogoff, and I. Wender. 1961. Bacterial oxidation of pyritic materials in coal. Appl. Microbiol. 9:491-496.

38. Starkey, R. L. and H. O. Halvorson. 1927. Studies
on the transformation of iron in nature. II. Concerning the
importance of microorganisms in the solution and precipitation of iron. Soil Sci. 24:381-402.
39. Sverdrup, H. U., M.W. Johnson, and R. H. Fleming.
1942. The oceans, their physics, chemistry and general
biology. Prentice-Hall, Englewood Cliffs, N.J.
40. Temple. K. L. and A. R. Colmer. 1951. The autotrophic oxidation of iron by a new bacterium: Thiobacillus
ferrooxidans. J. Bacteriol. 62:605-611.
41. Temple. K. L. and E. W. Delchamps. 1953. Autotrophic bacteria and the formation of acid in bituminous
coal mines. Appl. Microbiol. 1:255-258.
42. Vernon, L. P., J.H. Magnum, J.V. Beck, and F.M.
Shafia. 1960. Studies on a ferrous-ion-oxidizing bacterium.
II. Cytochrome composition. Arch. Biochem. Biophys.
88:227-231.
43. ZoBell, C. E. 1946. Marine microbiology. A monograph
on hydrobiology. Waltham, Mass. Chronica Botanica Co.

DISCUSSION

Dr. Werner Stumm (Harvard Univ.): We have conducted
some purely chemical studies on oxidation mechanisms of
manganese and especially on the colloid chemical properties
of manganese dioxide and it was interesting to see that quite
a lot of the phenomena observed in sea water and fresh water
can be reasonably well explained by exclusively chemical
hypotheses. This does not mean that I want to deny that
bacteria can play a role but, for example, I wonder with
respect to your slide on bacterial acceleration of manganese
adsorption, whether you have really conclusive evidence for
such a bacterial acceleration.

If one looks into the colloid chemical behavior of various
manganese dioxides and their various combinations, one finds
that these manganese dioxides behave as ion exchangers and
they have very remarkable ion exchange capacities depending
on pH, very small variations in hydrogen ion concentrations
which might be due to bacterial reactions which have nothing
to do with the manganese.

With respect to your remarks that manganese nodules
are better absorbents than manganese dioxide, it depends
entirely on the crystallographic structure of manganese
dioxide. One can produce all kinds of multivalent manganese

oxides. I would generally agree that it is a very good
working hypothesis to assume that such manganese oxides
are essentially combinations between bivalent and tetravalent
manganese.

Dr. Ehrlich: I think I have nothing further to add to that.

Dr. Claude ZoBell (Scripps Institution of Oceanogr.):
While it is clear in my mind, based upon our own laboratory
observations, that types of bacteria found with these manganese nodules do, indeed, bring about the precipitation of
manganese, I wanted to hear Dr. Ehrlich comment whether
he thinks it is due to a direct oxidation of manganous ion to
the manganic form or, as indicated by the previous question,
whether it may be more an indirect activity due to change in
pH or, additionally, redox potential changes which may take
place in micro environments and may substantially accelerate
the precipitation of both manganese and iron.

Dr. Ehrlich: My working hypothesis, of course, has been
that it is enzymic oxidation of manganese, but I do not have
data at present to substantiate this hypothesis. The pH changes
are such -- the pH with peptone added and bacteria developing,
never rises to 8, below which spontaneous oxidation of
manganous manganese has been reported to be very slow.
Above 8, it will oxidize very quickly; we observe that in the
test tube. This has been one of my major bases for the
working hypothesis on which I am proceeding.

Dr. E. G. Mulder (Landbouwhogeschool, Wageningen):
I would draw attention to the stimulative effect of hydroxy
acids on the non-enzymatic oxidation of manganese. In the
presence of citric acid and malic acid, for instance, there
may be non-enzymatic oxidation of manganese at pH values
between 7.5 and 8.0, which is much lower than normal.

Dr. Ehrlich: We do not observe accelerated manganese
adsorption, which we assume to be due to manganese oxidation,
in the presence of glucose, which may be the source of such
acids through microbial action. If anything, there is a release
of manganese by certain bacteria from the nodules in the
presence of glucose and peptone. I suppose there is a possibility for such acids to be formed.

Dr. D. Pramer (Rutgers Univ.): I would like to ask Dr.

Ehrlich his opinion as to the mechanism by which these organisms survive and even grow in environments such as he described; that is, an acid environment in which there is a high concentration of soluble copper. Is this a matter of resistance on the part of, say, the components of these organisms to copper toxicity, or is it a matter of permeability, or what?

Dr. Ehrlich: In the literature such tolerance has been ascribed to specific genetic properties. Many papers mention training, which, I assume, means the selection of particularly resistant mutants that tolerate copper, and this may well be part of the story. But there is also the tolerance to iron which these bacteria possess without any training.

My explanation for this tolerance is one, based on permeability. One never finds any accumulation of iron oxides inside the cell. Therefore I think that the iron and probably the copper, or any other metal which may or may not be oxidized by these bacteria, never gets into the cells. To keep the iron out, the bacteria require very acid pH because this theoretically would keep the cell surface at a relatively positive surface charge and this might prevent the penetration of these metals into the cells. At pH 7 these organisms not only do not grow, but they die, their viability being lost in a relatively short time. Acid pH here, I think, is of particular importance to the cell in keeping these substances out. The oxidation probably goes on at the cell surface. In the work of Vernon et al. (42) , and also in the work of Blaylock and Nason (5, 6) it appears that cytochrome c, which apparently is directly involved in these oxidations, is a member of the membrane component of enzymes.

Dr. Mulder: Years ago, we studied the effect of microorganisms on copper and found that microorganisms which produced H2S precipitated large amounts of copper. It appeared that this copper which was precipitated by the H2S was not available to microorganisms, Aspergillus, for instance.

Dr. Ehrlich: The copper that I think Dr. Pramer and I were referring to is dissolved copper, 0.8 g per liter, which remains in solution.

Dr. R. L. Starkey (Rutgers Univ.): We studied, in the past, the copper tolerance of certain fungi, and we found

that they were able to grow in a solution containing glucose
and saturated with copper sulfate at as low a pH as zero.
If you raise the pH, the copper is toxic, as Dr. Ehrlich
said, so that around neutrality the cell is exceedingly sensitive to copper. Around the critical range of pH 4 to 5, there
is a turning point below which they are exceedingly tolerant
and above which they become increasingly sensitive to
copper in the form of soluble copper sulfate.

4

THE ECOLOGICAL ROLE OF PHOSPHORUS IN WATERS
WITH SPECIAL REFERENCE TO MICROORGANISMS

John E. Phillips
Department of Biology
Dalhousie University
Halifax, Nova Scotia, Canada

The low phosphorus concentration in natural waters compared with that required to support phytoplankton growth in
laboratory tanks (reviewed by Hutchinson, 1957) supports
the belief that the phosphorus level might normally limit the
productivity of lakes and oceans. When attempts were made
to increase the productivity of marine and fresh-water ponds
by adding large amounts of phosphorus it was invariably
found that nearly all of the added nutrient disappeared within a few days (Smith, 1945; Orr, 1947; Pratt, 1949; Holden,
1961). The theory that this loss was associated with stimulated growth, while true in part, demanded reconsideration
when it was discovered that radiophosphate (P^{32}) in trace
quantities diminished in the water in the same exponential
manner as large masses of fertilizer (Hayes et al., 1952;
Rigler, 1956). It now appears that there is a continual exchange of phosphorus between the water and the solids within natural waters and that the quantitative distribution of
phosphorus between the phases represents a state of dynamic,
if normally fluctuating, equilibrium. That is to say, were
the opposite technique followed of taking up phosphorus from
the water on, say, ion exchange resins, a continuous replacement from the solids would be expected.
      The purpose of this paper is to consider the importance
of microorganisms in the exchange of phosphorus between
the water phase, the sediments, higher plants, and zooplankton.

The experiments which I shall describe were carried
out in the laboratory using samples of water brought to the
laboratory with precautions taken to prevent undue multiplication of microorganisms. In the initial experiments
8-oz, wide-mouth jars containing 150 ml of filtered water
were used, to which plants, zooplankton-like organisms or
antibiotics (terramycin and tetracycline) were added as
desired. To study the exchange at the mud-water interface,
a 1 cm layer of superficial lake sediment could be centri-
fuged to the bottom of the jar before the addition of the water
(Fig. 1). All systems were set up in duplicate, and results
to be presented represent pooled results. The water was
continually mixed by bubbling through the system either air
or nitrogen which was first passed through a bacteria-
retaining filter. This treatment also served to produce oxidizing and reducing (i.e. anaerobic) conditions respectively.

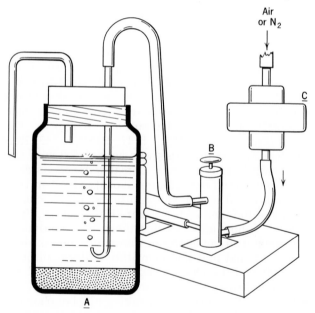

Fig. 1—An artificial mud-water system A, with gas jet connected to a
   needle valve B, and an aerosol bacterial filter C. Sterile apparatus
   was used and precautions against contamination taken so that the only
   opportunity for entrance of foreign bacteria was for about 15 sec.
   during collection of samples (Hayes and Phillips, 1958).

When using antibiotics, periodic checks were made to ensure that they were both toxic to bacteria and non-toxic to the plants and animals. The artificial systems, once set up at 4 C in the dark, were allowed to stand for one week so that a chemical and biological equilibrium might be reached. After this period, less than 1 ml of a sterile solution of carrier-free radiophosphate was added to the water and the decline in radioactivity in the water followed. It should be stressed that the absolute amount of phosphorus added was negligible compared with the amount already in the water. The isotope merely indicated the rate of exchange of phosphorus in the steady state and did not represent net movement.

Exchange with the Mud and Higher Plants. Before studying the phosphorus exchange at the mud-water interface, it was necessary to determine whether the exchange in the artificial systems represented that under conditions more closely approaching those in the lake itself. The preparation of an artificial system involves the destruction of the natural physico-chemical and biological layering of the surface muds. If layering were in any way peculiar and important to the phosphorus exchange in lakes, different results would be expected with natural Jenkin cores in which the mud-water interface was undisturbed. The exchange of radiophosphate with the mud of natural and artificially prepared Jenkin cores is shown in Fig. 2. The two systems apparently are identical in behaviour. Obviously, if any heterogeneous structure of the natural mud-water interface is important at all in the phosphorus exchange, it is quickly re-established when the mud surface is disturbed.

This experiment will serve to illustrate several general findings concerning the phosphorus exchange with the mud:

(1) When bacteria are inactivated by antibiotics or by heat sterilization there is a much more rapid loss of radiophosphate to the mud. This probably represents exchange of the radioisotope for unlabelled phosphate in precipitates and on the surface of colloidal particles in the mud (Einsele, 1938; Ohle, 1953; MacPherson et al., 1958).

(2) With one exception, in more than 100 artificial mud-water systems representing samples from 8 lakes of varying

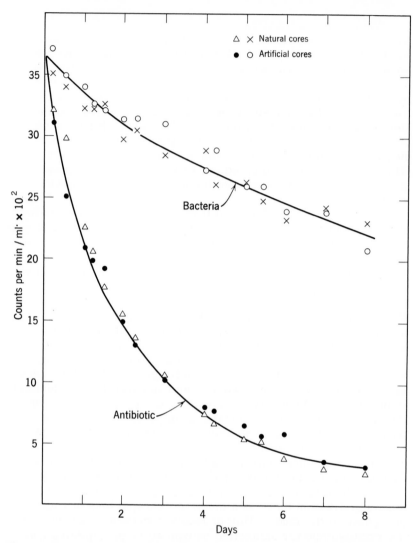

Fig. 2—The amount of radiophosphorus remaining in Grand Lake water over mud in natural and artificial Jenkin cores with and without antibiotic, i.e., bacteria absent and present (Hayes and Phillips, 1958).

productivity, the amount of radiophosphorus remaining in the water at equilibrim was greater in the control systems in which bacteria were active than in the corresponding

systems to which antibiotic had been added. This indicates
a higher concentration of exchangeable phosphorus in the
water.

(3) The above observation was true whether the system
was treated with nitrogen or air; i.e., was aerobic or was
anaerobic, as normally occurs in the hypolimnion of many
lakes during summer stratification.

(4) The ability of the water bacteria to retain so large
a proportion of the exchangeable phosphorus in the water
suggests that the microorganisms within the superficial
layers of sediment, which considerably out-number those in
the water per unit volume, are normally relatively inactive,
at least in the phosphorus exchange.

We turn now to a similar series of experiments in which
mud was omitted and the solid phase consisted of a 2 g
sprig of a higher fresh-water plant, e.g., the pipewort
(Eriocaulon). In the absence of bacteria, Eriocaulon very
rapidly takes up radiophosphate and reaches an equilibrium
within 1 day at which time only 10 per cent of the radiophosphorus remains in the water (Fig. 3). Here, as with
mud, the effect of bacteria is to reduce the rate of exchange
of radiophosphorus with the plant and to hold most of the
phosphorus (70 per cent)in the water. Similar results were
obtained with other of the higher plants (Fig. 3) more commonly found in Nova Scotia lakes, the bladderwort (Utricularia)
and the peat moss (Sphagnum), suggesting that these observations may hold for higher aquatic plants in general.

Two experiments were done with a layer of sediment at
the bottom of the bottle and with added plants thus placing all
three components in competition (Fig. 4A). In terms of wet
weight, the quantity of mud was 20 times that of the plant
(Eriocaulon). The ability of the plant to remove so great a
quantity of radiophosphorus from the water when the mud
control was unable to do so in the presence of bacteria indicates the considerably greater affinity of higher plants for
phosphorus compared with the sediments. In turn, the uptake
of radiophosphorus by higher plants can not match, on a
weight for weight basis, the activity of bacteria in retaining
phosphorus in the water.

These experiments suggest that there normally exists a
competition between the various solid phases for phosphorus
in natural waters so that the phosphorus in all phases represents
a potential reserve of phosphorus for any one of the living

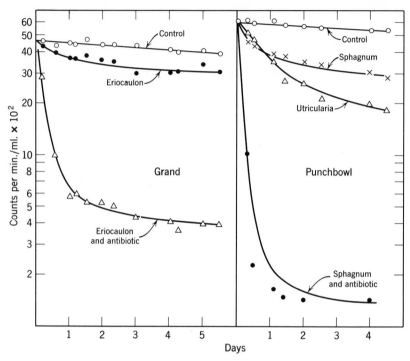

Fig. 3—Radiophosphorus remaining in aerated water (without added mud) from Grand Lake (primitive) and Punchbowl (acid bog) containing plants with and without antibiotic. The plants used were the pipewort (Eriocaulon), the bladderwort (Utricularia), and the peat moss (Sphagnum) (Hayes and Phillips, 1958).

components (e.g., plants or bacteria) should other conditions become more favourable for the development of the latter. Seen in such a context, the actual phosphate concentration in the water may bear little relation to productive capacity of natural bodies of water. As an example, the large fall-out of plankton following a bloom might be expected to increase bacterial activity at the mud surface of a lake by providing an energy source and thus alter the phosphorus exchange.

Approximately 0.3 g - aliquots of dead sterilized plankton were added to Grand Lake mud-water systems and to other

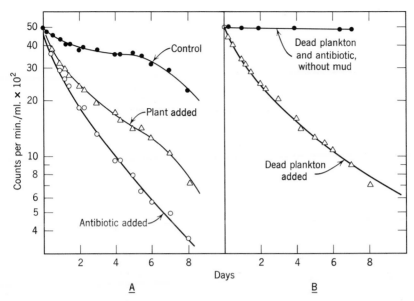

Fig. 4—A. Amount of P³² remaining in an aerated Grand Lake mud-
water system to which 2 g of Eriocaulon sprigs or 30 mg of tetracycline was added. B. Effect of adding dead plankton in the presence
and absence of bacteria. Comparing the lowest curve of A with the
top one of B it is shown that mud is necessary for the inorganic exchange of P³² and that sterile plankton will not serve as a substitute
for mud (Hayes and Phillips, 1958).

systems without mud but containing antibiotic. The plankton
immediately sedimented to the bottom of the systems. Dead
sterile plankton of itself is unable to adsorb significant
quantities of radiophosphate by a colloidal mechanism or by
other means (Fig. 4B). In the presence of bacteria, however,
there is an increased loss of radiophosphate to the mud compared with that in the control (Fig. 4A). This is undoubtedly
associated with increased activity of the mud bacteria. A
similar uptake of phosphorus by bacteria attached to falling
organic matter in natural waters is probably of importance in
the natural cycle.

Figure 4A illustrates another phenomenon which was
common to most experiments. While the control mud-water
systems seemed to reach equilibrium after 3 to 8 days, a

gradual loss of radiophosphorus continued over a period of
weeks until practically none remained in the water. This
decline is attributed to the fall-out of radiophosphorus in
the bodies of bacteria, since 89 per cent of the activity lost
could be recovered on a microbiological filter disc placed
on the bottom of the jar and since the fall-out did not occur
when antibiotics were added to the systems.

The exchange with zooplankton. The uptake of radiophosphorus by invertebrates was studied by a previous
graduate student of our department, E. Harris (1957).
Gammarus were set up with and without terramycin. In these
experiments the radiophosphorus activity within the body of
the animals was determined over periods of time following
the addition of the tracer to the water (Fig. 5). In the absence
of bacteria there is negligible uptake, indicating that direct
adsorption of inorganic phosphate does not occur appreciably
either through the body wall, intestine, or gills. The rapid
uptake of radiophosphorus by Gammarus in the presence of
bacteria (more recently confirmed by Rigler, 1961) is in
general agreement with various recorded experiments which
show that higher invertertebrates obtain their food by digestion
of particulate matter (in this case, bacteria) rather than by
direct adsorption of dissolved inorganic or organic compounds.
Microorganisms appear to play an essential role in withholding
phosphorus from other solid phases such as the sediment and
thus making it available to the zooplankton and, hence, to
higher groups in the food chain.

The organic exchange within the water. It is well known
that most of the phosphorus in natural waters, say 80 to 90
per cent in the summer, is in an organic form, either as
dissolved compounds or contained within particulate matter.
The most obvious explanation of the remarkable ability of
bacteria to hold phosphorus in the water is that they rapidly
take up radiophosphate and either retain it in their bodies or
release it as non-participating, dissolved organic compounds.
According to this theory, the conversion of radiophosphate to
dissolved organic radiophosphorus might involve two consecutive first-order reactions so that, following addition of radiophosphate, periodic measurements of the activity in the three
forms (dissolved inorganic, particulate and dissolved organic)
might exhibit the pattern shown in Fig. 6A. If the reactions
were reversible, the activity in each phase should reach an
equilibrium value rather than proceed to completion with all

the activity in the final form (i. e. , dissolved organic).

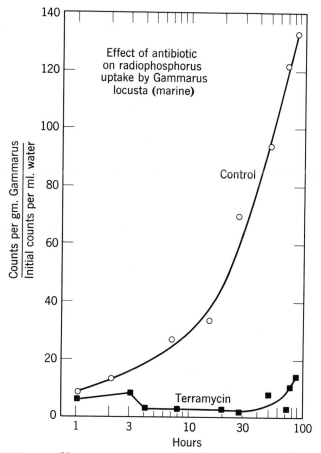

Fig. 5—Uptake of P^{32} by marine <u>Gammarus</u> after antibiotic treatment.
Specimens were washed in sterile sea water, then treated for 1 hr
on each of two successive days with terramycin in a concentration
of 100 mg per 100 ml water. After treatment the animals were transferred to flasks of sterile sea water for the experiment. Checks
were made for bacterial growth in each flask as animals were removed from it. No flask was completely free but there was reduction to as few as 5 colonies per ml. Evidently the intermediary activity of bacteria is necessary to permit inorganic phosphorus to be
used   (Harris, 1957).

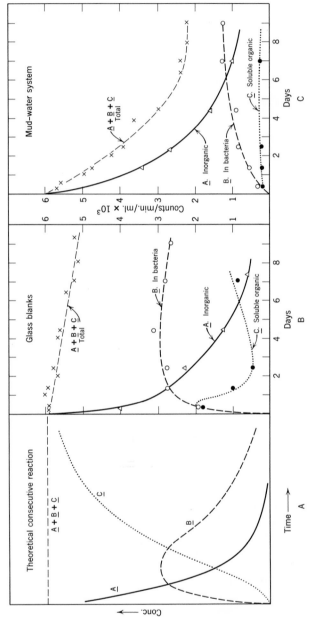

Fig. 6—Left: Pattern of an irreversible consecutive first-order reaction of type A → B → C. The second step is half as fast as the first. Center: Forms of P³² as they vary with time in an aerated bottle of Punchbowl water. Right: The same in a mud-water system, set up as shown in Fig. 1 (Hayes and Phillips, 1958).

In the following experiments, particulate radiophosphorus was estimated either from the activity retained on membrane filters (0.5 μ pore diameter, Millipore) or from the difference in the activity of filtered and unfiltered water. Dissolved organic radiophosphorus was estimated from samples of particulate-free supernatant following precipitation of the inorganic radiophosphate as a phosphomolybdate complex. Inorganic radiophosphate was estimated directly from the activity of the washed precipitate or indirectly as the difference in activity between filtered water before and after precipitation.

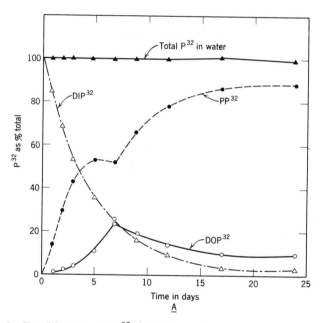

Fig. 7—A. Equilibration of P^{32} (added as a trace amount of dissolved inorganic orthophosphate DIP) with the phosphate system of sea water collected near Halifax, N.S., in June 1960. The experiment was carried out in darkness and at the in situ temperature of the water. DOP: dissolved organic phosphate; PP: particulate phosphate.

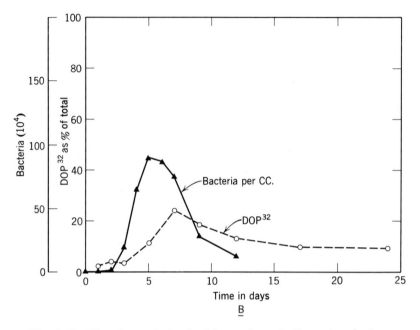

Fig. 7-B̲. The change in bacterial members in the water during
the equilibration shown in A̲. The dissolved organic P   curve
from A̲ is shown again here for comparison with the curve of
bacterial numbers (Watt and Hayes, 1963).

Experiments were carried out with water from several
lakes, both in the presence and absence of mud and antibiotics
(Figs. 6B, C). The loss of inorganic radiophosphate from the
water was accompanied by a rapid increase in particulate
P^{32} and the subsequent appearance of dissolved organic
radiophosphorus as predicted. Since all the activity remained
in the form of inorganic phosphate in the presence of antibiotics
it is certain that the particulate activity represents radiophosphorus incorporated within bacteria rather than adsorption
on inanimate particles.   There is no evidence for a direct
conversion of phosphate to dissolved organic phosphorus within the water itself. Since the exchange generally approached
an equilibrium, the conversion of dissolved inorganic phosphate
to dissolved organic phosphorus through the intermediate
activity of bacteria is obviously a reversible process.

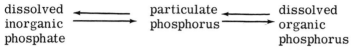

A similar but more rapid incorporation of radiophosphate by
phytoplankton has been observed (Hayes and Phillips, 1958;
Rigler, 1956).

More recently, Watt and Hayes (1963) have demonstrated
the same exchange in freshly collected sea water (Fig. 7A)
and have further investigated the source of the dissolved organic
phosphorus. Quite often a maximum is observed in the curve
for this component (Figs. 6B, 7A). When the equilibrium is
closely followed this dissolved organic maximum is invariably
found to coincide with a minimum in the particulate radiophosphorus curve. Estimations of bacterial numbers in the
water during the above experiment indicated that the dissolved
organic maximum occurred during a decline in bacterial
numbers (Fig. 7B).

The same results were obtained for sea-water bacteria
and a pure culture of the myxophytic alga, Nostoc, when
their growth was stimulated by adding nutrient broth to the
sea water, (Figs. 8A, B). The curve for particulate radiophosphorus followed closely the bacterial growth curve
measured as optical density. No dissolved organic phosphorus
appeared during the growth phase, suggesting that living
bacteria and phytoplankton do not normally release organic
phosphorus. The appearance of significant quantities of
dissolved organic radiophosphorus is associated with a decline
in cell numbers and is presumably due to the death and decay
of microorganisms.

To study the nature of the return reaction (i. e., from
organic to inorganic), a solution of natural, dissolved organic
radiophosphorus compounds was prepared utilizing the fact
that the common seaweed, Fucus vesiculosus, like fresh-
water plants, takes up radiophosphate from the water but
neither takes up nor releases dissolved organic phosphorus.
Sprigs of sterile Fucus were repeatedly added to a large
container of sea water which had equilibrated with radiophosphate for three days, at which time 30 per cent of the activity
was in the dissolved organic form. The dissolved organic
radiophosphorus content was thereby increased to 87 per cent
of the total activity. The remaining inorganic phosphate

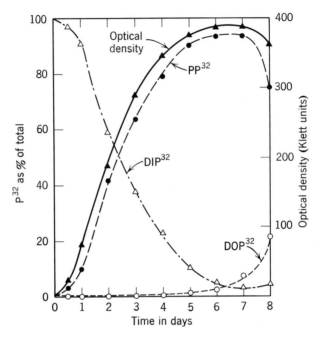

Fig. 8—A. Bacterial and phosphorus changes in aged sea water to which
organic nutrients and dissolved inorganic radiophosphate were added. The optical density is taken to be proportional to the number of
bacterial cells.

could be almost completely removed by filtration of the sea
water through a filter of 10 mμ pore diameter, so that 99
per cent of the remaining activity was in the dissolved organic
fraction.

The addition of this solution to freshly collected sea
water was followed by a slow decline of dissolved organic
radiophosphorus in the water (Fig. 9). This was accompanied
by a complementary increase in particulate radiophosphorus
while inorganic radiophosphate only appeared several days
later. On the other hand, all the activity remained in the
dissolved organic fraction for at least 1 month under sterile
conditions. The conclusion to be drawn from these experiments
is that there is no direct reconversion of dissolved organic
phosphorus to inorganic phosphate without intermediate incorporation into bacteria.

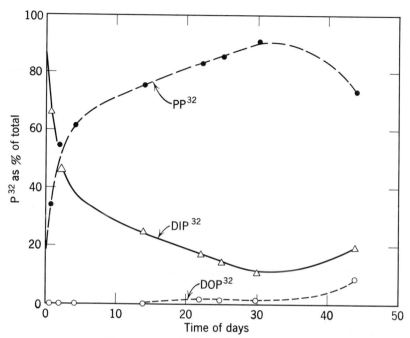

Fig. 8 —B. Equilibration of dissolved inorganic radiophosphate with a growing population of Nostoc. There was a noticeable death of algae after the thirtieth day (Watt and Hayes, 1963). DOP: dissolved organic phosphate; PP: particulate phosphate.

The dissolved organic radiophosphorus in equilibrated sea water has been separated into at least six fractions by unidimensional descending paper chromatography using 25 per cent trichloroacetic acid and acetone in a ratio of 1:3 as the solvent (Watt and Hayes, 1963). The peaks of activity were determined with a radiochromatogram scanner (Fig. 10). Peak V represents orthophosphate; peaks I, III and IV have been tentatively identified as nucleotides or polynucleotides on the basis of their adsorption on Norit A charcoal (Fig. 10). The non-adsorbed peaks II, VI and VIII may represent phosphorylated carbohydrates, although this is still a matter of speculation.

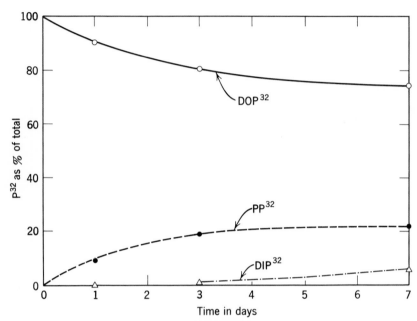

Fig. 9—Equilibration of dissolved organic radiophosphorus with freshly
collected sea water (mean of 5 trials). The equilibrations were carried out in darkness, at the in situ temperature of the water (Watt
and Hayes, 1963). DOP: dissolved organic phosphate; PP: particulate phosphate.

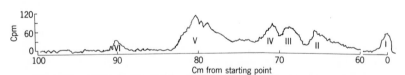

Fig. 10—Radiochromatogram scanner record of naturally occurring
dissolved organic radiophosphorus compounds from sea water labelled with P^{32}. Ordinate: counts per minute.

Integration of turnover times. There is now sufficient information from experiments here described and the literature (references given by Hayes and Phillips, 1958) to warrant a preliminary integration of time relationships of the several phosphorus reactions which might occur in a lake or bay (Fig. 11). The four kinds of lines are used as qualitative indicators of time. The exchange rates are expressed as turnover times; that is, the time required for the loss from a phase (e. g., mud, water, or bacteria) of as much phosphorus as is present in that phase. All values are in days except for one 5-min entry.

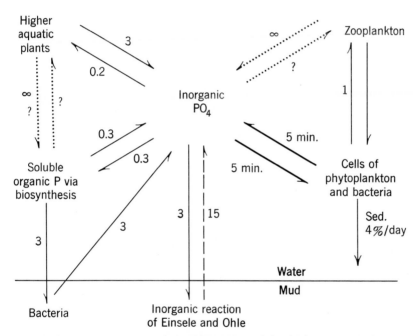

Fig. 11—Transformations of phosphorus in a lake with turnover times for different equilibria. Very heavy lines indicate the first reaction with suspended cells, time in minutes. Other times in days. Lighter solid lines are reactions at intermediate speeds—two or three orders of magnitude slower than the initial one. Dashed line is the return from mud by inorganic release, a still slower turnover. Dotted lines at top indicate reactions too slow to measure, called infinitely slow by comparison with the rest (Hayes and Phillips, 1958).

On adding phosphate to water, the immediate reaction is
the transfer through the bodies of unicellular suspended forms
of life. The turnover time for this reaction may vary between
5 min and several hours, presumably depending on a number
of factors such as temperature, light, cell density and
availability of nutrients. Next, there occurs, within a matter
of hours, a slower incorporation of inorganic phosphate into
organic forms, some of which are released as dissolved organic
compounds as a result of death and decay of microorganisms.
This component represents a large reserve of phosphorus in
the water which is presumably not available to the other solid
components and which can only be made available by bacterial
reconversion to phosphate. The exchange with the mud on
the left indicates the fallout of dead organisms and hence
potential dissolved organic phosphorus which may be re-
generated in the water or at the mud surface.

On the basis of present evidence the exchange with higher
plants seems to involve only dissolved inorganic phosphate
for which the turnover time is of the same order as the organic
exchange. Conversely the exchange with zooplankton, which
occurs primarily through feeding on microorganisms and
excretion, has a turnover time in terms of 1 to 2 days.

The lower part of Fig. 5 brings in the sediment surface.
When bacteria are inactive the turnover time for the inorganic
exchange with the sediment is 3 days for water, while the
return to water is slower, at 15 days. At the right, bacteria
are noted to fall out at a few per cent per day, representing
phosphorus which is more or less permanently lost to the mud.
This is for artifical bottle systems. In natural waters this
value is probably subject to wide variation.

LITERATURE CITED

Einsele, W. 1938. Über chemische und Kolloid-chemische
    Vorgänge in Eisen phosphat-systemen unter limnochemischen
    und geologischen Gesichtspunkten. Archiv. fur Hydrobiol.
    33: 361-387.

Harris, E. 1957. Radiophosphorus metabolism in zooplankton
    and microorganisms. Can. J. Zool. 35: 769-782.

Hayes, F.R., J.A. McCarter, M.L. Cameron, and D. A.
    Livingstone. 1952. On the kinetics of phosphorus exchange
    in lakes. J. Ecol. 40: 202-216.

Hayes, F.R. and J. E. Phillips. 1958. Lake water and
sediment. IV. Radiophosphorus equilibrium with mud,
plants, and bacteria under oxidized and reduced conditions.
Limnol. Oceanogr. 3:459-475.
Holden, A. V. 1961. The removal of dissolved phosphate
from lake waters by bottom deposits. Verh. Internat.
Verein. Limnol. 14:247-251.
Hutchinson, G. E. 1957. A Treatise on Limnology. Wiley.
New York.
MacPherson, L.B., N.R. Sinclair and F. R. Hayes. 1958.
Lake water and sediment. III. The Effect of pH on the
partition of inorganic phosphate between water and oxidized
mud or its ash. Limnol. Oceanogr. 3:318-326.
Ohle, W. 1953. Phosphor als Initialfaktor der Gewässer-
eutrophierung. Vom Wasser 20:11-23.
Orr, A.P. 1947. An experiment in marine fish cultivation.
II. Some physical and chemical conditions in a fertilized
sea-loch (Loch Craiglin, Argyll). Proc. Roy. Soc. Edin.
B. 68:3-20.
Pratt, D.M. 1949. Experiments in the fertilization of a
salt water pond. J. Mar. Res. 8:36-59.
Rigler, F. H. 1956. A tracer study of the phosphorus cycle
in lake water. Ecology 37:550-562.
Rigler, F. H. 1961. The uptake and release of inorganic
phosphorus by Daphnia magna Straus. Limnol Oceanogr.
6:165-174.
Smith, M.W. 1945. Preliminary observations upon the
fertilization of Crecy Lake, New Brunswick. Trans. Amer.
Fish. Soc. 75:165-174.
Watt, W. D. and F. R. Hayes. 1963. Tracer study of the
phosphorus cycle in sea water. Limnol. Oceanogr. 8:
276-285.

DISCUSSION

Mr. H. T. Victoreen (Philadelphia Suburban Water
Company): Many water utilities send out to their customers,
through mains, water which is almost totally devoid of
orthophosphate, perhaps a figure as low as 0.02 mg per liter
may be typical. These same utilities add to their water,
frequently, as much as 1 or 2 mg per liter of hexametaphosphate for corrosion control. Do we have any information
about the availability of this metaphosphate? Must the micro-

organisms wait patiently for spontaneous hydrolysis of the
hexametaphosphate in order to utilize the orthophosphate, or
can they accomplish this themselves, and can they derive
energy from these low energy phosphate bonds?

Dr. Phillips: I have no information on this. It is something we have not looked into at all.

Dr. John Sieburth(Univ. of Rhode Island): In your last
slide (Fig. 11) you showed a very slow regeneration of
phosphate by the zooplankton. In the last several years,
Conover showed tremendous excretion rates of phosphate
by zooplankton, presumably by the Entomostraca. Would
you care to comment on that?

Dr. Phillips: I think I showed a rapid exchange, i. e.,
a turnover time of one day for the zooplankton in the bottle
experiments. Other people, such as Conover, noted much
longer turn-over times, up to several days for other species.

Dr. Sieburth: Would you anticipate that the gut flora of
these zooplankton would be much more efficient than planktonic bacterial flora? Would you care to guess as to the
relative importance of these floras?

Dr. Phillips: I know of the experiments of Marshall and
Orr and of Rigler (1961). The former authors rinsed the
organisms off first and, presumably, had them sterile and
then put them in a sterile solution of radiophosphate. According to Rigler, in this case, it was possibly the bacteria
within the gut which fixed the phosphate and allowed them to
acquire the phosphate from the water.

Dr. D. Pramer (Rutgers Univ.): In your initial slide
(Fig. 1) you indicated that some studies were made under
anaerobic conditions. What differences, in general, were
there?

Dr. Phillips: According to the mechanisms of Einsele
and Ohle, one would expect a much higher concentration of
phosphate in the water under the anaerobic conditions; that
is, under reducing conditions the phosphorus could be released
from the mud since much of the phosphorus is in the mud as
ferric phosphate. On reduction this is changed to the more
soluble ferrous form and one would expect the phosphorus to
be released. The problem with these experiments was that

we found , although we had anaerobic conditions, only in some
of the systems were reducing conditions achieved as determined
by measuring the redox potential. For example, in the acid-
bog lakes we observed good reduction after bubbling the
systems for one day with nitrogen gas. But in other systems
we still had not observed reducing conditions after several
weeks. I purposely mention this point because, obviously,
we did not have reducing conditions in all experiments. In
the systems which were reduced, we did, in the absence of
bacteria, have a higher concentration of phosphate in the
water at equilibrium, but the effect of bacteria seemed to
overpower this inorganic mechanism. In the presence of
bacteria there was no uniform difference between the aerobic
and anaerobic systems.

5

IRON AND MANGANESE BACTERIA

R. S. Wolfe
Department of Microbiology
University of Illinois

It is my purpose here to discuss some of the properties
of the iron and manganese bacteria as well as to discuss
present concepts of certain members of the group. These
organisms have been one of my scientific hobbies for several
years; in discussing them I shall draw upon the observations
of others as well as my own. I regard them as a hobby
because a full-time study of these organisms is too difficult
to be profitable. Our knowledge of the iron and manganese
bacteria is very primitive.

The nature of the oxidation of the ferrous ion to the ferric
state and the biological implications of this reaction have been
established for many years. The following reaction, in which
ferrous carbonate is oxidized to ferric hydroxide, may be
utilized by iron bacteria, as suggested by Baas-Becking, et
al., in 1927 (1):

$$4 \ FeCO_3 + O_2 + 6H_2O = 4 \ Fe(OH)_3 + 4 \ CO_2 + 81,000 \ cal$$

$- \Delta \ F298 = 40,000$ cals (Baas-Becking and Parks).

Stephenson (2) has estimated (assuming a biological
efficiency of 5 per cent) that to produce 0.5 g of cell carbon
from CO_2, 224 g of ferrous iron would be required. Starkey
(3) has estimated that the ratio of iron oxidized to cell material
formed may be as high as 500 to 1. These calculations serve
to emphasize the magnitude of the problem faced by iron-
oxidizing organisms as well as to explain the large depositions
of ferric hydroxide produced by these organisms.

The oxidation of ferrous ions by oxygen at physiological pH is a rapid chemical reaction. Organisms which depend upon this oxidation of ferrous ions to ferric ions as a source of energy, at pH values near 7, must compete with non-biologically mediated oxidation. To compete effectively, then, these iron-oxidizing organisms must establish themselves at a propitious point between the source of ferrous ions and air. Iron bacteria, therefore, are gradient organisms and are not likely to compete under highly aerobic or under strongly reducing conditions. The Eh-pH environmental limits of iron bacteria in an estuarine environment have been studied by Baas-Becking and colleagues (4), as shown in Fig. 1. The reducing potential and pH of the environment of various deposits of iron bacteria were determined and plotted as shown here, these values roughly indicate the Eh-pH environmental limits of the iron bacteria observed by Baas-Becking. In the physiological pH range of about 5 to 8, the Eh, in millivolts, may range from +200 to +500.

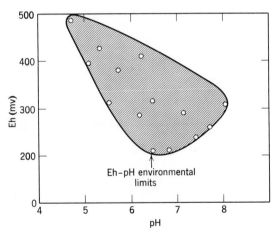

Fig. 1—Eh-pH limits of iron bacteria in an estuarine environment (Redrawn from Baas-Becking et al. (4).

One of the best examples of a gradient organism is Gallionella. The twisted stalks of ferric hydroxide secreted by this organism are its trade mark and are familiar to

water works personnel. As shown in Fig. 2, 3, and 4,
fragments of these stalks are easily recognized in natural
deposits of iron bacteria. It was not until the work of
Cholodny in 1924 that the bean-shaped bacterial cell was
discovered attached to the stalk and the true nature of the
twisted stalk as a secretion product of the cell was revealed
(5). Several years ago Dr. A. E. Vatter and myself made
a study of this organism using the electron microscope (6).
As shown in Fig. 5, the stalks are actually composed of many
strands of ferric hydroxide. The secretion of the stalk from
one side of the cell is an unique phenomenon, the mechanism
of which is unknown. A close examination of the strands of
the stalk reveals a discontinuous process of strand secretion.
A thesis on Gallionella has been published by van Iterson (7),
confirming these structural properties. In addition, her
micrographs reveal flagella on certain cells; however, her
proposal for a life cycle in this organism is speculative and
has not gained favor.

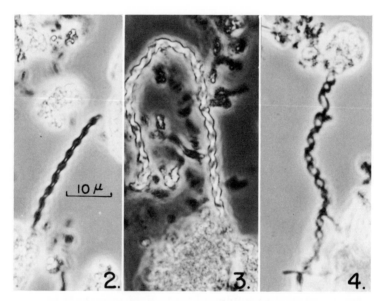

Figs. 2, 3 and 4—Stalk fragments of Gallionella as found in nature.
Phase-contrast photomicrographs (Taken with the assistance of
Mr. N. Ryckman).

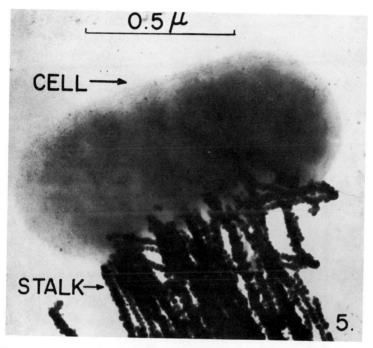

Fig. 5—Electron micrograph of Gallionella showing cell and secreted stalk of ferric hydroxide (Taken by Dr. A. E. Vatter).

It was in the laboratory of Professor C. B. van Niel that I first obtained successful enrichment cultures of Gallionella. Ferrous sulfide was chosen as a source of reduced iron. The reducing nature of this compound as well as its low solubility proved advantageous (8). In these enrichments growth of Gallionella was always initiated in a narrow zone, as shown in Fig. 6. The white deposit near the center of the tube represents colonies of Gallionella. The organism is sessile and, as the cells grow and divide, the stalks increase in length and bifurcate, forming fluffy balls about one mm in diameter. Growth occurs at room temperature in a simple medium consisting of CO_2, NH_4Cl, phosphate, mineral salts and FeS. Addition of CO_2 greatly stimulates growth and no growth occurs anaerobically (8, 9). Oxygen is the final electron acceptor. The gradient nature of the environment also is diagramed in Fig. 6. The region where

Gallionella grows is the region where deposition of ferric
iron occurs in uninoculated tubes. The organisms grow in
the gradient at the point where they can compete for ferrous
ions as well as for oxygen.

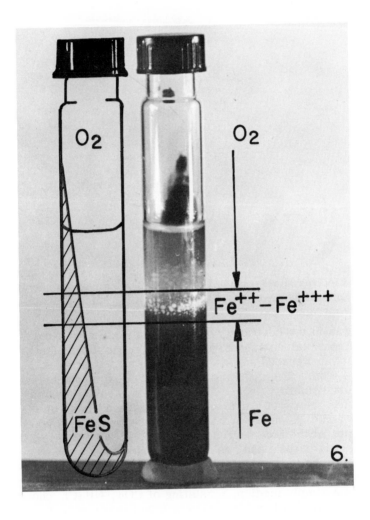

Fig. 6—Enrichment culture of Gallionella showing gradient nature of
growth.

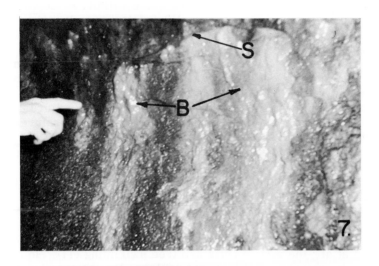

Fig. 7—Natural enrichment of iron bacteria. (S), seepage crack;
(B), masses of iron bacteria, yellow-brown in color.

In natural iron springs or seepages this phenomenon also
exists. A natural seepage area is shown in Fig. 7. Water
containing ferrous ions seeps through the vertical rock wall
and immediately below this area iron bacteria, including high
concentrations of Gallionella, are found. Water seeping
through the mass of bacteria provides a continuous supply of
ferrous ions. Although it is doubtful whether Gallionella has
ever been obtained in pure culture it is probably the best
example of a true iron bacterium which grows well in neutral
solution; it clearly defines this mode of life.

In contrast to the status of Gallionella, there is contro-
versy surrounding the status of the sheath-forming iron bacteria. Anyone who has ever looked at deposits of iron bacteria
with the microscope has observed the familiar forms shown
in Fig. 8 and 9. These hollow iron pipes have been known by
the name, Leptothrix ochracea, for many years. That ferric
hydroxide is deposited in the sheath is easily demonstrated;
however, factors concerning this deposition are controversial

at the present time. One concern is the validity of Leptothrix
ochracea. Is this organism a valid species or is it just a form
of another chlamydobacterium, such as Sphaerotilus? The
sheath, in the presence of iron-containing water, may be
merely a vehicle for the chemical deposition of ferric iron.
Pringsheim (10), starting with pure cultures of Sphaerotilus
natans, was able (by adjusting the nutrient as well as the
iron content of the medium) to reproduce in pure culture
various forms of iron bacteria described in the literature.
Pringsheim, therefore, regards Leptothrix as a form of
Sphaerotilus. Under conditions where ferric iron is being
deposited it does not take much imagination to visualize a
purely chemical deposition over the sheaths of Sphaerotilus
so that it would resemble the forms shown in Fig. 8.
Sphaerotilus has been studied by a number of investigators,
and it may be grown under a variety of nutrient conditions.
In a rich, yeast extract-tryptone medium, sheaths may not be
found at all; the motile cells are free swimming (11). In a
medium containing 0.5 per cent peptone, Dr. Elizabeth Gaudy,
in our laboratory, observed voluminous slime formation (12).
I mention this to emphasize the diversity of forms shown by
this organism, depending upon the source of nutrients provided. Table 1 presents a summary of Pringsheim's study
of the forms of Sphaerotilus natans. Form eutrophica shown
at the top is the form typical of polluted streams. Form
ochracea is the iron-pipe form found under conditions of high
iron concentration. Pringsheim regards this form as synony-
mous for Leptothrix ochracea. Other forms are also presented.
        In contrast to the work of Pringsheim, Beger and Bringmann
(13) consider Leptothrix and Sphaerotilus to be different. Paul
Prave has presented a lengthy article documenting his studies
on the growth of Leptothrix ochracea under conditions where
iron was oxidized (14). If his data actually represent growth,
as he intends, then this is evidence for biological oxidation
of iron by Leptothrix. His photographs show only empty sheaths
with no cells. More recently, Mulder and van Veen (15) have
studied 30 pure cultures of Sphaerotilus and Leptothrix and
have divided them into 5 groups, also presented in Table 1.
Group I was typical S. natans consisting of long filaments and
large cells. The organisms grew well in highly nutrient
solution. If the water contained iron, ferric iron was deposited
on the sheaths. In group II, the organisms possessed poor
ability to tolerate high nutrients, and oxidized manganese only

TABLE 1: A comparison of the observations of Mulder and Pringsheim
on the forms of Sphaerotilus and Leptothrix

E. G. Pringsheim (10) Forms of Sphaerotilus natans	Mulder and Van Veen (15) 30 strains of Sphaerotilus and Leptothrix (5 groups).
I. Form eutrophica (found in ponds and polluted streams).	I. Typical S. natans, long filaments, large cells, Fe^{+++} deposited on sheaths; no Mn^{++} oxidation; grows on rich media.
II. Form ochracea (found in water high in iron, this form has the following synonyms: Leptothrix ochracea, Leptothrix major, and Chlamydothrix ochracea).	II. Resembles S. natans. Retarded Mn oxidation, prefers low nutrients.
III. Form dichotoma (found in water low in iron and organic substances, this form has the synonym Cladothrix dichotoma).	III. Resembles S. natans. Oxidizes Mn. well. IV. Resembles S. natans. Grows well on high nutrient media. Deposits enormous amounts of manganic oxide.
IV. Form sideropus (synonyms: Chlamydothrix sideropus and Leptothrix sideropus).	V. Leptothrix discophora. Small cells; grows poorly on organic nutrients; oxidizes large quantities of Mn^{++}.
V. Form fusca (synonym: Clonothrix fusca).	(VI.) Leptothrix ochracea. (Enrichment cultures only) Short brittle sheaths, mostly empty. Cultivated in running, artificial ditch water.

after some time, whereas in group III the organisms, though
similar oxidized Mn^{++} well. The organisms in group IV
grew well on highly nutrient media but, in the presence of
Mn^{++}, deposited large amounts of manganic oxide. The
members of group V resembled Leptothrix discophora, grew
poorly on organic nutrients, and deposited large quantities
of manganic oxide. Leptothrix ochracea was obtained in

enrichment cultures and was clearly different from the other
organisms, possessing short brittle sheaths mostly empty.
Cells left the sheaths early and quickly formed new ones.
    An excellent example of a filamentous organism which
deposits both iron and manganese in its sheaths is the one
shown in Fig. 10. This low power photograph depicts the
hairlike growth of the dark brown filaments. We were unable
to cultivate this organism. Although we once obtained some
black colonies of Gallionella in a mineral medium containing
manganous salts, we were never able to subculture the colonies
in the same medium, so the filamentous, chlamydobacteria
such as Leptothrix discophora are the organisms which have
been studied most intensively as to the oxidation of manganous
compounds. The energetics of manganous oxidation are not
as favorable for the bacteria as those of ferrous oxidation;
less energy is available to the cells. This fact may account
for the large amounts of manganic oxide formed by Leptothrix
discophora, for instance, although it is by no means certain
that this oxidation actually yields energy for the organism.
Of the cells of the organism shown in Fig. 10, 12 per cent
of the total dry weight was an oxide of manganese and 10 per
cent was an oxide of iron.
    Another unique iron bacterium is the one shown in Fig. 11.
This organism was named Leptothrix trichogenes by Cholodny,
and Pringsheim has summarized its history (16). This organism, in my experience, is not common. I have found it
only in certain iron springs in high concentration. Even with
a good source of material it is difficult to locate the cells
microscopically in encrusted specimens; to my knowledge it
has not been cultivated.
    So far, we have been considering organisms which oxidize
iron or manganese at physiological pH. Oxidation of iron by
members of the Thiobacillus group has recently been well
established (17, 18, 19, 20, 21). These organisms grow well
under acid conditions where ferrous ions are not so readily
oxidized. They are isolated mostly from acid mine drainage.
In a medium at about pH 2.8, containing salts, with ferrous
sulfate as the energy source (under conditions of vigorous
aeration), growth is accompanied by a dramatic precipitation
of orange-red ferric iron, which does not occur in sterile
controls. Cells are typical, Thiobacillus-type cells. On the
basis of a nutritional study, Unz and Lundgren (22) propose
that Thiobacillus ferrooxidans of Colmer, Temple, and Hinkle

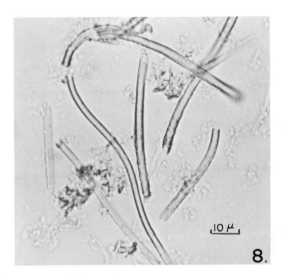

Fig. 8—Fragments of "Leptothrix ochracea" from a natural enrichment.

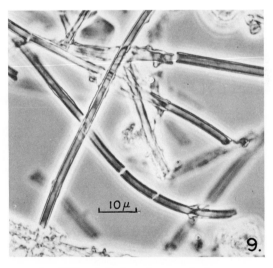

Fig. 9—Fragments of "Leptothrix ochracea," phase contrast photomicrograph. (Taken with the assistance of Dr. J. C. Ensign).

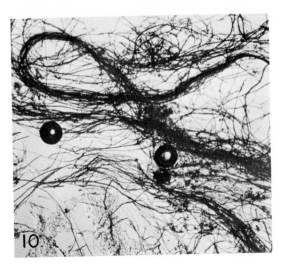

Fig. 10—Low-power photomicrograph of a filamentous iron- and manganese-depositing bacterium.

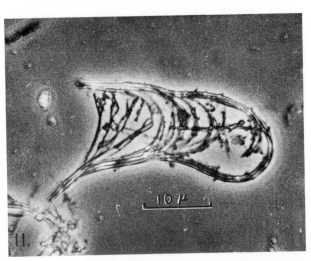

Fig. 11—Phase contrast photomicrograph of Leptothrix trichogenes, kindly provided by Mr. Arne Zimmergren, Malmo, Sweden.

(17, 18), be the type species of this group, and that
Ferrobacillus ferrooxidans of Leathen and Braley (19) and
Ferrobacillus sulfooxidans of Kinsel (20) be considered as
strains of this organism. The autotrophic mode of life which
depends on the oxidation of ferrous iron is best studied, at
the biochemical level, using these organisms.

In 1870, Cohn published a group of sketches of an organism which he had found and named Crenothrix polyspora
(23). This organism has become widely confused as an
iron-depositing bacterium; one attempt to clarify its morphological properties has been made (24). If cell types such as
those designated (A) in Fig. 12 only are found, it is impossible on the basis of a microscopic examination to distinguish this organism from Sphaerotilus natans. Cell-forms
designated (B) and (C) in Figure 12 are unique to Crenothrix,
however, and are not observed in Sphaerotilus. The round,
non-motile, conidia-like cells produced in large numbers
are derived from rod shaped cells. There is much to be
learned about the biology of this organism. Although Crenothrix is frequently found imbedded in masses of iron bacteria,
colonies are easily located by their colorless nature. As
shown in Fig. 13, the colonies consisting of hundreds of
filaments appear white by reflected light. The encrusted
iron bacteria in which the colony is situated are barely visible.
This is a low power photomicrograph taken through a dissecting microscope. Until this organism is cultivated in an
artificial medium it will remain an enigma.

The last 100 years of work with the iron bacteria have
been largely devoted to descriptive information. With the
cultivation of Thiobacillus ferrooxidans and the iron and
the manganese forms of the chlamydobacteria, it can be
expected that the next few years will see radical advances
in the enzymology of ferrous and manganous oxidation. This
is what really attracted my attention to the iron bacteria; the
possibility of studying the enzymology of the oxidation of
ferrous ions. Thiobacillus ferrooxidans is probably the
cellular material of choice for these studies.

There are two essentials for autotrophic existence: the
organism must obtain adenosine triphosphate for driving
synthetic reactions, and it must obtain reducing potential
for the reduction of CO_2 to the carbohydrate level. How do
autotrophic iron bacteria which oxidize ferrous ions at a
potential more positive than -0.32 volts, the E^1_0 for

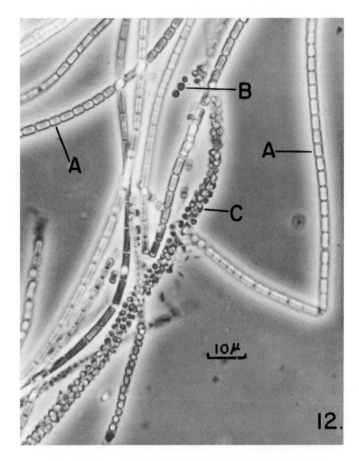

Fig. 12—Phase contrast photomicrograph of Crenothrix polyspora.
(A), typical bacillus cells within a sheath similar to that of
Sphaerotilus natans; (B) and (C) non-motile, sperical cells (con-
idia) unique to Crenothrix.

diphosphopyridine nucleotide, obtain reducing potential? Is
it possible that they carry out a reversal of oxidative phosphorylation to obtain reduced diphosphopyridine nucleotide?
The problem of adenosine triphosphate generation is also
an intriguing one. The enzymic steps in iron oxidation
where the potential drop is great enough to generate an an-
hydride phosphate bond remain to be demonstrated.

Fig. 13—Low-power photomicrograph of a natural enrichment of Crenothrix polyspora. Masses of trichomes appear white by reflected
light.

I point out these two problems, in conclusion, as only
two examples of the many interesting biochemical problems
awaiting study using various species of iron and manganese
bacteria.

LITERATURE CITED

1. Baas-Becking, L.G.M. and G. S. Parks. 1927. Energy relations in the metabolism of autotrophic bacteria. Physiol. Revs. 7:85-106.
2. Stephenson, M. 1950. Bacterial metabolism. Longmans, Green, and Co. New York. p. 266.
3. Starkey, R. L. 1945. Precipitation of ferric hydrate by iron bacteria. Science 102:532-533.
4. Baas-Becking, L.G.M., F. E. J. Wood, and I. R. Kaplan. 1956. Biological processes in the estuarine environment VIII. Iron bacteria as gradient organisms. Proc. Kon. Ned. Akad. v. Wet., B. 59:398-407.
5. Cholodny, N. 1924. Zur Morphologie der Eisenbakterien, Gallionella und Spirophyllum. Ber. Deut. Botan. Ges. 42: 35-44.
6. Vatter, A. E. and R. S. Wolfe. 1956. Electron microscopy of Gallionella ferruginea. J. Bacteriol. 72:248-252.
7. Van Iterson, W. 1958. Gallionella ferruginea(Ehrenberg) in a different light. Thesis. Amsterdam.
8. Kucera, S. and R. S. Wolfe. 1957. A selective enrichment method for Gallionella ferruginea. J. Bacteriol. 74: 344-349.
9. Wolfe, R. S. 1958. Cultivation, morphology, and classification of the iron bacteria. J. Am. Water Wks. Assoc. 50:1241-1249.
10. Pringsheim, E. G. 1949. The filamentous bacteria Sphaerotilus, Leptothrix, Cladothrix, and their relation to iron and manganese. Phil. Trans. Roy. Soc. London. Ser. B. 233: 453-462.
11. Stokes, J. L. 1954. Studies on the filamentous sheathed iron bacterium Sphaerotilus natans. J. Bacteriol. 67:278-291.
12. Gaudy, E. T. and R. S. Wolfe. 1961. Factors affecting filamentous growth of Sphaerotilus natans. J. Appl. Microbiol. 9:580-584.
13. Beger, H., and G. Bringmann. 1953. Die Scheidenstruktur des Abwasserbakteriums Sphaerotilus und des Eisenbakteriums Leptothrix im elektronenmikroskopischen Bilde und ihre Bedeutung für die Systematik dieser Gattungen. Zbl. Bakt. II, 107:318-334.
14. Prave, P. 1957. Untersuchungen über die Stoffwechselphysiologie des Eisenbakteriums Leptothrix ochracea Kützing. Arch. Mikrobiol. 27:33-62.

15. Mulder, E. G. and W. L. van Veen. 1962. The Sphaerotilus-Leptothrix group. VIII Int. Cong. Microbiol. Abstracts p. 50.

16. Pringsheim, E. G. 1949. Iron bacteria. Biol. Revs. Camb. Phil. Soc. 24:200-245.

17. Colmer, A. R., K. L. Temple, and M. E. Hinkle. 1950. An iron-oxidizing bacterium from the acid drainage of some bituminous coal mines. J. Bacteriol. 59:317-328.

18. Temple, K. L. and A. R. Colmer. 1951. The autotrophic oxidation of iron by a new bacterium: Thiobacillus ferrooxidans. J. Bacteriol. 62:605-611.

19. Leathen, W. W. and S. A. Braley. 1954. A new iron-oxidizing bacterium: Ferrobacillus ferrooxidans. Bacteriol. Proc. p. 44.

20. Kinsel, N. A. 1960. A new sulfur-oxidizing iron bacterium, Ferrobacillus sulfooxidans sp. n. J. Bacteriol. 80:628-632.

21. Beck, J. V. 1960. A ferrous ion-oxidizing bacterium. I. Isolation and some general physiological characteristics. J. Bacteriol. 79:502-509.

22. Unz, R. F. and D. G. Lundgren. 1961. A comparative nutritional study of three chemoautotrophic bacteria: Ferrobacillus ferrooxidans, Thiobacillus ferrooxidans, and Thiobacillus thiooxidans. Soil Sci. 92:302-313.

23. Cohn, F. 1870. Brunnenfaden (Crenothrix polyspora). Beitr. Biol. Pflanz. 1:108-131.

24. Wolfe, R. S. 1960. Observations and studies of Crenothrix polyspora. J. Am. Water Wks. Assoc. 52:915-918.

DISCUSSION

In the discussion of Dr. Wolfe's paper, Dr. Mulder presented a discussion at length on the Sphaerotilus-Leptothrix group at Dr. Wolfe's invitation. Dr. Mulder rewrote his remarks in part from the transcription of the discussion, and they are presented in the immediately following pages as a separate paper.

The general discussion of both Dr. Wolfe's and Dr. Mulder's presentations will be found in the pages following Dr. Mulder's paper.

6

SOME OBSERVATIONS OF THE
SPHAEROTILUS-LEPTOTHRIX GROUP

E. G. Mulder
Laboratory of Microbiology
University of Illinois

In the last five years we have isolated a considerable number of sheath-forming bacteria of the Sphaerotilus-Leptothrix group. Morphological and physiological characters of the isolated strains were studied (3, 4). In order to grow the organisms under more or less natural conditions, and to compare pure cultures with crude enrichment cultures, an apparatus (Fig. 1) was used for continuous culture in slowly-running, sterile soil extract, containing ferrous iron ("artificial ditch water"). In addition we cultivated the organisms on agar media and in culture solutions in the absence or presence of manganese salts, particulary manganous carbonate. In separate experiments the effect of various nitrogenous and carbon compounds and of a number of vitamins was tested.

The latter experiments revealed that the members of the Sphaerotilus-Leptothrix group can be grown in synthetic media containing glucose as the carbon source, aspartic or glutamic acids as nitrogen sources and vitamin B_{12} as the only vitamin. Many strains are able to utilize inorganic nitrogen compounds. Vitamin B_{12} can be replaced by methionine.

A common feature of the bacteria belonging to this group is the presence within the cells of globules of poly-β hydroxybutyric acid, serving as reserve material (2, 3, 4).

By comparing the morphological and physiological characters of the isolated organisms, at least five different types were distinguished. Type I is the sewage bacterium, Sphaerotilus natans, an organism with long, strongly-cohering sheaths which are often filled to more than 75 per cent with large rod-

98

form cells (Fig. 2). Organisms of this type have been isolated from running waste water, activated sludge and sporadically from running ditch water containing precipitated ferric hydroxide.

Fig. 1—Apparatus for growing iron bacteria in running artificial ditch
water. 1, cylinder containing ironstone soil; 2, Seitz-filter; 3, outlet for taking samples of filtered iron-containing soil extract (artificial ditch-water); 4, distribution of the artificial ditch water
amongst Erlenmeyer vessels of higher set, 5; 6, inoculation tube;
7, gas cylinder; 8, inlet gas mixture (O_2,1; CO_2,5; N_2, 94, per cent);
9, Erlenmeyer vessels of lower set with outlet (cotton plugs of
lower vessels present during sterilzation of apparatus only).

S. natans grows well with a variety of carbon compounds, of which it may utilize relatively high concentrations.

On agar media with 5 g glucose and 5 g peptone per liter the colonies of S. natans have smooth edges, as contrasted to the filamentous colonies obtained with a more limited nutrient supply (Fig. 3 and 4). In the smooth colonies practically no sheaths are present (Fig. 5).

In sterile, running ditch water containing ferrous iron, S. natans is able to grow slowly, depositing ferric hydroxide

in and on its sheaths (Fig. 6 and 7). Although under these
conditions the sewage organism behaves like an iron bacterium,
it is clearly different from Leptothrix ochracea which, according to Pringsheim (5, 6), is identical with S. natans.
Sphaerotilus natans, when growing in iron-containing ditch
water in the apparatus of Fig. 1, kept some of its typical
characters (formation of long sheaths, partly filled with
cells; Fig. 6) which were never seen in the crude enrichment
cultures of L. ochracea when growing under the same conditions (Fig. 8). Leptothrix ochracea formed rather short
sheaths almost entirely free of cells. Further evidence
that L. ochracea is not identical with S. natans is provided
by the fact that isolates from the enrichment cultures of
L. ochracea very seldom resembled S. natans, whereas the
latter could easily be re-isolated after it had been grown as
an iron bacterium.

Strains of type I are unable to oxidize manganous salts.
Under certain conditions, the cells of these strains may be
packed with globules of poly-β-hydroxybutyric acid (Fig. 9).

Types II and III include organisms with large cells which
resemble S. natans morphologically, but differ from it in
utilizing relatively low concentrations of organic nutrients.
In contrast with S. natans, strains of these types are able to
oxidize manganous carbonate to black manganic oxide. Strains
of type II oxidize manganese more slowly ("retarded manganese
oxidation") than those of type III. These types have been
isolated from activated sludge and waste water, as well as
from running ditch water containing iron precipitates.

In liquid media, the isolated strains of type II form fungus-
like flocks consisting of short trichomes, radiating from a
common holdfast (Fig. 10). Since a similar type of growth
has been observed under natural conditions by Dorff (1) and
described by him as Leptothrix lopholea, we introduced the
name L. lopholea Dorff for organisms of type II.

Organisms of type III, when cultivated in running, iron-
containing ditch water in the apparatus of Fig. 1, resemble
Leptothrix ochracea much more closely than is true of
Sphaerotilus natans. Their iron-containing sheaths are much
shorter than those of S. natans, when growing under similar
conditions, and empty sheaths occur much more frequently
(Fig. 11). Although the possibility that type III is identical
with L. ochracea is not ruled out, we believe that it is
different and therefore we introduced the name Leptothrix

pseudo-ochracea n. sp. for the strains of type III.
L. ochracea as it occurs in natural waters was studied
as a crude culture in artificial ditch water in the apparatus
of Fig. 1. The organism is able to form large masses of
almost empty sheaths (Fig. 8) by a continuous migration of
the cells from the sheaths. In some instances, cells leaving
their sheaths were found to have formed already a new
sheath within the old one.

Types IV and V are strong manganese oxidizers. The
manganic oxide is present in large amounts in, on, or outside the sheaths. However, both types are clearly different.
Type IV is an intermediate form between types I (S. natans)
and V (Leptothrix discophora). Cultivated in media containing
glucose and peptone, it behaves like a typical S. natans, re-
sponding to relatively high concentrations of these nutrients.
In poor media containing manganous salts, large amounts of
black-brown manganic oxide are formed. The oxide may be
present as a smooth, continuous layer in or on the sheaths,
as numerous small granules, or as irregular masses on the
sheaths (Fig. 12, 13 and 14).

On agar media well-supplied with sugars and peptone,
large, white, smooth colonies are formed, in contrast
with the black-brown, filamentous colonies on media con -
taining low amounts of organic nutrients but excessive amounts
of manganous carbonate (Fig. 15 and 16).

Although the name Leptothrix discophora or L. crassa
has been used in literature for manganese-oxidizing organisms
of both types IV and V, we reserved this name for type V and
introduced the name Leptothrix cholodnii n. sp. for type IV.
Strains of this type have been isolated from iron-containing
ditch water and some from activated sludge.

Type V, Leptothrix discophora, generally has considerably
smaller cells than type IV. It requires only small amounts of
organic nutrients; higher amounts do not favour and often
inhibit growth. On all agar media tested, the size of the
colonies is considerably smaller than that of the other types
(Fig. 17 and 18).

L. discophora has a pronounced capacity to oxidize
manganous compounds. Colonies are filamentous (on poor
media containing manganous carbonates; Fig. 18) or smooth
(on media containing glucose and peptone, particularly when
widely spaced; Fig. 17). Under certain conditions they may
be surrounded by a black-brown halo of manganic oxide

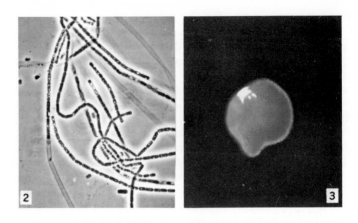

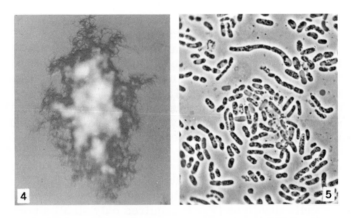

Figs. 2-5—Type I (Sphaerotilus natans). Fig. 2—Ensheathed cells grown in mineral salts solution containing 1 g glucose and 1 g peptone per liter; 810 x.
Fig. 3—Smooth colony on mineral salts agar, containing glucose, 5 g, and peptone, 5 g, per liter; colonies widely spaced; 14.5 x.
Fig. 4—Filamentous colony on mineral salts agar, containing glucose, 1 g, and peptone, 1 g, per liter; colonies crowded; 14.5 x.
Fig. 5—Cells without sheaths, grown on mineral salts agar containing 5 g glucose and 5 g peptone per liter; 810 x.

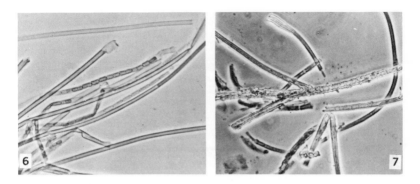

Figs. 6 and 7—Ensheathed cells and empty sheaths in running artificial ditch water in the apparatus of Fig. 1; 810 x.

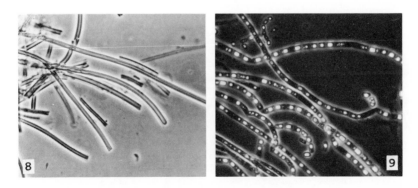

Fig. 8 -Crude culture of L.ochracea in the apparatus of Fig. 1; 810 x.
Fig. 9—Globules of poly-β-hydroxybutyric acid in ensheathed cells of S.natans; 810 x.

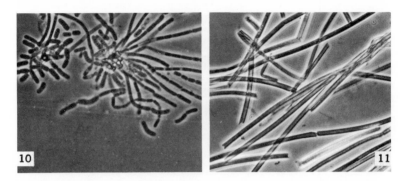

Fig. 10—Type II (Leptothrix lopholea) in mineral salts medium containing glucose, 2.5 g, and peptone, 2.5 g, per liter; 810 x.
Fig. 11—Type III (Leptothrix pseudo-ochracea) in running artificial ditch water in the apparatus of Fig. 1; 810 x.

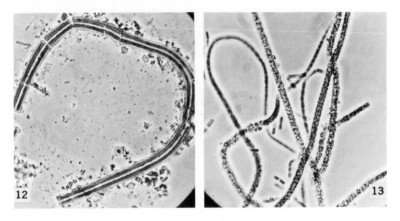

Fig. 12, 13 and 14—Type IV (Leptothrix cholodnii) in mineral salts medium containing glucose, 0.2 g, peptone, 0.2 g, and $MnSO_4 \cdot 1H_2O$, 25 mg, per liter. Figs. 12 and 14 strain 5; Fig. 13 strain 1; 810 x.

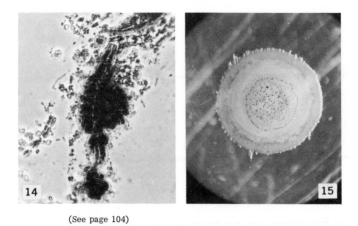

(See page 104)

Fig. 15 and 16—Type IV (L.cholodnii); smooth colony on mineral salts
agar containing glucose, 1 g, and peptone, 1 g, per liter (Fig. 15);
6.8 x, and filamentous colony on manganous carbonate agar containing
sodium citrate, small amounts of yeast and beef extracts and 2 g MnCO$_3$
per liter (Fig. 16); 9 x.

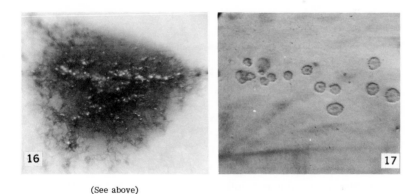

(See above)

Fig. 17-21—Type V (Leptothrix discophora). Fig. 17—Smooth colony
on mineral salts agar containing glucose, 5 g, and peptone, 5g, per
liter; 18.5 x.

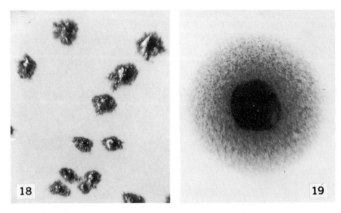

Fig. 18—Filamentous colony on manganous carbonate agar containing sodium citrate, small amounts of yeast and beef extracts and 2 g $MnCO_3$ per liter; 14.5 x.
Fig. 19—Smooth colony surrounded by halo of manganic oxide on medium containing glucose, 1 g, peptone, 1 g, and $MnSO_4 \cdot 1H_2O$, 5 mg, per liter; 30 x.

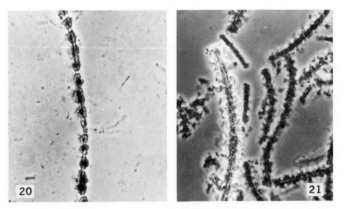

Fig. 20—Manganic oxide precipitated on sheaths in the vicinity of the cells (in nutrient solution containing mineral salts, glucose, 0.2 g, peptone, 0.2 g, and $MnSO_4 \cdot 1H_2O$, 25 mg, per 1); 810 x.
Fig. 21—Ferric hydroxide precipitated on the sheaths (in running ditch water of the apparatus of Fig. 1); 810 x.

(Fig. 19). In nutrient solutions containing manganous sulphate, manganic oxide is precipitated in or on the sheaths (Fig. 20). In iron-containing, running, ditch water, organisms of this type grow better than those of the other types. Under these conditions they form irregular flocculent masses of ferric hydroxide which are surrounding the sheaths (Fig. 21).

ACKNOWLEDGEMENT

The photographs in this paper were originally published in: Mulder, E. and W. van Veen. 1963. Investigations on the Sphaerotilus-Leptothrix group. Antonie van Leeuwenhoek 29:121-153.

They are reproduced again with the kind permission of the publishers of Antonie van Leeuwenhoek Journal of Microbiology and Serology.

LITERATURE CITED

1. Dorff, P. 1934. Die Eisenorganismen. Pflanzenforsch. H. 16. Hrsg. von R. Kolkwitz. G. Fischer, Jena.
2. Mulder, E. G., M. H. Deinema, W. L. van Veen, and L. P. T. M. Zevenhuizen. 1962. Polysaccharides, lipids and poly-β-hydroxybutyrate in microorganisms. Rec. Trav. Chim. Pays-Bas 81:797-809.
3. Mulder, E.G. and W. L. van Veen. 1962. The Sphaerotilus-Leptothrix group. VIIIth Intern. Congr. for Microbiol. Montreal. Abstr. B 12.7.
4. Mulder, E. G. and W. L. van Veen. 1963. Investigations on the Sphaerotilus-Leptothrix group. Antonie van Leeuwenhoek J. Microbiol. Serol. 29:121-153.
5. Pringsheim, E. G. 1949 a. The filamentous bacteria Sphaerotilus, Leptothrix, Cladothrix and their relation to iron and manganese. Trans. Roy. Soc. (London) Ser. B. 233:453-482.
6. Pringsheim, E. G. 1949 b. Iron bacteria. Biol. Revs. 24:200-245.

DISCUSSION

Mr. J. Zajic (Kerr-McGee Oil Ind.): A comment for Dr. Mulder. In your comments about the deposition of the manganese it is assumed that there is an intracellular enzyme. If there were an extracellular enzyme, I think that there would also be oxidation and deposition.

Dr. Mulder: We do not believe that enzymes are involved. There is a very large halo around the colonies, perhaps four or five times larger than the colony, so it looks improbable, in my opinion, that we have to do with enzymes. I am not quite sure what is active, but I do not belive it is an enzyme. It may be a question of a chemical reaction catalyzed by some excreted substance. I mentioned previously that hydroxy acids may, in very low concentrations, stimulate the oxidation of manganous to manganic oxide; but we have not yet studied that in this connection; it is possible, however, that there is excretion of some hydroxy acid which catalyzes the reaction.

Dr. Wolfe: Several years ago, to test Pringsheim's results, we took sheaths of Sphaerotilus natans which were well formed in an organic medium, then killed the cells by various techniques, and then added water containing ferrous ions. There was deposition of ferric hydroxide in the sheaths and I, therefore, lost interest in this problem and assumed that Pringsheim was right.

But I would like to ask, Dr. Mulder, have you tried dead cells?

Dr. Mulder: We very recently had some indication that dead cells can deposit manganese.

Mr. R. H. Culver (Camp, Dresser & McKee): I would like to ask Dr. Wolfe several questions. Would these organisms grow under anaerobic conditions?

Dr. Wolfe: We have never been able to grow chlamydobacteria or Gallionella under anaerobic conditions in any way.

Mr. Culver: Do they require an acid pH or will they grow under alkaline conditions?

Dr. Wolfe: Speaking again about Gallionella, we were never able to grow it lower than pH 6.5.

Dr. Mulder: In general, the pH for chlamydobacteria is 6.8 or 7.

Mr. Culver: Will they grow above pH 6.8?

Dr. Mulder: They grow up to pH 8.

Mr. Culver: I ask this from a practical viewpoint, because

there are many acid waters in New England in which these
organisms, or organisms resembling these, occasionally
grow, and if we could raise the pH of this water to 9 or so
to get rid of them, it would be a practical approach to the
control of them.

Would adding 2 mg per liter of phosphate to the water for
the control of corrosion tend to stimulate these if the water
system were infested with this type of organism?

Dr. Wolfe: I think that it would create quite a natural
enrichment, on a continual basis. Phosphate may be
limiting in certain waters. In my experience, wherever
phosphate is added for a long time there will be enrichment
and trouble.

Dr. A. H. Romano (Univ. of Cincinnati): I would like to
know how Dr. Wolfe convinced himself that the ferric hydroxide was secreted rather than simply deposited on the organic
matrix of Gallionella.

Dr. Wolfe: The fact that the individual strands of the
stalk are not continuous but seem to be formed in little
globules in a chain suggest that it may be formed in some
kind of a depression or vacuole; but there is no evidence for
it.

Dr. Romano: Dr. Mulder, you grew these organisms in
a continuous flow of soil extract to which was added the iron
and manganese. Is it possible that the growth was entirely
at the expense of organic matter in the soil extracts rather
than by oxidation of the minerals?

Dr. Mulder: Yes, that is possible.

Dr. Romano: Does anyone have evidence to show a
significant amount of carbon dioxide fixation; that is, to
show that a major proportion of the total carbon assimilated
by the cell comes from carbon dioxide which, of course, is
another characteristic of autotrophy?

Dr. Wolfe: I can't speak for the chlamydobacteria, but
with Gallionella one obtains no growth unless CO_2 is added
to the culture medium. And although it was not done with
radioactive CO_2, we once attempted to look for ribulose
diphosphate but we did not have enough material.

Dr. Romano: I believe Neisseria gonorrheae will not grow unless there is some carbon dioxide in the medium, too.

Dr. Wolfe: That is true, but there was no other carbon source in a purely inorganic culture medium.

Dr. Romano: I think this indicates that I remain rather skeptical about all of these organisms except for Thiobacillus ferrooxidans as real iron bacteria, if we were to apply the term strictly.

Dr. Wolfe: I am convinced that Gallionella is an autotroph, although at present we cannot prove it.

Dr. M. Alexander (Cornell Univ.): Would Dr. Wolfe care to speculate how an organism which gets only 10 kilocalories per gram of iron can form adenosine triphosphate?

Dr. Wolfe: It is one of the interesting problems one might be able to attack with extracts.

Dr. W. Stumm (Harvard Univ.): I want to comment about iron oxidation or manganese oxidation by dead or living organisms. It is relatively easy to create synthetic chemical systems in which such oxidations and juxtapositions can be observed, for example, even at the pH of 6, where manganese is certainly not oxidized. One merely lowers a grain or small crystal of calcite into the medium and manganese dioxide will be heavily deposited on the calcite crystal, despite the fact that the bulk of the solution is at pH 6. One can produce the same situation with a crystal of iron phosphate. We should be aware that there are many such catalysts which can mediate these oxidations.

Dr. Wolfe: Pringsheim deserves an enormous amount of credit for examining the literature on iron bacteria. There are literally dozens of descriptions of organisms which are actually due to such nonbiological precipitations. These have been given Latin names which are carried in the literature.

Dr. Orgel (Colgate-Palmolive Co.): Perhaps we are overlooking the fact that there are facultative autotrophs. Hydrogenomonas facilis, for one, is facultative. With all organic carbon excluded and with CO_2 as its sole source of carbon, it grows, but it grows slowly as an autotroph; but it grows heterotrophically on common organic substrates.

Dr. Mulder: We have studied the effects of purely in-organic media on these organisms. In the absence of any organic material there is no growth. With added Vitamin B_{12}, which is necessary for these organisms, there is no growth. In the presence of the yeast extract there is some growth, then you add the carbonate in large amounts. The possibility exists of the bacteria deriving the amino acids and vitamins from the yeast extract. We had an increase in yield but it may have been due to the presence of small amounts of impurities in the manganese, so we have to await our ex-periments with radioactive carbon dioxide before we can say more.

Dr. Robert Speck (Campbell Soup Co.): Dr. Wolfe, you mentioned a pH range of 5 to 8 and 200 to 500 millivolts as environmental limits. Are these for specific organisms?

Dr. Wolfe: These limits were determined by Baas-Becking in an estuarine environment in natural deposits.

Dr. Speck: Would you care to comment, in a general sort of way, on the chlorine resistance of the iron and manganese bacteria?

Dr. Wolfe: Massive doses (50 to 100 mg per l) are sufficient for cleaning out isolated pipes, but they become resistant to small doses (3 to 5 mg per l).

Dr. Norman Davis (Mass. Inst. Technol.): Van Iterson demonstrated a filterable form of Gallionella. Has anyone seriously attempted to verify this? Has anyone attempted to follow subsequent developments of the submicron sporal bodies to see if they do, indeed, revert to full-size bacterial forms?

Dr. Wolfe: Concerning van Iterson's thesis, I mentioned that some parts of her work had not gained favor and, to my knowledge, the filterable forms have not been confirmed. Her micrographs are excellent, but this portion of her thesis is very speculative.

Concerning Crenothrix polyspora, I forgot to emphasize that, to my knowledge, this organism has never been culti-vated in pure culture. For the past eight months we have had absolutely negative results. We cannot imagine what it may require.

Dr. Alexander: You mentioned the ribulodiphosphates in

one of the organisms. Is there any evidence for any of the
intermediates, or any of the enzymes of the pentose cycle in
any of the iron bacteria, other than Thiobacillus ferrooxidans?

Dr. Wolfe: No. To my knowledge it has not been investigated in other iron organisms. Pure cultures have been
the problem so far.

Dr. Ehrlich (Rensselaer Polytechnic Inst.): Dr. Mulder
may very well be right that manganese nodules are not of
direct biological origin or that bacteria directly contribute
to their formation, but I prefer still to maintain my stand
for which there are some lines of supporting evidence that
I did not mention in my talk. One of these is that not all the
bacteria that we find in the nodules help to accelerate manganese deposition on nodules. Secondly, not all the bacteria
in the nodules help to reduce the manganese in the nodular
substance. Thirdly, low peptone concentrations favor the
acceleration by bacteria of manganese deposition much more
than high peptone concentrations do. These indirect lines of
evidence suggest to me that there is some biological function
involved here which may be enzymatic.

Dr. Mulder: I do not say that microorganisms are not
important in the oxidation of manganese. Often you will find
organisms which produce manganic oxide only in the presence
of, say, hydroxy acids, but these chlamydobacteria are real
manganese oxidizers. They are manganese oxidizers more
so than the organisms which are found in large numbers in
the soil. When once manganese oxidation has started, it
goes on in a chemical way.

7

DETERIORATION OF ORGANIC
MATERIALS BY MARINE ORGANISMS

Waldimero Coscarelli
Bell Telephone Laboratories, Inc.
Murray Hill, New Jersey

The interest of the Bell System in the performance of organic materials in a marine environment stems from the expanding use of submarine telephone cable. There currently exists about 20, 000 nautical miles of such cable, with further installations in progress and planned. Since installations of this type are costly to service and repair, every effort is made to select materials that provide trouble-free service for a minimum of 20 years. While considerable published data is available on the behavior of organic materials, such as wood, jute, hemp, Malayan gum, and similar materials in a marine environment, there is a paucity of information on the resistance of synthetic materials such as plastics, elastomers, casting resins, and laminates.

The principal biological agents of concern in the deterioration of organic materials are marine borers and microorganisms, with particular emphasis on bacteria.

Marine borers are predominantly mollusks or crustaceans which have acquired the capacity to excavate hard materials -- particularly rock, wood or shell -- in which they find shelter and protection. The principal marine animals responsible for the deterioration of cellulosic materials are molluscan borers of the genera Teredo and Bankia, and the crustacean, Limnoria. Several accounts on the ability of teredos to attack submarine cables are reported in a bibliography prepared by Clapp and Kenk (3). In most instances, the susceptible constituents were confined to cellulosic materials such as jute and hemp and, infrequently, to

gutta percha insulation. Four cable faults due to teredo
attack have been recorded over a 70-year period in the Gulf
of Corinth (5). This represents 13 to 15 per cent of all
faults reported during that span. Lawton (8) reported slight
teredo scorings on the polyethylene insulation of an experimental, armorless, submarine telegraph cable after seven
years of exposure. Damage was confined to splice joints
wrapped with untreated jute for mechanical protection during
laying. There is one report of a teredo attack on lead-
covered submarine cable (6).

Another important family of boring mollusks is the
Pholadidae, commonly known as the burrowing clams. Lead-
sheathed submarine cables have been penetrated by these
borers. Bartsch and Rehder (1), as well as Snoke and Richards
(12), reported boring by these organisms in the lead sheath
of submarine cables in shallow water.

Limnoria, the gribble, is primarily but not exclusively
a wood-boring isopod. For example, there are a few references which suggest that Limnoria has bored into gutta percha
Chilton (2) reports the activity of Limnoria in the splice of a
submarine cable in about 60 fathoms off the New Zealand coast.
According to Preece (10), Limnoria was responsible for the
failure of the Holyhead-Dublin cable in 1875, and Jona (7)
frequently found Limnoria in cables recovered from the
Adriatic Sea.

Although the ability of microorganisms to break down
simple or complex organic molecules in a marine environment does not reside exclusively within bacteria, most of
the information available in marine microbiology is restricted to this group. Bacteria contribute to the biology of
the sea by participating in a variety of processes which liberate
carbon, nitrogen, phosphorus, and other essential elements
in utilizable forms.

Bacteria are not evenly distributed in the ocean, even
though the marine environment is relatively uniform with
respect to chemical composition and other properties. A
preponderance of bacterial population usually occurs in sea
water near land, irrespective of the depth or temperature of
the water. Bacteria were found in depths as great as 5,621
fathoms under pressures of 1000 atmospheres (9) and at
temperatures as low as -5 C (11).

This brief outline is not meant to summarize nor to review
the history of organic materials in a marine environment, for

it is beyond the scope of this paper to do so, but, rather, to
point out the complexities that must be considered in the
proper design of a research program. To obtain fundamental
data on the performance of materials in a diverse marine
environment that covers over 70 per cent of the surface of
the earth is an almost boundless task. The practical parameters which were finally established were based on a number
of considerations. The basic inertness or relative rates of
attack by bacteria could be determined best under controlled
laboratory conditions. However, because of the relatively
rapid activity of marine borers under natural conditions, and
because of their critical cultural requirements, it was decided
that borer tests would be conducted in the field. Results obtained from such a natural exposure would serve also to
complement the laboratory microbiological portion of the
program.

The integrated program is outlined in Fig. 1. Results
from the conductor test and the analysis of cable samples
from service are presently being evaluated and will be
published in the future.

Marine exposure of materials. The marine borer program
was initiated in 1954 by the Bell Telephone Laboratories in
cooperation with the William F. Clapp Laboratory, Incorporated, Duxbury, Massachusetts. Wrightsville Beach, North
Carolina, and Daytona Beach, Florida were selected as the
test sites for the natural exposure of test materials because
of the severe and diversified borer activity at these locations.
At present, over 70 materials involving some 600 individual
specimens have been exposed (4, 13). Included are thermo-
setting and thermoplastic materials, casting compounds,
rubbers, glass-reinforced plastics, and natural and synthetic
fibers. Where possible, test specimens are made in rod or
tube form about one inch in diameter and three feet long to
simulate cable shape. Fibers and tape samples are wrapped
around 3/4 -inch diameter methyl methacrylate rods three
feet long. About 26 specimens are mounted in each rack in
such a manner that a split, creosoted, two-by-four-inch board,
which serves as a structural support, fastens them together
at a point six inches from the top. One split, untreated, two-
by-four-inch board is fitted to the specimens about 14 inches
from the top and serves as a bait piece to lead boring organisms
from the susceptible wood into direct contact with each test

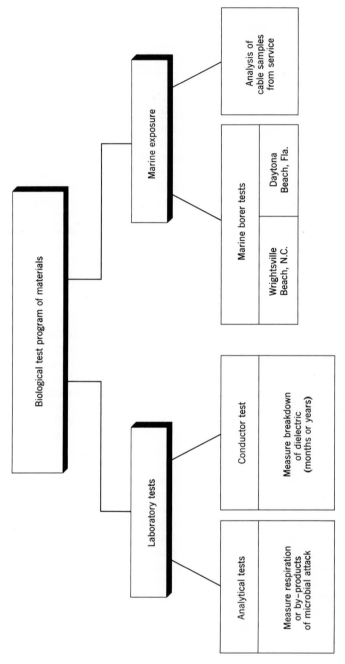

Fig. 1—Outline of marine biological test program.

specimen. The unbaited portions of the test rack serve to uncover whether the embryonic borers can attack the samples directly from the water or sediment without the assistance of a susceptible material. Figure 2 shows a typical rack before exposure. Each rack is submerged in the ocean so that approximately the bottom ten inches of each specimen is embedded in the bottom sediment, where an active microbial population is present. The balance of the rack is exposed to the sea water and its diversified marine life. Annually the racks are removed, and one out of four replicate specimens from each material is cleaned of all fouling (Fig. 3) and examined for evidence of deterioration. It is desirable to maintain the status quo of the test specimen with respect to fouling for as long as possible, since this association creates a favorable environment for boring organisms and microbial activity. Consequently, where conditions permit, inspections are rotated so that a test specimen is examined only once in four years. Apart from the normal fluctuation in fouling, the nature of the test material can influence the degree to which fouling occurs on the specimen. Materials with a waxy, or a hard, smooth surface such as polyethylene, for example, generally show light adherence, whereas fouling on elasto-meric materials is difficult to remove. Fouling also adheres tenaciously to most of the fibers.

The extent and type of deterioration to these materials provide a basis for segregating them into four broad classes:

Class I. No deterioration. No observable changes in the basic material. Superficial alterations due to color changes, barnacle impressions, or purely mechanical damage resulting from fouling are included.

Class II. Borer activity under bait piece only. Includes abortive attempts by borers (principally the teredo) to penetrate the material after egressing from the bait piece.

Class III. Borer attack or other deterioration in nonbaited area. Deterioration of materials in this category is the result of pholad, chemical, and microbial activity.

Class IV. Materials destroyed. Materials in this class are completely deteriorated by either borer, bacteria, fungi, mechanical action, or various combinations of these.

The performance trends of these materials for varying periods of as long as seven years of exposure are presented in the first section of this paper.

Fig. 2—A typical test rack used in marine borer test (prior to exposure).

To date, materials listed in Table 1 have shown no apparent
chemical or biological deterioration, but various degrees of
mechanical damage due to calcareous fouling have occurred
on the fibers. Polyethylene, with but one exception which
will be noted later, has resisted borer penetration. Laminates
have shown little structural change, but substantial changes
in electrical properties have been detected. The natural and
styrene-butadiene rubber jackets, as well as two coal tar
treated jute materials, showed no signs of deterioration.

Fig. 3—Typical test rack removed from ocean exposure showing every fourth specimen cleaned for annual inspection. Bottom portion of the rack was embedded in the sediment and is relatively free of fouling.

It should be noted that the exposure time for this group of materials ranges from one to seven years.

Materials that suffered numerous abortive grooves from boring organisms under the bait piece area but were not attacked elsewhere on the sample are listed in Tables 2 and 3. It can be expected that proneness to borer activity under the bait piece will be exhibited early during the exposure test and that continued exposure would serve to indicate the frequency of attack. Perhaps it would be well to emphasize here that slight differences in material structure could spell the

TABLE 1: Class I: No deterioration

Material	Exposure to Date (Yr)
Laminates:	
Epoxy, glass cloth	1
Epoxy, glass cloth	1
Polyester, glass mat	1
Natural fibers:	
Jute + American coal tar	1
Jute + English coal tar	1
Plastics:	
Acrylonitrile-vinyl chloride copolymer (fiber)	7
Polyamide (fiber)	7
Polyacrylonitrile (fiber)	7
Polyethylene, ASTM 1A3, melt index 2.0	5
Polyethylene terphthalate (fiber)	7
Poly (vinyl chloride) DOP, semirigid	6
Vinyl chloride, acetate copolymer (fiber)	7
Rubbers:	
Natural rubber jacket	7
Styrene-butadiene rubber jacket	7

difference between success and failure of a material. For example, polyamide presented here (Table 2) has suffered no borer penetration, whereas data will be presented later which includes another type of polyamide that was penetrated by pholads within the first year of exposure.

Apart from the abortive pholad attempts, rubbers (Table 3) have held up remarkably well throughout the test. Butyl jacket has shown a slight tendency toward surface cracking but physical tests have failed to reveal significant changes in any of the properties measured. There has been no indication of microbial activity on the elastomers.

Poly (vinyl chlorides) are difficult to classify because some, depending upon the compounding of the plasticizer used, resist borer penetration (Table 3) whereas others (Table 4) are penetrated by pholads after three to four years of exposure. The designation "poly (vinyl chloride)" is used by the American Society for Testing and Materials for resins prepared by the polymerization of vinyl chloride alone.

TABLE 2: Class II: Borer activity under bait piece only; (Plastics)

Material	Exposure to Date (Yr)
Acrylonitrile - butadiene - styrene	5
Polyamide (natural)	2
Polyamide (black)	2
Polyethylene, ASTM 1A4, melt index 0.3	7
Polyethylene, ASTM 1A4, melt index 0.3	7
Polyethylene, ASTM 1A4 + antioxidant, melt index 0.3	7
Polyethylene + antioxidant + 5 per cent butyl, ASTM 1A4, melt index 0.3	5
Polyethylene (black) ASTM 111C3, melt index 0.5, density 0.96	6
Polyethylene (natural) ASTM 111A3, melt index 0.5, density 0.96	6
Polyethylene, ASTM 111A3, melt index 0.3, density 0.96	2
Polypropylene	3
Polytetrafluoroethylene	2

TABLE 3: Class II: Borer activity under bait piece only

Material	Exposure to Date (Yr)
Rubbers:	
Butyl jacket, mineral oil plasticizer	7
Natural rubber insulation, zinc oxide loaded	7
Neoprene jacket, mineral oil plasticizer, red lead cured	7
Neoprene jacket, mineral oil plasticizer, red lead cured + clay	7
Nitrile-butadiene rubber, dibutylphthalate plasticizer	7
Plastics:	
Poly (vinyl chloride), TCP, flexible, natural	7
Poly (vinyl chloride), DOP, flexible, natural	7
Poly (vinyl chloride), DOP, flexible	6
Poly (vinyl chloride), acrylonitrile rubber/polyester, flexible, black	6

Physical measurements, as determined by the Shore A
durometer, indicate that no significant changes in hardness
occur. Characteristically, vinyls which contain lead stabi-
lizers changed color from natural to black because of the
reaction between sulfide in the surrounding environment and
the lead.

TABLE 4: Class III: Borer attack or other deterioration
not restricted to baited area; (Plastics)

Material	Exposure to Date (Yr)	Deterioration After (Yr)
Polyamide (natural)	2	1
Polyamide (black)	2	1
Polyethylene + butyl cable compound	7	5
Polymonochlor-trifluoroethylene (tape)	7	3
Poly (vinyl chloride), plasticizer, flexible	7	4
Poly (vinyl chloride), black, semirigid	6	3
Poly (vinyl chloride), natural, semirigid	6	4
Poly (vinyl chloride), TOF plasticizer, flexible	6	3
Poly (vinyl chloride), polyester plasticizer	6	4
Poly (vinyl chloride), unplasticized rigid	7	6

The two polyamides at the top of Table 4 are the formulations susceptible to pholad attack that were mentioned
earlier, and listed below them is the only polyethylene
penetrated by a pholad, and then at only one point. This
material is a mixture, and not a polyethylene homopolymer.

Ironically, polymonochlor-trifluorethylene is the only
tape which was attacked by borers and not destroyed by
the mechanical damage usually caused by fouling organisms.

Both the epoxy and silica-filled styrene polyester have
suffered borer damage outside the baited area (Table 5). A
pholad entry into the epoxy resin was noted in the fourth
year of exposure. Since then, there have been numerous other
penetrations. The silica-filled styrene polyester sustained
its first pholad entry after seven years of exposure. The
entry is somewhat surprising in view of the silica incorporated
in its formulation. One theory suggests that pholads may

be able to burrow into materials harder than their aragonite shells because these materials are often friable and the harder grains that are broken off serve as an abrasive at the point of the burrowing (16). The surface hardness of the polyester decreased by 20 per cent but no changes were observed in the epoxy.

TABLE 5: Class III: Borer attack or other deterioration
not restricted to baited area

Material	Exposure to Date (Yr)	Deterioration After (Yr)
Casting resins:		
Epoxy, clear	7	4
Styrene polyester, silica filled	6	6
Natural fibers:		
Cyanoethylated jute	5	3
Rubbers:		
Neoprene (MgO, ZnO cured)	7	6
Silicone rubber	7	2
Styrene-butadiene rubber insulation	7	7

Cyanoethylated jute remains in relatively good condition although it is beginning to show signs of microbial attack.

None of the rubbers have exhibited any visual signs of microbial attack. More serious than the borer activity on silicone rubber is its tendency to show laminar separations in a circumferential direction. Although this may be a manufacturing imperfection, it has been apparent on all the replicates. Numerous abortive pholad entries, as well as superficial horizontal cracks were observed on neoprene.

Tapes removed because of mechanical damage caused by fouling organisms are listed in Table 6. In no case was there any evidence of deterioration due to microbial action.

The synthetic fibers were attacked by borers and microorganisms soon after exposure and within a maximum of four years were completely destroyed. A photomicrograph of cellulose acetate fiber showing microbial deterioration of the fiber surface is shown in Fig. 4.

Despite various preventive treatments, natural fibers have performed poorly in the ocean environment. Untreated

TABLE 6: Class IV: Materials destroyed

Material	Destroyed After (Yr)
Plastic tapes:	
Polytetrafluoroethylene	7
Polyethylene terphthalate	7
Polystyrene	7
Synthetic fibers:	
Cellulose acetate (secondary) yard	1
Cellulose acetate (secondary tow)	2
Cellulose triacetate	4
Natural fibers:	
Jute rove, untreated	1/2
Jute rove, cutched (lime fix)	1/2
Jute yarn + dodecyl dimethyl benzyl	
ammonium cyclopentane	1/2
Jute yarn + zinc naphthenate	2
Jute yarn + anthracene oil + coal tar pitch	4
Jute yarn + copper naphthenate + petroleum	
asphalt and petroleum wax	3
Jute rove + melamine + copper-8-	
quinolinolate	3
Jute rove + cutch + copper sulfate +	
potassium chromate	3
Jute + road tar 9 + copper naphthenate	5
Jute yarn + road tar 9, creosote + copper	
naphthenate	5

jute and jute treated with cutch or dodecyl dimethyl benzyl ammonium cyclopentane lasted only six months. These, as well as the others, were attacked by fungi, bacteria, and Limnoria. The use of creosote and allied compounds increases the life span of the jute, but its effect is soon dissipated through the leaching action of the ocean. In certain instances pholads have bored through the fibers and penetrated the methyl methacrylate supporting rod (Fig. 5).

This portion of the paper can best be summarized by stating a few general observations. Deterioration is confined primarily to attack by marine borers. There have been few chemical changes in the basic materials. Most of the plastic materials have resisted the attack of borers and microorganisms, the exceptions being the poly (vinyl chlorides) and polyamides

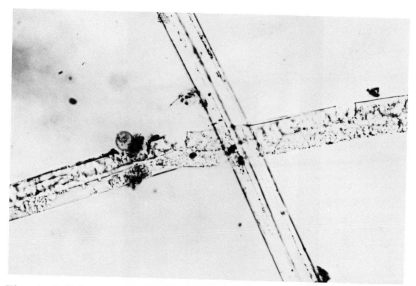

Fig. 4—Cellulose acetate fiber showing extensive surface erosion after one year of marine exposure.

where half the number of different types of these materials were penetrated by pholads. Rubber samples have performed well but are beginning to show signs of degradation, as evidenced by the borer penetrations and surface cracking. The emergence of new synthetic fibers, such as polyamide, gives promise of providing materials which can resist the attack of borers and microorganisms better than treated natural fibers.

Laboratory bacterial tests. Data obtained from studies (13, 14, 15) performed in the laboratory on the resistance of organic materials to aerobic bacteria and anaerobic sulfate-reducing bacteria are presented in the second half of this paper.

The general features of the test procedure are shown in Fig. 6. The four primary constituents of the test are aged sea water, raw sea water, test materials as the sole organic carbon source, and ocean bottom sediment.

Where possible, the test materials were about four mils (0.102 mm) thick and of sufficient volume to provide in each

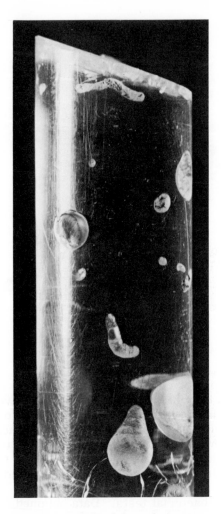

Fig. 5—Section of methyl methacrylate rod showing penetration by pholads. One of the mollusks can be seen protruding from the rod above and to left of center.

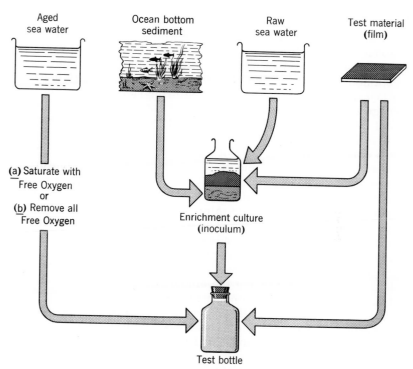

Fig. 6—Flow chart of laboratory bacteriological test.

60 ml test bottle a total surface area of 12.9 cm^2. Materials other than film specimens were either cut in a fashion to produce an equivalent surface area, as in the case of elastomers, or weighed to 50 mg portions when materials were employed in granular form.

Prior to testing, raw sea water was obtained and a portion was filtered and aged for eight weeks. For aerobic studies, the sea water was aerated for 16 hours in a carboy with oxygen, and sustained under a slight positive oxygen pressure until after the test bottles were filled. For anaerobic studies, the aged sea water was boiled vigorously for 10 minutes and then maintained under slight nitrogen pressure until after the test bottles were filled. The amount of organic matter present in aged sea water at the time of the test never exceeded 1.0 mg per l.

The inoculum was prepared by an enrichment culture
technique. To portions of raw sea water and marine sediment
(about 1: 1 by volume) was added some of the material to be
tested, and an aliquot of pooled marine enrichment cultures
obtained through the courtesy of Dr. ZoBell, Scripps Institution
of Oceanography. The latter were prepared from a wide
range of organic materials including elastomers, carbohydrates,
coal products and other aromatic compounds. The cultures
were incubated for six weeks at 25 C at which time 1.0 ml
was used to inoculate 10 l of aged sea water. Aerobic cultures
were incubated at 5 C and 20 C, whereas anaerobic cultures
were incubated only at 20 C. The 20 C temperature is representative of certain shallow water environments and would be
expected to support higher microbial activity, in contrast to
the 5 C temperature more characteristic of the ocean bottom
at a depth of about 1000 meters, where microbial activity
would be expected to be proportionally less.

The extent of degradation under aerobic conditions was
determined by measuring the amount of dissolved oxygen
that was consumed (commonly known as the biochemical
oxygen demand test, BOD). The amount of sulfide produced
by sulfate-reducing bacteria was used to determine the degree
of anaerobic deterioration. In Fig. 7 are listed the salient
reactions that occur during these determinations.

The individual materials tested are similar to those in
the marine exposure program and include casting compounds,
elastomers, natural and synthetic fibers, polyethylene,
polypropylene, poly (vinyl chloride), and other thermoplastics.

Oxygen consumption values (Table 7) on variously formulated polyethylenes clearly indicate that these materials are
not degraded by aerobic bacteria nor are they susceptible
under anaerobic conditions (Table 8) to sulfate reducers. For
anaerobic studies the incubation period was extended to 16
weeks to provide adequate time for changes to occur.

The deterioration of poly (vinyl chloride) varies in ac-
cordance with the plasticizer used (Table 9). Every poly
(vinyl chloride) tested, with one exception, shows some
distinct oxygen consumption above the control. The lone
exception is the semiflexible poly (vinyl chloride) which
contains no added external plasticizer. Materials plasticized with polyesters, fatty-acid type compounds, indicate,
because of their rapid oxygen depletion rate, that they are
the most susceptible formulations.

Winkler oxygen determination in BOD test

(a) Oxidation of manganous hydroxide in a highly alkaline solution

$$2H_2O + O_2 + 2Mn(OH)_2 \rightarrow 2Mn(OH)_4$$

(b) Acidification in the presence of an iodide

$$Mn(OH)_4 + 4HCl \rightarrow MnCl_2 + Cl_2 + 4H_2O$$

$$Cl_2 + 2NaI \rightarrow 2NaCl + I_2$$

(c) Free iodine titrated with a standard thiosulfate solution

$$I_2 + 2Na_2S_2O_3 \rightarrow Na_2S_4O_6 + 2NaI$$
starch indicator   starch indicator
(blue)   (colorless)

Hydrogen sulfide determination in anaerobic test

$$H_2S + I_2 \rightarrow 2HI + S$$

(Starch indicator remains blue following completion of reaction)

Fig. 7—Reactions involved in laboratory marine analytical test.

Poly (vinyl chlorides)compounded with nitrile rubber or tri-ethylhexyl phosphate are attacked at equal rates whereas di-2-ethylhexyl phthalate reached maximum oxygen consumption only after a prolonged lag period. Of the poly (vinyl chloride) which contained no added external plasticizers only the rigid plastic, listed at the top of Table 10 is utilized. This material contained 8 to 10 times as much fatty acid lubricant as the other compounds.

One might be tempted to speculate, on the basis of results listed in Table 10, that polyester A, for example, is more susceptible to bacterial action than jute. It is more likely, however, that the rate of bacterial growth, as reflected by the specific indicators, on plasticized materials, may be profoundly influenced by the ability of the plasticizer to leach out into the surrounding medium.

TABLE 7: Oxygen consumption by marine bacteria at 20 C
in BOD test with polyethylene as the only source of organic carbon

Test Material[a]	O_2 Consumption (mg/l) After Weeks of Incubation			
	1	2	4	8
2.0 Melt index[b]	2.2	3.7	6.0	10.2
0.2 Melt index (source A)	0.8	1.6	2.4	10.9
0.2 Melt index (source B)	1.4	3.4	5.2	10.8
0.2 Melt index + antioxidant	0.9	3.0	6.2	8.5
0.2 Melt index + 5% butyl rubber + antioxidant	0.2	3.8	5.8	—[c]
0.7 Melt index (high density) + antioxidant	0.9	4.3	7.4	9.3
Controls (inoculated sea water)	1.5	5.3	8.3	11.2

[a]Except where noted polymers are low density grades manufactured by the high pressure process.
[b]ASTM D1238.
[c]Samples accidentally destroyed.

The salient features of Table 11 can best be described by comparing these results with those in Tables 9 and 10.

Materials that are resistant under aerobic conditions are not degraded anaerobically. Poly (vinyl chlorides) plasticized with either tricresyl phosphate, di-2-ethylhexyl phthalate, or tri-2-ethylhexyl phosphate are attacked aerobically but not anaerobically. Note that polyesters exceeded all plasticizers in sulfide production.

Poly (vinyl chloride) resin (Table 12) itself is not degraded under either test condition. This strongly suggests that the resinous materials, per se, is resistant to microbial action and that additives, such as lubricants and plasticizers, must be looked upon as the susceptible constituents.

Of the two casting resins tested, only the silica-filled polyester shows some indication of attack under aerobic conditions alone; however, the oxygen consumption values are low and inconclusive. Anaerobic studies with these materials are presented in Table 13. In the anaerobic

TABLE 8: Hydrogen sulfide production by marine bacteria at 20 C in anaerobic sea water test with polyethylene as the only source of organic carbon

Test Material [a]	H_2 S Production (mg/l) After Weeks of Incubation			
	4	8	12	16
2.0 Melt index [b]	0.22	0.32	0.22	— [c]
0.2 Melt index (source A)	0.22	0.29	0.45	— [c]
0.2 Melt index (source B)	0.22	0.32	0.26	0.38
0.2 Melt index + antioxidant	0.22	0.64	0.35	0.58
0.2 Melt index + 5% butyl rubber + antioxidant	0.22	0.32	1.31	0.24
0.7 Melt index (high density) + antioxidant	0.22	0.22	0.29	0.45
Controls (inoculated sea water)	0.10	0.64	0.70	0.58

[a] Except where noted polymers are low density grades manufactured by the high pressure process.
[b] ASTM D1238.
[c] Insufficient samples.

environment, the low sulfide values indicate that the silica-filled styrene polyester is not degraded.

The degradation of elastomers at 5 C and 20 C is summarized in Figs. 8 and 9. At 5 C, butyl jacket and neoprene jacket, which is a butadiene acrylonitrile copolymer, were the only elastomers which did not utilize all of the available oxygen. The black portion of the bar graph represents the average daily consumption rate of oxygen and can be used to indicate the relative rates of attack between different elastomers. At 20 C, all elastomers utilized the total available oxygen. Natural jacket is degraded at a rate comparable to the more susceptible elastomers whereas the GR-A jacket and the neoprene jacket with zinc and magnesium oxide, remained among the more resistant rubbers. Based on the calculated rates of oxygen uptake, elastomers incubated at 20 C were, in general, consumed ten times faster than at the lower temperature.

Poly (vinyl chlorides) were attacked rather slowly at the lower temperature (Fig. 10), and with the exception of those

materials which contained polyester plasticizers, none consumed more than 30 per cent of the total oxygen supply.
Oxygen consumption values presented in Fig. 11 indicate that
poly (vinyl chlorides) incubated at 20 C are degraded five
times as fast as at 5 C. Jute, listed as a separate item in
Fig. 12, was attacked twice as fast at 20 C than at 5 C.
     Materials not attacked in either the BOD or anaerobic
tests are listed in Table 14. None of the polyethylenes,
synthetic fibers, or thermoplastics such as polytetrafluoro-
ethylene, polycarbonate, or polyamide were utilized by either
aerobic or anaerobic bacteria. Internally plasticized poly
(vinyl chloride) as well as the resin itself were inert to
bacteria but all externally plasticized poly (vinyl chlorides)
were utilized aerobically at both temperatures tested (Table
15).
     Few of the poly (vinyl chlorides) were degraded anaero-
bically; those degraded being restricted mainly to formulations
containing polyesters and nitrile rubber. Aerobically, all
elastomers were degraded, but only natural and butyl rubber
proved to be susceptible anaerobically.

TABLE 9: Oxygen consumption by marine bacteria at 20 C in BOD
         test with poly (vinyl chloride) plastics as the only
         source of organic carbon

Plasticizer	O_2 Consumption (mg/l) After Weeks of Incubation			
	1	2	4	8
Nitrile rubber/polyester C	10.3	12.9	21.4	[a]
Nitrile rubber	9.2	12.3	18.7	[a]
None[b]	3.7	4.2	6.5	10.5
None[b]	4.0	5.5	8.4	11.0
Tri-2-ethylhexyl phosphate	11.7	14.4	23.1	[a]
Di-2-ethylhexyl phthalate (DOP) Shore A62	6.4	8.4	11.5	[a]
Polyester E/DOP	[a]			
Controls (inoculated sea water)	3.5	4.5	7.1	9.7

[a] All free O_2 in sea water consumed.
[b] Semiflexible PVC copolymer.

TABLE 10: Oxygen consumption by marine bacteria at 20 C in BOD
test with poly (vinyl chloride) plastics, epoxide casting
resin or jute as only sources of organic carbon

Test Material	O_2 Consumption (mg/l) After Weeks of Incubation			
	1	2	4	8
PVC - no plasticizer (rigid)	11.1	12.9	11.6	18.7
PVC - tricresyl phosphate	9.5	13.2	21.6	22.2
PVC - di-2-ethylhexyl phthalate (DOP) Shore A88	9.1	13.4	19.7	20.7
PVC - polyester A	19.3	22.2	a	a
Epoxide casting resin	—	4.1	5.1	4.2
Jute	10.0	15.0	16.5	a
Controls (inoculated sea water)	6.8	6.8	7.7	7.7

[a] All free O_2 in sea water consumed.

TABLE 11: Hydrogen sulfide production by marine bacteria at 20 C in
anaerobic sea water test with poly (vinyl chloride)
plastics, epoxide casting resin, or jute as only sources
of organic carbon

Test Material	H_2S Production (mg/l) After Weeks of Incubation			
	4	8	12	16
Poly (vinyl chloride) plastics				
No plasticizer (rigid)	1.90	3.50	4.20	5.60
Tricresyl phosphate	0.22	0.22	0.64	0.38
Di-2-ethylhexyl phthalate				
Shore A88	0.26	0.26	0.26	0.61
Polyester A	2.60	38.40	38.40	47.70
Nitrile rubber/polyester C	1.50	7.00	19.98	18.60
Nitrile rubber	4.10	9.60	12.40	11.50
No plasticizer [a]	0.22	0.22	0.90	0.51
No plasticizer	0.32	0.64	1.89	1.02
Tri-2-ethylhexyl phosphate	0.26	0.96	1.86	0.99
Di-2-ethylhexyl phthalate				
Shore A62	0.22	0.22	1.09	0.58
Polyester E/DOP	12.20	61.40	94.10	82.90
Epoxide casting resin	0.16	0.64	0.86	0.48
Jute	1.90	13.40	38.60	52.20
Controls (inoculated sea water)	0.10	0.64	0.70	0.58

[a] Semiflexible PVC copolymer.

TABLE 12: Oxygen consumption by marine bacteria at 20 C in BOD
test with polyethylene, polyester casting resin or poly
(vinyl chloride) resin as only source of organic carbon

Test Material	O_2 Consumption (mg/l) After Weeks of Incubation			
	1	2	4	8
Polyethylene 0.7 melt index (high density), natural + antioxidant	3.0	3.3	6.0	6.5
Polyethylene 0.7 melt index (high density), black + antioxidant	2.9	4.1	7.1	7.0
Silica-filled, styrene polyester	5.5	7.0	9.3	12.1
Poly (vinyl chloride) resin	4.2	4.1	7.3	7.2
Controls (inoculated sea water)	2.5	3.8	6.7	6.7

TABLE 13: Hydrogen sulfide production by marine bacteria at 20 C in
anaerobic sea water test with polyethylene, polyester
casting resin or poly (vinyl chloride) resin as only source
of carbon

Test Material	H_2S Production (mg/l) After Weeks of Incubation			
	4	8	12	16
Polyethylene - 0.7 melt index (high density), natural + antioxidant	0.35	0.58	0.90	1.12
Polyethylene - 0.7 melt index (high density), black + antioxidant	0.26	0.48	0.38	0.74
Silica-filled styrene polyester	0.83	0.83	1.02	1.02
Poly (vinyl chloride) resin	0.48	0.58	0.58	0.58
Controls (inoculated sea water)	0.45	0.86	0.91	0.91

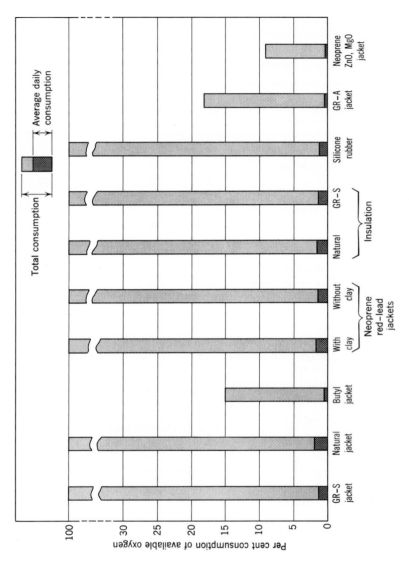

Fig. 8—BOD test on elastomers, 8 weeks at 5 C.

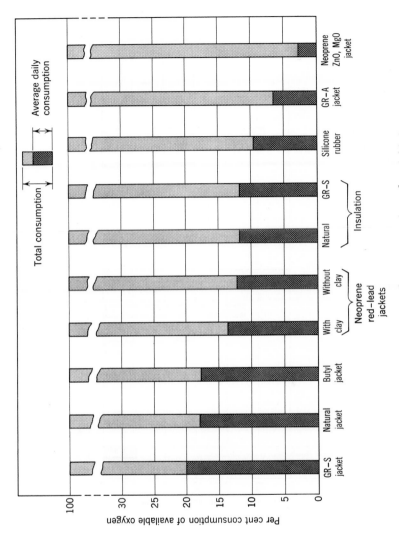

Fig. 9—BOD test on elastomers, 8 weeks at 20 C.

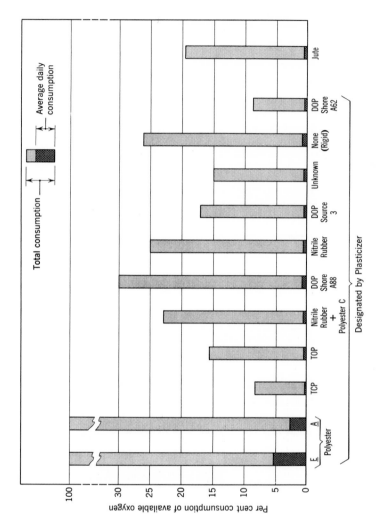

Fig. 10—BOD test on poly (vinyl chloride) plastics and jute, 8 weeks at 5 C.

TABLE 14: Materials not attacked in
either BOD or anaerobic tests

Poly (vinyl chloride)	Polypropylene
Semiflexible copolymer A	Polypropylene + antioxidant
(no plasticizer added)	
Semiflexible copolymer B	Other materials
(no plasticizer added)	Polyamide (source 1, 2, and 3)
Pure poly (vinyl chloride)	Polyethylene terephthalate
resin	Polytetrafluoroethylene
	Cellulose triacetate
Polyethylene	Cellulose acetate
2.0 melt index, standard	
molecular weight	Casting Compound
0.2 melt index (source A),	Epoxide casting compound
high molecular weight	
0.2 melt index (source B),	
high molecular weight	
0.2 melt index + antioxidant	
0.2 melt index + 5% butyl	
rubber + antioxidant	
0.7 melt index (high density)	
+ antioxidant	
0.7 melt index (high density)	
+ carbon black +	
antioxidant	

TABLE 15: Materials attacked in either BOD or anaerobic tests

	BOD Test		Anaerobic Test
Incubated at 20 C		Incubated at 5 C	Incubated at 20 C
Poly (vinyl chloride)			
Plasticizer			
Polyester E		Polyester E	Polyester E
Polyester A		Polyester A	Polyester A
Nitrile rubber/polyester C		Nitrile rubber/polyester C	Nitrile rubber/polyester C
Nitrile rubber		Nitrile rubber	Nitrile rubber
None (rigid)		None (rigid)	None (rigid)
Tricresyl phosphate (TCP)		Tricresyl phosphate (TCP)	
Tri-2-ethylhexyl phosphate		Tri-2-ethylhexyl phosphate	
(TOP)		(TOP)	
Di-2-ethylhexyl phthalate		Di-2-ethylhexyl phthalate	
(DOP) Source 3		(DOP) Source 3	
Di-2-ethylhexyl phthalate		Di-2-ethylhexyl phthalate	
(DOP) Shore A88		(DOP) Shore A88	
Di-2-ethylhexyl phthalate		Di-2-ethylhexyl phthalate	
(DOP) Shore A62		(DOP) Shore A62	

Elastomer

Natural rubber jacket	Natural rubber jacket	Natural rubber jacket
Natural rubber insulation	Natural rubber insulation	Natural rubber insulation
Butyl rubber jacket	Butyl rubber jacket	Butyl rubber jacket
GR-S jacket	GR-S jacket	
GR-S insulation	GR-S insulation	
GR-A jacket	GR-A jacket	
Neoprene red lead jacket (with clay)	Neoprene red lead jacket (with clay)	
Neoprene red lead jacket (without clay)	Neoprene red lead jacket (without clay)	
Neoprene ZnO, MgO jacket	Neoprene ZnO, MgO jacket	
Silicone rubber	Silicone rubber	

Natural Fiber

Jute	Jute	Jute

Casting Resin

Styrene-polyester, silica filled		

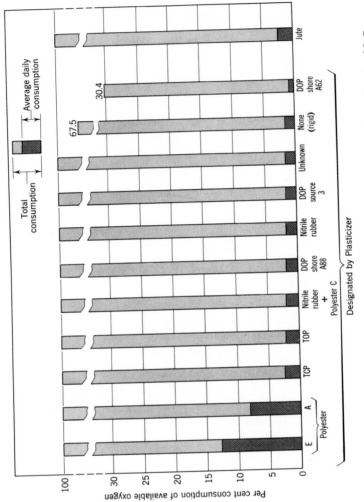

Fig. 11—BOD test on poly (vinyl chloride) plastics and jute, 8 weeks at 20 C.

Conclusions. In conclusion, we can note that many interesting comparisons can be drawn from the results of both programs. Polyethylene has shown negligible deterioration both in the laboratory and in ocean exposure. Casting resins have resisted bacterial attack but are penetrated by pholads.

The susceptibility of elastomers in laboratory studies indicates that bacteria may be implicated in the surface cracking phenomenon beginning to appear on ocean exposure specimens after seven years. Longer exposure may shed some light on this point. Synthetic cellulosic fibers are degraded in the ocean environment by borers and microorganisms, and preliminary laboratory studies indicate some susceptability to bacteria. Although gross observations of poly (vinyl chlorides) subjected to ocean environments do not reveal signs of microbial activity, laboratory studies provide ample evidence that these materials, depending upon formulation, can be utilized by bacteria under certain optimum conditions.

These discrepancies, if they can be called that, point to the value of a multiphasic program and to the ultimate collation of facts which can be used as a guide in the selection of resistant materials.

ACKNOWLEDGEMENTS

I wish to express my appreciation to Mrs. Steinberg and Messrs. Connolly and Snoke whose data have provided the basis for this paper. A debt of gratitude is due to the many members of the Chemical Research Department who cooperated by furnishing the test materials, and in particular to Mr. J. B. DeCoste who coordinated the efforts related to this program within his department. Special thanks are also due to Professor Claude E. ZoBell of the Scripps Institution of Oceanography for his many helpful suggestions and comments with regard to the laboratory portion of the program, and to Mr. A. P. Richards of the William F. Clapp Laboratories, In corporated, for his valuable assistance in connection with the marine borer test program.

The data from references 13 and 14 are reprinted by permission of the American Telephone and Telegraph Company.

LITERATURE CITED

1. Bartsch, P. and H. A. Rehder. 1945. The West
Atlantic boring molluscs of the genus Matersia, Miscellaneous
Collections 104, Smithsonian Institute, Vol. 11, Washington,
D. C.
2. Chilton, C. 1916. The Gribble (Limnoria lignorum,
Rathke) attacking a submarine cable in New Zealand. Ann.
and Mag. Nat. Hist. 18:208.
3. Clapp, W. F. and R. Kenk. 1956. Marine borers: A
preliminary bibliography, Parts I and II, Library of Congress,
Technical Information Division, Washington, D. C.
4. Connolly, R. A. 1963. Effect of seven-year marine
exposure on organic materials. Materials Res. and Standards,
3:193-201.
5. Heezen, B. C., M. Ewing, G. L. Johnson. 1960. Cable
failures in the Gulf of Corinth: a case history. Lamont Geological Observatory, Palisades, New York.
6. Henley W. T. 1935. Notes on everyday cable problems.
Distribution of Electricity. 8:1896-1898. W. T. Henley's
Telegraph Works Co., Ltd., London.
7. Jona, E. 1913. I cabi sottomarini dall'Italia all Libia,
Atti della Soc. Ital. per il Progr. delle Sci. 6:263-292.
8. Lawton, C. S. 1959. More about non-armored cable,
Trans. Am. Inst. Electr. Engrs. p. 5.
9. Morita, R. Y. and C. E. ZoBell. 1956. Bacteria in marine
sediments. Office of Naval Research, Res. Rev. p. 21.
10. Preece, G. E. 1875. On ocean cable borers. Telegr.
Jour. and Electr. Rev. 3:296-297.
11. Sanborn, J. R. 1930. Certain relationships of marine
bacteria to the decomposition of fish. J. Bacteriol. 19:375-382
12. Snoke, L. R., and A. P. Richards. 1956. Marine borer
attack on lead cable sheath. Science. 124:443.
13. Snoke, L. R. 1957. Resistance of organic materials
and cable structures to marine biological attack. Bell
System Tech. J. 36:1095-1127.
14. Steinberg, P. L. 1961. The resistance of organic
materials to attack by marine bacteria at low temperatures.
Bell System Tech. J. 40:1369-1395.
15. Steinberg, P. L. 1961. Resistance of organic materials
to marine bacterial attack. In developments in industrial
microbiology, vol. 2 Plenum Press, New York.
16. Turner, R. D. 1954. The family Pholadidae in

the Western Atlantic and the Eastern Pacific, Part I:
Pholadinae, Johnsonia 3:1-64.

DISCUSSION

Dr. D. Pramer (Rutgers Univ.): Did you supplement sea
water with nitrogen?

Dr. Coscarelli: Yes, it was supplemented with ammonium
nitrogen only.

Mr. Zajic (Kerr-McGee Oil Ind.): Your tests were done
under very adverse conditions. Do you have a series of
comparable studies, or do you plan to, say, run these tests
with 3 or 4 percent inocula and to grow the organisms and
test them under more ideal conditions of aeration and agitation?

Dr. Coscarelli: The rationale behind these studies is to
attempt to simulate conditions that we may expect on some of
our cables. This has been the basic reason for the selection
of the temperatures and conditions. It is true that one may,
depending on culture conditions, get information a little more
readily, but I do not think it would alter the end result.

Mr. Zajic: I think that we would know what would happen
to some of these materials if we selected microbes that
could break them down very rapidly. My approach to the
problem would be twofold.

Dr. Sieburth (Univ. of Rhode Island): These cables are in
a psychro-habitat, and I wonder whether we pay enough attention
to testing materials with organisms which grow preferentially
in the coldness of the marine environment. We have organisms
which will grow optimally at 3 C, but will not grow above
15 C. Furthermore, if one uses organisms which prefer
warmer temperature in a test under 5 C, the test is too artificial. Would you care to comment on any precautions you
have taken to select or obtain organisms that will grow obligately or prefer the cold?

Dr. Coscarelli: We did not preferentially select organisms
that develop at a specific temperature. This is not a completed
program. We intend to extend the studies along these lines
and in related fields, such as hydrostatic pressure studies.

Dr. Orgel (Colgate-Palmolive Co.): Is the boring effect

enzymatic or simply mechanical disruption of a matrix? Is it quite different than in the case of microbial deterioration?

Dr. Coscarelli: The type of damage caused by borers is readily distinguishable from microbial deterioration. Penetration of the material is due to mechanical abrasion and is not enzymatic. There may be some nebulous conclusions drawn from some of the fibrous materials that are either attacked by borers or mechanically damaged, but usually the difference in the method is quite evident and leaves no doubt.

Dr. Iain Anderson (Univ. of Mass.): With reference to the last question, have you any clue as to what is inherent in the nature of your polyethylenes and other substances which renders them so resistant to this mechanical grinding attack? Inasmuch as you did say that these borers will go into rock and shell, what is it about the nature of these artificial fibers which will prevent it?

Dr. Coscarelli: That is not an easy question to answer. I can tell you, for example, that with polyethylenes the one penetration that occurred was into a polyethylene which contained as a mixture five percent butyl. With cross-linked polyethylenes we have had absolutely no penetration. How one can attribute the resistance of these materials to some of these items, I do not know.

I made some comparisons earlier with polyamides. One polyamide that was penetrated was made by a process using caprolactam; the resistant polyamide was made with hexamethyldiamine plus adipic acid. The formulations result in materials which have similar physical properties and therefore we cannot draw significant conclusions.

Dr. S. Green (Wallerstein Co.): Have you related the BOD (biochemical oxygen demand) values to actual physical destruction of the various coverings? Is there a relationship between BOD and COD (chemical oxygen demand)?

Dr. Coscarelli: I am familiar with the BOD studies only and the best way I can answer your question, would be to say that there is a correlation between the materials that have been degraded in the laboratory and those that have been degraded under natural exposure.

Dr. F. A. Rosenberg (Northeastern Univ.): Have you made studies on specific bacteria which attack specific materials?

Dr. Coscarelli: We are only beginning to gather some information on this aspect of the program.

Dr. Anderson: I have found, with some of the cellulosic materials immersed in the bay of Woods Hole, that the first organisms of which there was any quantity when the materials had started to deteriorate were cytophaga.

Dr. John M. Sharpley (Sharpley Labs.): Was there any attempt to add an anti-bacterial material to the plasticizers in the process of manufacturing?

Dr. Coscarelli: No, we would be more interested in developing or selecting materials that are resistant to microorganisms per se.

Dr. Edward A. Zuraw (Gen. Dynamics): Have submarine cables been modified as a result of these studies? Have some of these materials that you find to be resistant been incorporated?

Dr. Coscarelli: The selection of some of the materials used in cable structures, has, in many cases been predicated by these studies. Many of the older cables were covered with jute, for example, and now jute has been replaced by synthetic fibers or a combination of synthetic fibers and jute.

8

PLANKTONIC AND BENTHIC BACTERIA
OF LAKES AND PONDS

Louise F. Potter
Windham College

In an aquatic environment there are at least three distinct habitats for microorganisms: the water, the mud, and the surfaces of stones, plants, and animals. The bacteria in the water may be termed planktonic, those of the mud benthic, and those inhabiting but not penetrating the surface of plants, animals, and stones "Aufwuchs" (Cooke, 1956; Seligo, 1905; and Young, 1945).

The material to be presented will be concerned with the aquatic environments of northwest Montana within the Flathead and Mission Valleys. Flathead Lake is the major body of water. It is an oligotrophic lake (Graham and Young, 1934; Young, 1935) approximately 35 miles (56 kilometers) long and 7 miles (11 kilometers) wide. The Deep Station is 110 meters deep (Potter and Baker, 1961). Rogers Lake is a small eutrophic lake north and west of Flathead Lake (Brunson and Nelson, 1952; Lauff, 1953). Swan Lake lies north and east of Flathead Lake. It is an oligotrophic lake larger than Rogers and smaller than Flathead Lake.

Twin Lakes are south of Flathead Lake in the terminal moraines of the Flathead Valley. Ninepipe is a reservoir south of Flathead Lake in the Mission Valley. These lakes range in area from 2.8 acres (1.1 hectares) to over 1600 acres (647 hectares; Schindler, 1954). The volume of water varies in Lower Twin Lake and Ninepipe because both areas are used as storage basins for irrigation water.

The ponds are south of Flathead Lake in the Mission Valley. These ponds are potholes under 60 meters in diameter and about 0.6 meters deep. The ponds studied (Schindler, 1954) are just a few of a large number of potholes found in the same area. All of these ponds are on the same type of soil.

Chemical analyses of the water of the lakes and ponds (Table 1) revealed that the waters of the Flathead Lake area are alkaline. The pH of most of these surface waters is 8.0 or above. These data are representative of the results of the chemical analyses (Potter and Baker, 1956, 1961; Potter, unpublished data).

TABLE 1: Chemical analyses of surface water

Lake or Pond	pH	Dissolved O_2 mg/l	NH_3 mg/l	NO_2 mg/l	NO_3 mg/l	PO_4 mg/l	Fe mg/l
Flathead Deep Station	8.2	10.0	0.00	0.00	0.02	0.40	0.00
Rogers Station No. 3	8.3	8.3	0.02	0.00	0.07	0.00	0.00
Swan No. 1	8.2	10.0	0.00	0.00	0.04	0.20	0.10
Pond No. 1	9.0	5.5	0.10	0.00	0.06	1.00	2.20
Pond No. 2	9.6	7.5	0.20	0.14	0.80	10.00	0.42
Pond No. 3	9.6	5.0	0.05	0.001	0.40	6.00	0.60
Pond No. 4	9.4	3.0	0.00	0.00	0.24	1.00	0.40
Upper Twin	8.4	11.0	0.00	0.00	0.02	0.00	0.00
Lower Twin	7.9	9.0	0.00	0.00	0.03	0.00	0.00
Ninepipe	9.7	11.0	0.00	0.00	0.03	0.50	0.00

Although Flathead Lake has several areas which are distinct habitats, the chemical analyses of Flathead Lake show that it is an oligotrophic and well-aerated lake. Often samples from the greatest depths were supersaturated with oxygen. The results presented here reveal small amounts of phosphates and nitrates. Other samples, however, contained traces or no detectable amounts of phosphate, nitrate, or iron.

Rogers Lake contained small amounts of the moieties listed. The other lakes resembled Flathead Lake. The ponds, however, are distinctly eutrophic or dystrophic. Although all ponds are similar in physical characteristics, they vary greatly in chemical characteristics. The ponds had lower concentrations of dissolved oxygen than the lakes and they contained significant to high amounts of the other chemicals.

A study of the bacterial populations of surface water samples of the lakes and ponds showed large fluctuations in the number of bacteria and the proportion of chromogens. Fred, Wilson, and Davenport (1924) and Graham and Young (1934) have demonstrated that microbial populations fluctuate greatly over a period of time. Even during a 24 hour period, fluctuation in the size of the population was significant. The changes in the size and chromogenic characteristics of the populations over a period of time, say 4 weeks, is significant. These changes were more often found in inlet areas, near shore areas, or in small ponds. The changes in water from Deep Station were less marked. The largest populations in Flathead Lake are often associated with algal blooms (Henrici, 1937; Potter and Baker, 1956), run off (Taylor, 1940), and surface contamination such as pollen drifts.

The data given in Table 2 are representative of the counts obtained. Consistently, Flathead Lake has the smallest bacterial population of the lakes and ponds. The lakes generally have smaller populations than the potholes.

TABLE 2: Bacterial populations of lakes and ponds

Lake or Pond	Water		Mud	
	bacteria per ml x 10^3	Chromogens (per cent)	bacteria per g x 10^6	Chromogens (per cent)
Flathead Deep Station	0.026	69	0.780	14
Rogers Station no. 3	1.090	29	0.0427	18
Swan Station no. 1	1.050	55	1.49	14
Pond no. 1	18.1	44	98.0	35
Pond no. 2	10.6	28	7.9	32
Pond no. 3	232.0	69	7.7	35
Pond no. 4	6.7	51	0.99	39
Upper Twin	0.53	19	0.05	33
Lower Twin	0.96	42	0.086	25
Ninepipe	7.9	83	14.1	27

Flathead Lake is a large oligotrophic lake and Rogers
Lake is a small eutrophic lake. Yet the variations in the
numbers of microorganisms from different areas in each
seemed to be more significant than the variations ascribable
to the type of lake.

A study of the benthic bacteria reveals that the deeper
the water over the mud, usually the smaller the bacterial
population, as noted by Henrici and McCoy (1938). The
characteristics of the bottom deposits are related to the
characteristics of the microbial populations. The number of
bacteria present in the Rogers Lake sample from the open
area was very low. The organic nature of the bottom indicates that bacteria are not actively decomposing the deposited materials as rapidly as they are being deposited. (In turn,
the small bacterial population suggests that the number present may be one of the limiting factors in decomposition.)

Pollution of an area results in changes in the sizes of
the bacterial populations of water and a reduction in the proportion of chromogens (Potter, unpublished data). In turn,
pollution may effect the populations of bottom deposits.

In basins having similar chemical characteristics, the
numbers are usually proportional to the size and depth of the
basin. The percentage of chromogens is usually higher in
water than in mud.

Although a study of Table 2 will reveal that neither the
number nor the character of the ecological factors affecting
planktonic and benthic populations is known, the assumption
can be made that there are autochthonous floras for water
and mud. Although there may be separate or distinct
differences in the types of organisms, there appear to be
distinct differences in the characteristics of a planktonic
versus a benthic population.

Further evidence supporting this assumption is apparent
in the morphology and the Gram reactions of cultures obtained
from dilution plates.

First, let us examine, in general, the representative data
(Table 3) on the morphology of the cultures. As noted with
counts, there are fluctuations in the qualitative characteristics.
The patterns of the variations suggest the possibility of some
colonization or clumping of bacteria in water -- possibly on
the surfaces of planktonic particles -- and in the mud. The
possibility of atypical samples or the effect, however temporary, of a marked change in the food available should not be

overlooked.

Gram positive spore-formers are frequently found in significant numbers in the mud and less frequently in water. Gram negative organisms are more numerous in water than mud. In water, Gram negative rods are most frequent. Although not shown in this table, cocci often are found in low numbers and occasionally in significant numbers (Potter and Baker, 1961), suggesting the presence of clumps or colonies. Thus, the distribution of morphological types lends further support to the theory of autochthonous floras in mud and in water.

TABLE 3: Gram reaction of bacteria

Lake or Pond	Water		Mud	
	Gram + Spore formers (per cent)	Total Gram - Organisms (per cent)	Gram + Spore formers (per cent)	Total Gram - Organisms (per cent)
Flathead Deep Station	6	86	50	35
Rogers Station no. 3	0	94	35	2
Pond no. 1	1	91	0	82
Pond no. 2	0	80	5	66
Pond no. 3	1	94	9	46
Pond no. 4	2	91	6	73
Upper Twin	0	99	52	19
Lower Twin	1	85	20	35
Ninepipe	3	95	10	54

A study of the vertical distribution of bacteria in the lakes indicates that the largest populations occur at the surface of the water. More information is presented in another paper (Potter and Baker, 1961); only representative data are presented here (Table 4).

In Flathead Lake (the Deep Station) and in Rogers Lake, the numbers of bacteria decrease significantly in the first 0.1 to 0.5 meter. In Flathead Lake the largest number was found at the 10-meter level. The significance of this larger number at 10 meters is not known. There is no evidence of a true thermocline or stratification at this depth (Potter and Baker, 1961).

TABLE 4: Vertical distribution of bacteria

Depth in Meters	Flathead Lake		Swan Lake		Rogers Lake	
	no. per ml	Chromo-gens (per cent)	no. per ml	Chromo-gens (per cent)	no. per ml	Chromo-gens (per cent)
0.0	26	69	1050	55	1090	29
0.1	—	—	—	—	79	68
0.5	3	53	—	—	—	—
1.0	10	50	—	—	275	88
2.0	5.4	27	—	—	121	91
4.0	—	—	—	—	80	76
4.5	—	—	—	—	150	85
5.0	—	—	59	11	—	—
10.0	31	51	182	35	—	—
17.0	—	—	163	31	—	—
20.0	10	70	—	—	—	—
30.0	—	—	252	34	—	—
40.0	20	70	—	—	—	—
100.0	6.4	34	—	—	—	—

Chromogens are usually predominant at all levels, with few exceptions. There does not appear to be a distinct pattern of distribution of chromogens or bacteria in relation to the depths at which samples were taken. There is, however, some evidence for vertical distribution patterns. Very few red-pigmented organisms were found in water samples. They were found in surface samples from the Deep Station a number of times but they were absent in deeper samples. Of more significance is the occurence of pink-pigmented organisms. In Big Arm water samples (Potter and Baker, 1961) these pink organisms were more numerous at the surface. Meager evidence is available from other stations in Flathead Lake suggesting that pink-pigmented organisms are most numerous in surface water.

There is, at least, suggestive evidence of autochthonous planktonic and benthic bacterial populations in aquatic areas. A study of vertical distribution reveals no distinct patterns, but does indicate that the largest populations are found at the surface. There is some evidence of a vertical

distribution pattern in certain groups of chromogens, at
least in Flathead Lake. It is my belief that the study of the
distribution of bacteria in a large oligotrophic lake, such
as Flathead Lake, will yield more typical information, as
temporary changes in the environment are far less marked
because of volume and subsequent dilution.

The Aufwuchs on non-living materials, stones and stumps,
and on living materials, plants and fish, were investigated
using the methods described by Potter and Baker (1961).

The bacterial populations found on the surface of stones
removed from the water, were many times larger than the
populations found in water. The variation in the number per
cm^2 (Table 5) was large; consistently larger numbers were
found on the top surfaces than on the bottom. The dilution
plates resembled those of water rather than of mud. The
colonies were predominantly chromogenic. There were few
typical, aerobic spore-former colonies. From the distribution of chromogens and colony types it would appear that
the Aufwuchs group is a flora more typical of water than of
mud.

The large numbers of bacteria found on stones may indicate that stones can serve as adhesion surfaces for
bacteria and that stones may absorb nutrients from the water
for the organisms.

The presence of algae on an object alter the surface and
nutritional characteristics of the area. One of the areas
sampled was a large stump partially covered with algae.
Swabs from alga-covered and alga-free areas had different
numbers of bacteria and percentages of chromogens. The
evidence, even though slight, indicates that the presence of
algae provides conditions suitable for the growth of more
chromogens and larger bacterial populations.

Emergent plants were swabbed for Aufwuchs populations.
Representative results are given in Table 6. The total
number of bacteria per cm^2 was variable and the percentage
of chromogens was variable over a wide range. The variations of different numbers of the same species in the same pond
were large. This information would suggest that the plant is
not a selective environment. An alternative suggestion is
that colonization by bacteria and growth of these bacteria is
not adequately represented by the population recovered from
a sample of 1 cm^2.

TABLE 5: Number of bacteria on submerged materials

Material	Location	Total no. per cm^2 x 10^3	Chromogens (per cent)
Stone	McDonald Lake	136	66
Stone	McDonald Lake	13	91
Stone (top)	Skidoo Bay	1810	74
Stone (bottom)	Skidoo Bay	15. 7	50
Stump (+ algae)	Skidoo Bay	2600	74
Stump (no algae)	Skidoo Bay	234	70

At present we can say that the Aufwuchs populations of plants are large and variable. The numbers, percentage of chromogens, and colony types may resemble those of either planktonic or benthic bacteria.

TABLE 6: Bacterial populations on plant surfaces

Location	Plant Surface	Total no. per cm^2 x 10^3	Chromogens (per cent)
Rogers Lake	Carex sp.	4.81	21.0
	Carex sp.	10.2	71.0
	Potamogeton sp.	11.5	11.0
	Potamogeton sp.	3.81	20.0
Pond no.1	Potamogeton sp.	196.0	17.0
	Potamogeton sp.	3.8	43.0
Pond no. 4	Sedge	331.0	33.0
	Sedge	6.0	55.0

Stones, stumps, and plants provide surfaces for growth of microorganisms. These organisms growing on, or adhering to, these surfaces could be washed off and become part of the planktonic bacteria.

More information is available on the Aufwuchs populations of fish (Potter and Baker, 1961). For 60 fish sampled, the majority (Table 7) carried between 1000 and 100, 000 bacteria per cm^2. Over 75 per cent of the fish had more than 50 per

cent chromogens. Morphological studies showed Gram
negative rods to be most numerous. The numbers and kinds
of bacteria present showed no relation to location or kind of
fish. Thus the Aufwuchs of fish resemble the planktonic
group of bacteria more than the benthic group.

The investigations on bacterial populations of fish indicate
that fish are important as passive carriers of bacteria in the
aquatic environment. Thus, in an aquatic environment, fish
may be important in the distribution of the planktonic bacteria.

TABLE 7: Characteristics of the bacterial
populations of fish

Total no. per cm^2	No. of fish	Chromogens (per cent)	No. of fish
0 - 10	0	0 - 10	6
10 - 100	0	11 - 20	0
100 - 1,000	6	21 - 30	1
1,000 - 10,000	20	31 - 40	4
10,000 - 100,000	26	41 - 50	2
Above 100,000	8	51 - 60	7
		61 - 70	6
		71 - 80	13
		81 - 90	19
		91 - 100	2

The number and types of planktonic bacteria in a body
of water will be determined by the nutrient materials in the
water. The influence of the components in the water of
Flathead Lake and some ponds was investigated.

Water samples from Flathead Lake and ponds no. 1 and
no. 4 were filtered, autoclaved, and reinoculated with water
from the same areas. For controls, water from each area
was treated with hydrogen peroxide before autoclaving.

Bacterial populations multiply in stored water samples
(Whipple, 1901; ZoBell and Anderson, 1936; Potter, 1960).
The hydrogen peroxide treated water supported no growth.
Water from Flathead Lake supported the smallest growth
(Table 8). Otherwise, reinoculated water supported good
growth of bacterial populations. The differences in the amount
and kinds of organisms growing in reinoculated water is de-

termined by the inoculum and the nutrients present in the
water. These nutrients are destroyed by hydrogen peroxide.

TABLE 8: Growth of Planktonic bacteria
in waters of different origin

Water	Inoculum	Chromogens (per cent)	No. per ml x 10^3
—	Deep Station	69	0.111
Deep Station	Deep Station	51	1410
Pond no. 1	Deep Station	89	3190
Pond no. 4	Deep Station	29	8400
—	Pond no. 1	82	157
Deep Station	Pond no. 1	23	119
Pond no. 1	Pond no. 1	13	1360
Pond no. 4	Pond no. 1	13	1110

Many other factors in the water affect the size and composition of the bacterial population. One of these factors is pH
(Potter, 1960). The influence of other factors -- inorganic
and organic compounds, including vitamins -- was investigated.
Water samples containing the additions given in Table 9, were
inoculated with water or mud. There were large increases
in the populations and significant shifts in the chromogen
populations. Only the addition of vitamin B_1 or a group of
B vitamins increased the percentage of chromogens in the
total population. With mud as an inoculum, all samples showed
increases in the proportion of chromogens. Using percentage
of chromogens as an indicator of the planktonic group of
bacteria, it appears that the dilution of benthic populations
and the additions of some substances enhance the planktonic
characteristics of the benthic populations.

The nutritional requirements of bacteria isolated from
mud and water of Flathead Lake Deep Station were examined
using Lochhead's et al., methods (1943, 1952, 1953, 1956,
1957). The cultures had been selected at random from
dilution plates. The morphological characteristics (Table 10)
are typical of the more populous members in the aquatic
environment. The cocci, which are few in the environment,
are not represented in this group. The group labelled "Arthrobacter" shows morphological characteristics of that group.

TABLE 9: Influence of enrichment on bacterial
populations of water and mud

Enrichment	Increase in per cent of chromogens	
	Water	Mud
None	+ 2	+ 33
Chlorophyll	− 29	+ 2
Ammonium chloride	− 1	+ 46
Sodium nitrate	− 17	+ 32
Vitamin B₁	+ 6	+ 37
Vitamin B₁₂	− 13	+ 49
Vit. B₁ + B₁₂ + Biotin + Niacin	+ 9	+ 16

TABLE 10: Morphological characteristics of cultures of
Flathead Lake

Type	No. of cultures	
	Mud	Water
Gram + rod	5	4
Gram − rod	10	55
Gram variable rod	17	17
Spore forming rod	28	4
"Arthrobacter"	8	3

Nutritional requirements were determined at both 20 C
and 4 C. Most organisms grew in at least one of the culture
media at 20 C but many organisms did not grow in any of the
culture media of 4 C even after 20 weeks incubation. At 20 C,
the largest number of bacteria from mud grew in base medium.
At 4 C, the largest group did not grow in any of the media.
Most cultures from water, at both temperatures, grew in the
amino acid or the yeast extract medium.

From Table 11 it can be seen that, at 4 C, many organisms
from both mud and water show increased nutritional requirements. Only a few cultures showed a decrease in nutritional
requirements at 4 C.

TABLE 11: Nutritional characteristics of bacteria of Flathead Lake

Medium	Mud cultures		Water cultures	
	20 C	4 C	20 C	4 C
Base	24*	9	10	9
Amino acids	10	13	23	25
Amino acids + growth factors	1	1	16	4
Yeast extract	22	13	23	35
Yeast extract + B_{12}	1	1	0	0
Yeast and soil extracts	3	4	5	4
No growth	2	18	6	8

* Entries represent the number of cultures which grew.

The information and results presented here suggest the presence of two groups of bacteria in the aquatic environment, namely, the planktonic and the benthic bacteria. The Aufwuchs group, in most samples, resembles more closely the planktonic bacteria.

The size and proportions of types of organisms in each group vary with changes in the environment. Many fluctuations in the characteristics of a population in water or mud are indicators of naturally occuring changes in the environment.

Many organisms are probably present in both the planktonic and the benthic group, but the populations have characteristic differences.

Only a few results of a few different techniques have been presented to indicate the characteristics of autochthonous groups in the aquatic environment. Much more information is needed before a fully satisfactory characterization of planktonic and benthic bacteria will be possible.

Author's present address: Department of Biology, Elmira College, Elmira, N. Y.

LITERATURE CITED

Brunson, R. B. and H. E. Nelson. 1952. A limnological
reconnaissance of three western Montana lakes. Proc.
Montana Acad. Sci. 12:45-61.

Cooke, W. B. 1956. Colonization of artificial bare areas
by microorganisms. Bot. Rev. 22:613-638.

Fred, E. B., F. C. Wilson, and A. Davenport, 1924.
Distribution and significance of bacteria in Lake Mendota.
Ecol. 5:322-339.

Graham, V. E. and R. T. Young. 1934. A bacteriological
study of Flathead Lake, Montana. Ecol. 15:101-109.

Henrici, A. T. 1937. Studies of fresh water bacteria. IV.
Seasonal fluctuations of lake bacteria in relation to
plankton production. J. Bacteriol. 35:129-139.

Henrici, A. T. and E. McCoy. 1938. The distribution of
heterotrophic bacteria in the bottom deposits of some
lakes. Trans. Wisc. Acad. Sci. 31:323-361.

Lauff, George. 1953. Contributions to the water chemistry
and phytoplankton relationships of Rogers Lake, Montana.
Proc. Montana Acad. Sci. 13:5-20.

Lochhead, A. G. and F. E. Chase. 1943. Qualitative studies
of soil microorganisms. V. Nutritional requirements of
the predominant bacterial flora. Soil Sci. 55:185-195.

Lochhead, A. G. and R. H. Thexton. 1952. Qualitative studies
of soil microorganisms. X. Bacteria requiring vitamin
B_{12} as growth factor. J. Bacteriol. 63:219-226.

Lochhead, A. G. and M. O. Burton. 1953. An essential
bacterial growth factor produced by microbial synthesis.
Can. J. Bot. 31:7-22.

Lochhead, A. G. 1956. Incidence in soil of bacteria requiring
vitamin B_{12} and terregens factor. Soil Sci. 82:237-245.

Lochhead, A. G. 1957. Qualitative studies of soil microorganisms. XIV. Specific vitamin requirements of the
predominant bacterial flora. Can. J. Microbiol. 3:35-42.

Potter, L. F. 1960. The effect of pH on the development of
bacteria in water stored in glass containers. Can. J.
Microbiol. 6:257-263.

Potter, L. F. and G. E. Baker. 1956. The microbiology of
Flathead and Rogers Lakes, Montana. I. Preliminary
survey of the microbial populations. Ecol. 37:351-355.

Potter, L. F. and G. E. Baker. 1961. The microbiology
of Flathead and Rogers Lakes, Montana. II. Vertical
distribution of the microbial populations and chemical
analyses of their environments. Ecol. 42:338-348.
Schindler, J. 1954. Taxonomy and ecology of algae in ponds
and lakes of the Flathead Basin, Montana (Exclusive of
the diatoms). Thesis, Mich. State College, East Lansing,
Mich.
Seligo, A. 1905. Über den Ursprung Fischnährung. Mitt.
Westgr. Fisch. -V., Danzig. Mitt. 17:52-56.
Taylor, C. B. 1940. Bacteriology of fresh water. I.
Distribution of bacteria in English lakes. J. Hyg. 40:
616-640.
Young, O. W. 1945. A limnological investigation of the
periphyton in Douglas Lake, Michigan. Trans. Am.
Microscop. Soc. 64:1-20.
Young, R. T. 1935. The life of Flathead Lake, Montana.
Ecological Monog. 5:91-163.
Whipple, G. C. 1901. Changes that take place in the bacterial
content of waters during transportation. Tech. Quart.
14:21-29.
ZoBell, C. E. and D. G. Anderson. 1936. Observations on
the multiplication of bacteria in different volumes of
stored sea water and the influence of oxygen tension
and solid surfaces. Biol. Bull. 71:324-342.

DISCUSSION

Dr. M. A. Benarde (Rutgers Univ.): Can you tell me
something about the sampling procedure for the surface counts
on fish, the counts you obtained, and whether there were any
differences, for instance, between sampling external surfaces
and gill areas?

Dr. Potter: In the sampling, we worked with the fisher-
ies people when they were collecting samples. While they were
studying distribution of fish we went out with them and took a
number of fish at random in each net set. The number was
sometimes the total of the fish they caught or, sometimes,
only one or two per cent. There were many kinds of fish.
As for the bacteria, we limited our swabbing to the side
of the fish, using aluminum foil having 1 cm^2 holes, which
we laid over the surface to delimit the sampling area.

Dr. Benarde: A cotton swab was used?

Dr. Potter: Yes, or alginate swabs. We found no difference in either technique.

Dr. C. ZoBell (Scripps Inst. of Oceanogr.): I was
particularly interested in your data on the vertical distribution of bacteria. Your table showed that at 0. 0 meters
you had the largest natural populations. I wonder at what
depth this was actually taken. Did you, like a good many
others, find a very high concentration of microorganisms
in the very surface film of water, which some have described
as the most interesting, the most significant millimeter of
water in natural bodies? Often we find from 10 to 1000 times
more bacteria in the topmost millimeter than in immediately
underlying layers.

Dr. Potter: We did skim those samples, but most of the
time in Flathead Lake there is a little rolling, so we could
not limit sampling to only the first millimeter or the first
10 mm. Our largest counts were obtained repeatedly in those
surface samples and, probably, in the surface film. That
is the area which is most contaminated, too. I think that
there are more atypical organisms there than in the deeper
areas.

Dr. Karl Wuhrmann (Swiss Fed. Inst.): I should like
to ask a question concerning the plate count method. I
suppose that these counts have been made on some nutrient,
as is conventionally done, but I should like to recall that
direct counts in lake waters, for instance, have shown that
significantly higher numbers of bacteria exist in these waters
than are found by plate counts and these differences amount
to, say, four, five, or six, potentials of ten. Will you
comment on this, especially as concerns the pure waters
which you investigated?

Dr. Potter: First, we wanted cultures of organisms, so
total counts alone were not sufficient for us. In order to
handle a certain volume of work and to be able to correlate
our information, we had to arrive at a standard method of
our own and, after trying a large number of different plating
media, we found that sodium caseinate agar gave us the greatest distribution of types and the highest number of organisms.
In this connection, although I presented the work on bacteria
only, Dr. Gladys Baker and I were interested in the fungal
population also. We found that the most satisfactory culture

medium for the heterotrophs and fungi was sodium caseinate
agar. I have done some work with membrane filters, but
only a little. I did a little with the direct count method.
Not only does one get very large numbers with the direct
count method, but one can introduce considerable error which
may be magnified by a factor of at least 10^4 or 10^6 if one is
not very careful.

Total numbers were not as important to us as the kinds
of organisms which were living together. Shall we find them
year after year? What are they doing there? That is what
we want to know primarily.

Dr. Donald Aulenbach (Rensselaer Polytech. Inst.): You
mentioned that there was no detectable thermocline in Flathead Lake. Is there any particular significance to its absence?
Do you attribute the lack of a thermocline to conditions in the
lake? With reference to the depth-distribution of bacteria,
if there were, say, complete mixing with no thermocline,
would this be a valid reason for having equal distribution of
bacteria? You did not give any data on temperature; I
presume you measured this?

Dr. Potter: We have the chemical analyses for vertical
distribution. We did look for a thermocline and for stratification. Usually, in an area where there is a thermocline,
not only is there a marked temperature difference, but there
is eventually a chemical stratification and stratification of
plankton. I have not worked on the planktonic organisms
larger than bacteria, but from information available from the
biological station, there seems to be no stratification at all.
The most positive piece of information we have is the
supersaturation with oxygen. The flow is from north to south
and the lake is so oriented that there is vigorous wind action
from west to east, so that the lake is very well mixed and
aerated.

Dr. F. Johnson (Princeton Univ.): I noticed 100 meters
was the maximum depth in one of your tables. Is that the
maximum depth in Flathead Lake?

Dr. Potter: No; 110 m is the maximum we have found so
far.

Dr. Johnson: It is not really very deep. I was thinking
of the hydrostatic pressure.

Dr. Potter: The pressure there is about 160 lb per in^2.

Dr. Johnson: In the sea, it is about one atmosphere for 10 m so that would probably not be an important factor, but I was particularly struck by the high pH and I wondered if you had thought about this with reference to temperature. I have heard not very much reference to temperature, and I happen to be particularly sensitive to this point, that the pH ran from 7.9 to 9.7; 9.7 is quite alkaline for most environments of heterotrophic bacteria, and it seemed to me that it would be understandable if the temperature were low enough, because the higher pH would be expected, on general principles --which often lead us astray--to have a denaturing effect on proteins.

If you permit this comment, I think it may be worth taking into account. I noticed yesterday that Dr. Kallio mentioned that some of his organisms would grow on some hydrocarbons at a low temperature but not at a higher temperature. I was about to comment that I suspected this would be the case and I suggest that you might find an analogous effect. The inter-relationship could be sought between temperature and pH just as between temperature and toxicity or availability of substrates.

Dr. Potter: The pH was so high in one area that we could not believe the information. We finally determined the pH by titrating for free alkali and calculating back. The result was pH over 13. Ammonia was coming off the area, but there were still many bacteria there.

Dr. Johnson: Were they familiar heterotrophic types?

Dr. Potter: They looked familiar, however, I never studied them further.

Dr. Johnson: Do you recall the temperature? Was it quite cold?

Dr. Potter: I do not remember the temperature, but surface waters above 19 C in that area would be unusual.

Dr. Johnson: Did you ever look at any of your cultures in the dark?

Dr. Potter: We found no luminous bacteria.

Dr. Johnson: They are nearly all confined to the sea or to brackish water, but I think it is still worthwhile, occasionally, to look at petri dishes in the dark.

Dr. Heukelekian (Rutgers Univ.): What is the geology of this area? Are the rocks igneous or calcareous?

Dr. Potter: Calcareous, with some igneous. I think the valley, itself, is mainly calcareous.

Dr. Heukelekian: Do you attribute the high pH of the waters to planktonic activity or to the geological formation?

Dr. Potter: There is not much free carbon dioxide. We cannot find much in Flathead Lake water by chemical analyses, but we can demonstrate that there is growth of bacteria on reinoculation. The main constituents seem to be carbonates and oxygen.

Dr. Louis Purkerson (Taft San. Eng. Center): Did you compare counts of streptomyces, molds, and yeasts with numbers of bacteria? Have you any information on the contribution of types and numbers of intestinal organisms by fish?

Dr. Potter: We have only a few of analyses of micro-organisms in the intestines of fish. In Flathead Lake there is a tremendous dilution volume. It is good fishing, but there is a lot of room for each fish. As for the fungal population, actinomyces, and yeast, I shall ask Dr. Baker to comment. I think we neglected the yeast the most, did we not?

Dr. Gladys Baker (Vassar College): In working together, I took care of the fungi; Dr. Potter looked at the bacteria and the actinomyces chiefly. Dr. Potter is correct in saying that yeasts are the most neglected area of this study, partly because sometimes I overlooked them or mostly because I overlooked them. I thought they were bacterial colonies. The high counts of yeast were made by Dr. Potter, who thought they were bacteria.

The fungi were quite varied in the lake. I think I should start with the fish population. We did not find any connection between kinds of fungi and kinds of fish. The fungi that were present on the fish were representative of the fungi found throughout the lake, in both the water and the mud. From the surface swabs, with only one exception, we did not find a fungus that was not reported from either the water or the mud.

You asked, too, about the intestional populations. A
few fungi were isolated from the gut samples and one of them
was an ascomycete. As many of you know, ascomycetes
sometimes are particularly adapted for intestinal passage,
so this was not surprising. Incidentally, it was an ascomycete
we had not found in any of the other samples.

The numbers of fungi in both the water and the mud are
very low. I cannot hold a brief for plate counts if one is
strict about counting plates having between 30 and 300 colonies
or, as mycologists lower the number sometimes, 10 colonies;
but by the method of accrual over the years, by using different
kinds of agars in addition to the sodium caseinate base agar,
we have accrued a number which now amounts to about 225
different kinds of fungi. They are predominantly imperfect.
We have had some basidiomycetes, including imperfect
basidiomycetes and including one enterprising little mush-
room that fruited in the plate; it was a small Coprinus. We
found, of course, some regular yeasts, and many that we
have to call "candida-like" organisms. We found a few
phycomycetes. I would say the phycomycetes were conspicuous by their absence from the water and the mud of
Flathead Lake, and that is very curious.

In the ponds that we have sampled from season to season
--and the water level in these particular ponds is quite
variable--some of chaetomiums and ascomycetes can be
recovered from mud, even when the pond is very well dried
down, as well as in a full season. So I think the fungus
population is there to stay.

9

RIVER BACTERIOLOGY AND THE ROLE
OF BACTERIA IN SELF-PURIFICATION OF RIVERS

Karl Wuhrmann
Institute of Water Supply, Sewage Purification
and Water Pollution Control at the Swiss
Federal Institute of Technology
Zurich, Switzerland

River bacteriology is certainly not a special discipline in microbiology. Flowing surface water as a bacterial habitat merits, nevertheless, all our interest, considering the many theoretical and practical questions involved. It must be realized, however, that the problems to be anticipated are of an ecological nature. This implies that neither single bacteria nor bacterial species can be the main objects of interest. What we ought to know are the factors responsible for the occurrence of certain communities of bacteria in a river and the effects these bacteria impose on their medium, i.e., the river water.

The presence of bacteria in rivers has, up to now, mostly been treated from two aspects, namely:

(a) bacteria as pollutants in regard to the uses of rivers for water supply and recreation, and

(b) indirect emphasis on bacteria in rivers, using oxygen consumption and changes in oxygen concentration in river water as parameters in the study of self purification.

It cannot be denied that, in general, the microbes, as an essential part of the biocenosis within the ecosystem of a river, are often unduly neglected. Let us regard, as an example, the role of bacteria as destroyers of organic pollution: a tremendous amount of information has been collected on so-called self-purification in rivers, using biochemical oxygen demand (BOD) or similar unspecific parameters, as scales for measuring the disappearence of pollutional materials

167

from the water. Nobody has asked, however, what kinds of
bacteria, what numbers, what metabolic rates, etc., are
responsible for the removal of a defined substance. As a
result of this situation, the term self-purification is much
more obscure than it would seem in regard to the volume
of paper already devoted to this subject!

It is our purpose, in this lecture, to look upon a river as
a habitat for bacteria and to discuss some practical problems,
like self-purification, from the point of view of bacterial
ecology. Time and space allows no more than tracing the
picture with some crude lines. It is hoped, however, that
they may initiate and stimulate future research.

Bacterial biotopes and distribution of bacteria in rivers.
The immense space represented by a river from the point of
view of a single bacterium is, in fact, a world partitioned
into a large number of most diversified biota for microbes.
As far as volume is concerned, the free-flowing water is,
in general, the biggest and most homogenous biotope. It is
necessary, however, to differentiate even this space into at
least two biota: there are (1) the bacteria suspended individually or in small aggregates in the free water, and (2)
the microbes which settle on the surface of either mineral
particles or on organic debris carried by the flow. We may
designate these bacteria as the epipsammic flora, in contrast
to the free, suspended flora. The investigations by Jannasch
(1956) have demonstrated that, in a river transporting, for
instance, noticeable quantities of silt, the epipsammic population embraces, by far, the majority of microbes. Some
figures from his numerations in the river Nile, assembled
in Table 1, are quite illustrative of this fact. Additional
information on the proportion of epipsammic and freely suspended germs in river water would be highly desirable.

We come, next, to the microbial populations living as
sessile organisms, either on the surface of macrophytes,
green algae, diatoms, etc., or on the surface of water
animals of all sizes. These bacteria represent the epiphytic
and the epizoic flora, respectively. (It is worthwhile to consider briefly the proportion of epiphytic and freely suspended
bacteria in, for instance, extremely clean and slightly polluted
rivers) Table 2 contains two examples of enumerations of
saprophytic germs (total count) found in two experimental
rivers (see page 170)fed with waters of different quality. The
density of growth of carrier plants in both rivers was rela-

TABLE 1: Number of freely suspended and epipsammic bacteria
in the River Nile (from Jannasch, 1956)

Relative particle density*	Total count 10^6/ml	freely suspended bacteria 10^6/ml	freely suspended bacteria of total (per cent)
2	9.21	0.002	0.02
4	18.1	0.007	0.04
10	10.8	0.002	0.02

* Photometric turbidity, susp. solids 50 - 280 mg/per l.

tively large, as is generally observed in shallow rivers. It
is surprising that the freely suspended microbes in the water
represent, with a proportion of much less than 1 per cent, such
a small part of the total population. From the figures in this
table we also have to conclude that the epiphytic bacteria must
exert a much larger part of the metabolic activity in a shallow
stream than the freely suspended microbes.

A third large group of biotopes for bacteria are the surfaces
of the stones and of the mud deposits on the river bed. The
epibenthic flora inhabiting these surfaces is still in immediate
contact with the flowing water. In polluted streams it is, in
general, especially numerous. We need only recall the large
masses of organisms formed, for instance, by species like
Sphaerotilus or Beggiatoa.

We have to call attention, finally, to the bacterial population
within the benthic deposits, i. e., the benthic flora which, in
many respects, meets ecological conditions similar to those of
water-logged soil. Most of these organisms are excluded from
direct contact with the flowing water and, hence, the species
composition in this biotope is not directly related to the ecological conditions within the free water. Consequently, the metabolic activity of the benthic flora is generally of minor importance
for the quality of river water. This fact has been clearly confirmed with the experimental investigations by Fair et al. (1941),
and is further supported by the considerations of Ruttner-
Kolisko (1962).

Bacterial species in rivers and the term "water bacteria".
By far, the majority of bacteria in rivers is of allochthonous
origin; i. e., they are introduced by the washings from soil or
with sewage. It is an idle undertaking, therefore, to start an

TABLE 2: Number of freely suspended and epiphytic bacteria in experimental rivers*

	I Ground water	II Ground water with 2% sewage
Flow velocity m/sec	0.16	0.16
Temperature °C	4.0	4.0
Carrier plants ("Aufwuchs")	Mosses (Fontinalis, Amblystegium) with little Hormidium and Diatoma	Long strands of Synedra and Diatoma with little Hormidium
Density of carrier growth g dry solids/m	60	30
Free susp. bacteria/ml ††	82	0.021×10^6
Free susp. bacteria/ml †	4.3×10^6	1.1×10^9
Epiphytic bact./g dry solids ††	1.5×10^6	4.1×10^6
Epiphytic bact./m	9×10^{10}	1.23×10^{11}
Total count/m	9×10^{10}	1.24×10^{11}
% free susp. bact. of Total	0.005	0.9

* Sampling point: 200 m of flow distance from feeding station.

† Volume of water per m river length = 52.41.

†† Plate counts: 1/10 plate count agar, 22 C, 10 days.

investigation on the kinds of species present (we are neglecting
here those types which must be emphasized from an hygienic
point of view; these few species are of no interest in ecological considerations). The soil being probably the original
habitat for most bacteria met in a river, they are confronted
in water with some fundamentally new ecological conditions.
It is worthwhile to consider briefly some of the pertinent
ecological differences between soil and flowing water and their
consequences for a mixed microbial biocenosis:

(a) In comparison to the water adhering to the surface of
soil particles or filling the capillaries in soil, the water in a
stream represents an extremely diluted medium. The low
concentration of nutrients is, however, partly compensated
for by the continuous replacement of the metabolic substrates
and the removal of eventually inhibiting metabolic end products
by the flow of the water. (Diffusion velocities for gases and
substrate molecules thus limit the metabolic rate of bacteria
in a turbulent liquid medium to a degree that is much less than
in soil.)

(b) A stream represents a rather homogenous medium in
space and in time, regarding both the chemical composition
and the physical conditions.

These two specific properties explain immediately the
unique mass developments of certain bacteria or fungi observed in streams which have no parallel in soil microbiology.
In this connection, we remember organisms like Sphaerotilus
natans, Beggiatoa species, the Thiobacillus, some of the iron
bacteria (Leptothrix), fungi such as Fusarium species or
or Leptomitus lacteus, and so on. All these organisms are
known to live in soil but they would never be able to grow there
in macrocolonies as they do in water, because of ecological
limitations already mentioned. It would, in fact, be very
difficult to nominate bacterial or fungal species which are
exclusively limited to open water. (The habit of designating
some of them, nevertheless, as typical "water" or even
"stream bacteria" is justified, however, by their potential
for massive development in nature under suitable conditions.

Besides the ubiquitous flora discussed above, dense)
populations of more specialized types may be found where a
stream represents unusal chemical conditions in regard to
its inorganic or organic composition, either because of the
soil characteristics in the drainage area or because of continuous pollution with special compounds such as hydrocarbons,

phenols, etc. Extensive growths of bacteria which are very
specific with regard to nutrient substrate may then occur in
rivers. It is a matter of taste whether such specialists
should also be designated as "water bacteria".

Summarizing this discussion, we conclude that the term
"water bacteria" has no taxonomic and only a small ecological significance. It would be realistic, therefore, to omit
this expression completely or to use it exclusively in a descriptive sense.

Flow velocity as an ecological factor for bacterial growth.
Besides the composition of the stream water as a growth
medium, one of the most characteristic features of a stream
as a biotope is the water current. It is well known that this
ecological factor exerts -- independently of all other conditions
-- a strong influence on the species distribution of invertebrate
and vertebrate water animals and of the autotrophic microphytes
(see, for instance: Ambühl, 1959, and symposium of the Societas Internationalis Limnologiae, 1961, on the influence of
current on running-water organisms). Does there exist a
similar influence on the bacterial populations in streams?
Our information is very meager in this respect. A classical
but, perhaps, rather singular example might be mentioned,
however; experiments show that, for instance, Sphaerotilus
natans or Leptomitus lacteus grow luxuriantly in a stagnant,
aerobic medium when kept in pure culture. In nature, however, these species demonstrate massive developments in
flowing water only. Experiments by Zimmermann (1960) in
model rivers with various current velocities gave a very
characteristic result as shown in Fig. 1. The graph represents,
in black columns, the growth intensity of several species
which were chosen as typical members of the biocenosis of
polluted rivers. There were three channels (Fig. 2) with
different slopes which were fed over the period of one year
the same water (ground water with addition of small amounts
of sewage). Three water qualities were tested (hence, three
years of observations underlie the graph of Fig. 1). It is
easily seen that typical zoogloea-forming bacteria, growing
in the most polluted water (I), were equally present at all
flow velocities. Sphaerotilus natans found a suitable medium
at the two pollution levels (I) and (II). In both these assays,
however, observable growth occurred only with water velocities
of at least 0.2 m per sec. None of the other species mentioned
in the graph demonstrates a similar steady reaction to water

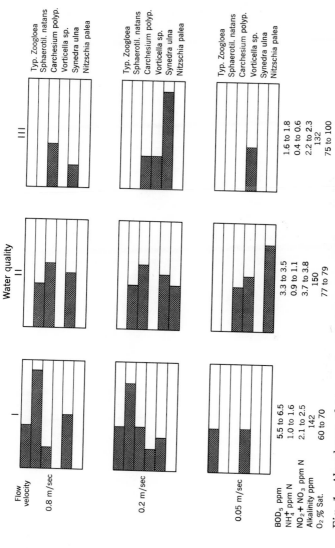

Fig. 1—Abundance of some microphytes in experimental rivers with various water qualities (I, II and III) as a function of the current velocity (0.8, 0.2 and 0.05 m/sec). Length of black columns: relative frequency (scale 0 – 5) of the organisms. Data from Zimmermann (1960).

Fig. 2—View of the channel system "small channels"
at the experimental station of the Institute for
Water Supply, Sewage Purification and Water Pollution Control at the Swiss Federal Institute of
Technology in Zurich. The 3 channels to the left
were used in the investigations by Zimmermann
(1960).

current independently of other variables. It is indicative
that, for instance, Leptomitus lacteus behaves in a very
similar manner when adequate milieu conditions are present

in nature. This fact leads to the conclusion that the effect of flow conditions on growth is but an indirect one. The most reasonable explanation is the competition exerted by the large number of commensal organisms living in the dense and rather voluminous masses of the filamentous host organisms. (As soon as the water velocity decreases below a critical value (probably dependent on the degree of pollution), the nutrition and the oxygen supply within this intimately coexisting world of organisms become inadequate for the largest consumers: i. e., in this case, Sphaerotilus or Leptomitus.) So far, no dependences of microorganisms on current have been reported which could not be explained by similar synecological effects. It is rather doubtful, therefore, whether flow velocity of the medium exerts any direct physiological influence essential for growth on any microorganisms ordinarily met in streams.

Microbial activity in self-purification. As already pointed out, one of the main ecological influences of bacteria in rivers is their effect on the degradation of organic substances suspended or dissolved in the water or deposited in sediments. The result of this metabolic activity forms an important -- and frequently the essential -- part of the overall reaction called self-purification.

In the following discussion, all non-microbial phases of self-purification, such as flocculation and sedimentation of organic or inorganic suspended solids, chemical oxidation of reduced substances, escape of volatile compounds into the atmosphere, and so forth, will be disregarded. We shall further restrain our discussion to reactions occurring exclusively in the free-flowing water and in the zone of the epibenthic biocenosis. Benthic decomposition, as defined in the work of Fair, Moore, and Thomas (1941), will not be considered. Self-purification, in the present discussion is understood, therefore, in a restrictive sense as the elimination of dissolved, chemically defined compounds from the water by the metabolic activity of organisms.

A tremendous amount of information on self-purification in rivers has accumulated in the past 50 years and, as long as we are satisfied with BOD values of river water and the oxygen balance in rivers, nothing new could be added. We have to admit, however, that all this work, informative as it may be, is a very poor basis for a thorough understanding of biological and chemical reactions in a river. Furthermore, it throws no light on the factors really governing the rate of decrease of a given charge of organic compounds while the charge is travelling downstream. It is not amazing, therefore, that our present knowledge of quantitative estimates of self-purification and the relationships of self-purification with ecological and hydrographic factors is still on a very low level I realize that it is plain heresy to make such a statement in the country where most of the impressive brainwork has been done for the elaboration of the BOD test and its application in the calculation of oxygen balances in streams. Full credit has to be given to the pioneer work of scientists such as Phelps, Streeter, and others, who established, for the first time, quantitative relationships between the pollution load of a river and the oxygen content of the flowing water. These workers also clearly recognized the metabolism of microorganisms as the driving force in this complicated system of reactions. It does by no means diminish their merits in the development of what may be called the "oxygen sag" concept of self-purification when we find today that the phenomenon of self-purification should be reconsidered on a new basis. There are two reasons which justify this thought:

(a) Defining self-purification as being essentially the removal of organic compounds from the water by the metabolism of microorganisms, its quantitative estimation must be based on the results of recognized analytical procedures for individual chemical compounds or, at least, for a known group of compounds. BOD values do not fulfill this requirement. BOD represents on overall value of the respiration of a numerically and taxonomically unknown population of microorganisms in a medium of, unknown composition and, thus, BOD is only very loosely correlated with the concentration and the kind of organic substances in a water sample.

(b) Although the oxygen concentration in a river is a key ecological factor, it is directly related neither to the individual mechanism of biological oxidative self-purification nor to the rate of the elimination of individual chemical compounds. Oxygen concentration may have an indicative value in self-purification observations. It has, however, no quantitative relationship to the reactions already occurring.

We realize that these statements shake the supporting columns of a well-established concept, and we are obliged, therefore, to propose new fronts of attack for the solution of the problem. In our opinion, there are two exigencies which have to be satisfied before any further progress can be expected:

(a) Clear-cut definitions of terms to be used in the study of self-purification must be established. The bases of the phenomena involved are the interactions between the association of organisms in a river and the rate of degradation of definite substances under various ecological conditions.

(b) It must be accepted that quantitative evaluations of individual chemical compounds, in relationship to quantitative and qualitative characterizations of the biocenoses in rivers, provide the only tools for an adequate measure and description of the phenomena occurring.

The general direction of future research as we see it now might be exemplified with some experimental questions such as the following:

(a) What is the rate of self-purification in any stretch of a stream for various organic substances as a function of the quantity and type of organisms present in the river bed?

(b) Assuming a state of equilibrium between the association of microorganisms and the permanent load and kind of organic pollution, what is the quantitative influence of external factors such as temperature, mineral turbidity, inorganic ion content, oxygen tension, hydraulic conditions, and so on, on the rate of self-purification suffered by known substances?

(c) How fast does the association of organisms adapt to new pollutional compounds in a river; or, in other words, how long is the lag in self-purification when a new waste is discharged into a water course?

This catalogue of questions could be easily supplemented by numerous other topics of similar theoretical and immediate practical interest.

At present, we are facing these problems with nearly complete ignorance. The finding of satisfactory answers is a very difficult task indeed, because we are dealing with at least three interdependent variables:

(a)   The kinds and quantities of polluting chemicals,

(b)   The types and quantities of organisms, and

(c)   The rate of degradation, i. e., self-purification.

In addition, downstream from a point of pollution, the intimate interaction between these three variables is continually changing until a new equilibrium between the biocenosis and the water, now free from decomposable material, is established. External, ecologically active factors such as temperature, flow conditions, mineral turbidity, inorganic

contents of the water, illumination, character of the river
bed, and so on, are superimposed on these interactions. We
are, therefore, confronted with a rather complicated dynamic
system in the length profile of a stream and it is obvious that
only very simple and well defined experiments can establish
a base line from which the complicated relationship in a
natural environment may then be attacked.

Definitions. Some of the expressions generally used in
connection with self-purification are much less clear than it
may seem from their extensive use in the literature. We
propose, therefore, the following definitions:

(a) Amount of self-purification (SP, Grösse der Selbst-
reinigung, taux d' autoépuration). Observed between two
points on the length profile of a stream, SP is the difference
in discharge of a specific compound at the two points.

$$SP = Q \ (c_0 - c_d) \qquad\qquad\qquad \text{g per sec (1)}$$

(b) Rate of self-purification (SR, Selbstreinigungsgew-
chwindigkeit, vitesse d' autoépuration): SR is the amount of
self-purification per unit flow distance and per unit time.

$$SR = Q \ (c_0 - c_d \ ) \ /d \ = Q \ (c_0 - c_d)/v \cdot t \quad \text{g per sec} \cdot m \quad (2)$$

(c) Specific elimination activity of the biomass (SE,
spezifische Selbstreinigungsleistung der Biomasse, activité
spécifique d'élimination de la biomasse): SE is the amount of
a substance removed by the biomass in the river bed over a
flow distance corresponding to 1 sec flow time.

$$SE = SR/G \qquad\qquad \text{g substrate per g biomass. sec (3)}$$

In the above definitions we use:

Q river discharge m^3/sec
c_0 concentration of pollutant at the upstream station g/m^3
c_d concentration of pollutant at the downstream station g/m^3
d flow distance   m
v flow velocity   m/sec
t flow time   sec
G biomass in direct contact with the flowing water in a
      river segment of the length corresponding to 1 sec
      flow time g/m

The quantity SE should vary with the quality of the biomass, other conditions being equal, if any true correlation
between self-purification and type of organisms in the river

bed exists. It is a proportionality factor in the relationship between the self-purification rate and the acting biomass in a river, for SR = SE · G.

(d) Self-purification capacity (Selbstreinigungsvermögen, capacité d'autoépuration): this expression is used with various meanings in the literature. Some authors think in terms of what was already defined as "amount of self-purification"; however, the term is mostly used in the sense of a potential capacity for self-purification. It is obvious that this capacity gains a definite meaning only with additional limiting parameters. We could define, for instance, as self-purification capacity, the amount of self-purification leading to predetermined oxygen depletion within the flow distance investigated. Other definitions might be used as well, however. In any case, self-purification capacity will be a variable value within the same river, dependant on the arbitrary definition given by the investigator. We shall not use this ill-defined term again until its meaning is better understood.

Self-purification as a function of quantity and composition of the river biocenosis, an experiment. We have tried to test the validity and usefulness of the foregoing definitions experimentally. It must be added immediately that the assays being described are not more than a first approximation to the problem. We are fully aware of the fact that one has to go through a long period of further investigations until any decisive answer can be given as to whether this approach to the problem of self-purification will be successful.

The following question has been formulated as a starting point: What is the quantitative relationship between the rate of self-purification in a river and the quantity and species composition of the biomass in continuous contact with the flowing water?

Obviously, an investigation of this kind in a natural water course must meet insurmountable difficulties due to the many uncontrollable variables which will interfere and may mask the main effects looked for. Artificial channels were used, therefore (description in Wuhrmann, 1957), where practically all essential ecological factors can be kept under strict control. Figures 3 a & 3 b give a general idea of these seven model rivers which are roughly 30 cm wide, 20 cm deep, and 210 m long, with a constant slope of 0.15 per cent. They are built of concrete with a smooth inner surface and may be fed with either river water, ground water, raw or purified sewage, or

any mixtures of these waters.   Chemicals may be added at will。
     The principle of the assays in connection with the above experimental question was the following: four of the channels were used with an identical discharge of 8 liters per sec. Three of them were fed with a mixture of ground water and sedimented raw sewage.   Sewage addition was 10 per cent in channel No. 1, 4 per cent in No. 3 and 2 per cent in No. 5.

Fig. 3a—View of the "large channel system" at the experimental station. Start of the channels at left. In the foreground, the ground water pumping station. In the background, the small channel system (Fig. 2) crossing the large channels.

Fig. 3b—View of the "large channel system" at the experimental station.
Upstream view towards feeding station (right). In foreground, over-
crossing of the system.

Channel 7 was not polluted at all; i. e., it received clean
ground water only. The feeding was started more than a
year ahead of the self-purification assays and thus a biocenosis
in complete equilibrium with the quality of the feeding water
and the other ecological factors was established. From time
to time, some of the vegetation, growing often in large masses,
had to be removed. This could be done without disturbing
the general character of the growth. The biocenoses at the
time of the experiments can be described in short as follows:
  Channel 1 (10 per cent sewage): River bed and sidewalls
completely covered with large masses of Sphaerotilus natans
over the entire length; in the first 50 m this growth partly
covered with fine sewage solids. From 100 m on, Nitzschia
(palea) and Synedra ulna overgrowing the floating Sphaerotilus
masses in increasing numbers downstream.
  Channel 3 (4 per cent sewage): From 0 to 25 m completely
covered with Sphaerotilus, sessile ciliates, and green filamentous algae (Hormidium and Ulothrix). Proportion of heterotrophic: autotrophic organisms ca. 1:1. Sphaerotilus gradually disappearing downstream and completely absent (macroscopically) from 150 m on. Rich vegetation of Synedra ulna,

Fragillaria capucina, Nitzschia (palea) over the entire length.
Diatoma vulgare abundant from 125 m to the end.

Channel 5 (2 per cent sewage): Rapidly decreasing, small
growth of Sphaerotilus from 0 to 100 m, overgrown with
Hormidium and Ulothrix. Rich diatom flora over the entire
length (Fragillaria capucina, Synedra ulna, less Nitzschia).
Diatoma vulgare dominating from 150 m to the end.

Channel 7 (clean water): From 0 to 150 m, Hormidium
and Stigeoclonium abundant. Channel bed and sidewalls with
more or less complete cover of diatoms (Diatoma and Ach-
nanthes over entire length, Meridion and Gomphonema
abundant from 0 to 50 m).

Even this fragmentary description shows that a considerable biological change in the length profile was developed.
The biological gradient was obviously due to self-purification
effects exerted on the organic pollutants introduced with the
small amounts of sewage into the channels.

During the self-purification experiments, the feeding of
sewage into the channels 1, 3, and 5 was stopped, the channels
washed through with clean ground water for about 1 hour and
then the pure substance to be assayed was added for an other
hour. By this method the already established biocenoses in
the channels were brought into contact with a single, known
substance which could be analyzed individually. During the
feeding of the test substance, several samples were taken
at various sampling stations along the length profile. The
concentration of the compound in equilibrium with self- purification at known flow distances could be gained by this procedure. The biomass was measured at the sampling points
in terms of dry solids per meter channel length and relative
chlorophyll content, giving the necessary information on the
quantity of biomass in contact with the test substance.

From such experiments, an estimate of the magnitude of
all terms defined in "Definitions" can be made.

Most of the pertinent data of an assay, using glucose as
a test substance, are assembled in Fig. 4. The uppermost
diagram for each of the four channels R_1 to R_7 summarizes
the composition of the biocenosis, as far as the relative
distribution of heterotrophic and autotrophic microphytes are
concerned. The second graph shows the quantity of the bio -
mass per meter channel length and its relative chlorophyll
content. It is seen that the density of the biocenosis decreases
downstream in all channels except in the clean water channel,
No. 7, where growth is more or less uniform. The increasing

chlorophyll content along the channels 1, 3, and 5 is a good demonstration of the change in character of the biomass due to self-purification effects in the preparative period of the assay. The third diagram gives the absolute concentrations of the test substance, glucose, at the sampling points (average values of four samples taken at 10 min intervals). It is obvious that, in channels 1, 3, and 5, a similar loss of about 3 mg per 1 of glucose occurred. In channel 7, however, no measurable self-purification was observed over the flow distance of 210 m. We find, therefore, as a first indication, that in a very clean river the amount of self-purification is very much smaller than in a river which is already polluted. This is self-evident from the microbiological point of view; quite often, however, it is ignored by many workers.

The rate of self-purification, as a function of the flow distance from the source of pollution, deserves much closer attention. According to conventional concepts based on BOD measurements, this rate should decrease according to an exponential function. From the last graphs in Fig. 4, it is evident that this exponential function is, at most, a rather optimistic approximation of what happens with a pure substance in a shallow river inhabited by a sessile biomass of noticeable size. Each of the four channels behaved differently.

The more or less heterotrophic channel No. 1 demonstrates in the first stretch a rather low rate of self-purification of about 3 mg glucose per 50 m per second. This part of the channel was packed with dense bacterial masses, covered partly with fine sewage solids. The contact of the biomass with the flowing water was rather superficial. In the next 100 meters, the large bacterial masses (mostly Sphaerotilus, with its commensal organisms) were floating freely in the characteristic form of a sheepskin and, hence, an intense water contact was established. In this part, the self-purification rate increased to about 3 times the value in the first stretch. In the final 50 meters, the Sphaerotilus masses gradually diminished and became overgrown by diatoms. The self-purification rate decreased considerably with this change in the biocenosis.

In channel No. 3, a high self-purification rate is observed in the first 50 m of flow where the free-floating algae, with their overgrowth of heterotrophic organisms (mostly Sphaerotilus and ciliates), offered a large contact surface with the flowing water. With decreasing total biomass downstream the SR diminished gradually.

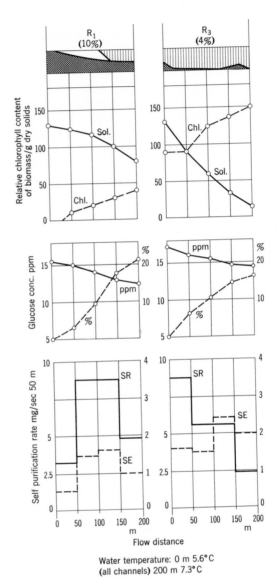

Water temperature: 0 m 5.6°C
(all channels) 200 m 7.3°C

Fig. 4—Results of a self-purification experiment in the large channels, No. 1, 3, 5, and 7, using glucose as a pollutant.

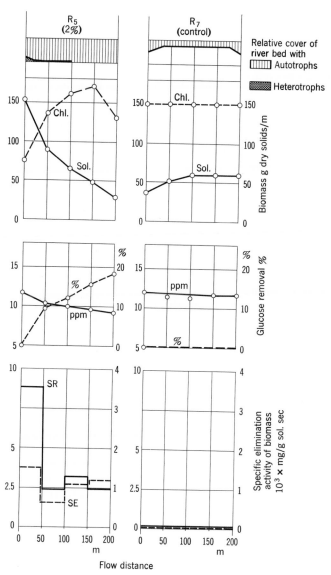

Flow distance

Flow velocity: 0.153 m/sec
Flow time: 0–200 m : 22 min

In channel No. 5, only the first 50 m were efficient in self-purification and further downstream the rate fell to a low value with the diminishing quantity of biomass and its change in species composition.

We conclude from these observations that the self-purification rate is highly dependent on the absolute quantity of biomass which is in intimate contact with the flowing water. This result would be quite normal in a river with a predominantly heterotrophic microflora, where we expect the oxidation rate of a substrate like glucose to be proportional to the number of organisms. In our experiment, however, this relation was also found in those channels in which autotrophic organisms were, seemingly, far more abundant than heterotrophic ones. The only exception was channel No. 7 where, in spite of a sizeable biomass, no measurable self-purification occurred.

Is it possible, now, to find relationships between the quality of the biomass and the self-purification rate in river. This is certainly not an easy question. However, our last proportion, the specific elimination activity of the biomass, SE, may give some indications. The diagrams in Fig. 4 demonstrate, indeed, significant differences for this proportion in the various stretches of the channels. Correlating the values of SE with the type of the organism associations, however, considerable difficulties of interpretation arise. We find, for instance, that the entirely heterotrophic flora in channel No. 1 eliminated not more, but even less, glucose than the seemingly much more autotrophic biocenosis in channel No. 3 or at the start of channel No. 5. It is obvious by this observation that additional factors besides the type of the macroscopically dominant organisms influence the specific elimination rate per unit weight of growth. In this respect, glucose was probably an unfavorable test substance for this special experimental question because it can be resorbed by heterotrophic and by autotrophic organisms as well. Many inconsistencies remain, however, even when we consider this physiological effect, and we have to admit that a number of open questions arise when we correlate self-purification and biological parameters.

We hope, however, that this work, although being of a laboratory nature and still at the beginning, will later uncover some of the fundamental relationships between the biocenosis and self-purification rates. These studies will have to include situations where the freely suspended and epipsammic flora forms the essential part of the biomass in a river.

To conclude this chapter, we find as an essential experi - ence, that, in self-purification studies, much more emphasis should be laid upon the simultaneous quantitative and qualitative estimate of the acting microorganisms on the one hand and the qualitative measure of self-purification of defined chemical compounds on the other hand. We think that sufficient empha- sis on both of these parameters will certainly lead to a much better understanding of the peculiar set of reactions and in- teractions called self-purification.

SUMMARY

In the first part of the paper river bacteriology is dis- cussed from an ecological point of view. Water current as a special feature of this habitat is assumed to be an important synecological factor but having no autecological significance for bacteria in rivers.

In discussing microbial self-purification, three terms are defined, namely: (1) amount of self-purification, (2) rate of self-purification, and (3) specific elimination activity of the biomass. Experimental data from assays in artificial channels, using glucose as a pollutional agent, are presented to demon- strate the significance of these terms.

ACKNOWLEDGEMENT

My best thanks are due to Dr. Eichenberger, Mr. Krähenbühl, and Dr. Mechsner of our institute, for their collaboration in the experimental part of this work. I also express my gratitude to Mr. Friederich, of our experimental station, for the operation and maintenance of the experimental channels.

LITERATURE CITED

Ambühl, H. 1959. Die Bedeutung der Strömung als ökologischer Faktor. Schweiz. Z. Hydrol. 21:133-264.

Fair, G. M., E. W. Moore, and H. A. Thomas. 1941. The natural purification of river muds and pollutional sediments. Sew. Wks. J. 13:270-307, 756-779.

Jannasch, H. W. 1956. Vergleichende bakteriologische Untersuchung der Adsorptionswirkung des Nil-Treibschla - mmes. Ber. Limnol. Flusstation Freudenthal 7:21-27.

Ruttner-Kolisko, A. 1962. Porenraum und kapillare Wasser-
    strömung in limnopsammal, ein Beispiel für die Bedeutung
    verlangsamter Strömung. Schweiz. Z. Hydrol. 24:444-458.
Societas Internationalis Limnologiae. 1962. Symposium
    Kastanienbaum. 1961. The influence of current on running-
    water organisms. Schweiz. Z. Hydrol. 24:353-484.
Wuhrmann, K. 1957. Die heutigen Einrichtungen für
    verfahrenstechnische Forschungen über biologische
    Abwasserreinigung und für Studien an Fliessgewässern
    in der Verschsstation Tüffenwies der EAWAG. Verbandsber.
    Schweiz. Abwasserfachleute, 44/2, 1-21.
Zimmermann, P. 1961. Experimentelle Untersuchungen über
    die ökologische Wirkung der Strömungsgeschwindigkeit
    auf die Lebensgemeinschaften des fliessenden Wassers.
    Schweiz. Z. Hydrol. 24:1-81.

DISCUSSION

Dr. Heukelekian (Rutgers Univ.): It may be inferred that,
in large streams where the surface area exposed to the volume
of water is relatively small, that attached growths do not
exert as much influence and, therefore, the self-purification
takes place in the flowing water at a rate different from those
you presented here.

I was very much interested in the statement about the
River Nile, where bacterial populations were greatest in
association with the silt and where the numbers of free-
floating bacteria were very small.

I have questions about your reference to free-floating
Sphaerotilus. Were the amounts the same in all four channels?
Was there more free-floating Sphaerotilus in the lower concentrations of sewage? Was there as large a quantity of
floating organisms in the 10 per cent channel as, say, in the
4 or 2 per cent channel?

Dr. Wuhrmann: I have to correct myself regarding the
expression "free-floating". The Sphaerotilus was, of course,
attached but the colonies were freely floating in the water as
streamers, so the water could flow through the colonies, in
contrast to the first channel, where the Sphaerotilus grew
more or less close to the bottom and was overlaid with sludge,
and consequently water contact was much less.

Dr. Heukelekian: Yes, but there must have been some

detachment of the attached growth. Was there any difference in the different channels?

Dr. Wuhrmann: There was a difference. In the channel with the highest growth, there was most detachment, of course.

Dr. Heukelekian: Do you believe, as Velz says, that Sphaerotilus can grow freely floating in the water and does not have to be attached, and that what one sees in the river as free-floating organisms actually grew while floating in the water, rather than previously while still attached?

Dr. Wuhrmann: That is a difficult question, but I suppose that most Sphaerotilus flocs we see free-floating in the river are detached organisms. They certainly live for a time, but I think, in time, they just die.

Dr. Mulder (Landbouwhogeschool der Wageningen): I am very much interested in the microbial flora on aquatic plants. Dr. Wieringa in our laboratory, is studying the growth of microbes on land plants and on forest plants and he has found that there is quite a microbial population on plants which depends on excretion of substances by the plants. In forest plants, he has found a flora of nitrogen-fixing organisms which depends on the excretion of sugar by the plants.

Is there any indication that the aquatic plants excrete some substances upon which this channel flora depends, or may use? Is there any indication that there is some relationship between the bacteria and the higher plants and lower plants such as the algae?

Dr. Wuhrmann: I cannot answer this question, for the moment, because in this phase of the investigation we are interested only in the numerical relationships and there has been no investigation of the kinds of organisms involved. But I am quite sure that excretions from the host play a role in the density of this growth because, if you observe with the microscope, for instance, a strand of Hormidium or Spirogyra, this strand is completely settled with bacteria, like a brush, and it is very difficult to conceive that these bacteria are there only because there is a physical substrate. I think they grow, partly because the medium close to the filament surface is better than the free flowing water, but I do not know exactly why.

Dr. John A. Winter (Academy of Natural Sciences of
Philadelphia): On the curves for self-purification, it
appeared that the channel with the highest sewage, which
was at 10 per cent, showed a lag, then a high level, then
a decreasing level going downstream. This occurred in
both the 6 per cent and the 4 per cent channels. Was this
not so? That is, the ten per cent curve, if one cut off the
initial portion, would be identical with the 6 per cent. I
wondered if you saw any indication in the high sewage-
content channel that the growth of Sphaerotilus, as one moved
down channel, became like the 6 per cent then like the 4 per
cent as the degradation occurred?

Dr. Wuhrmann: Unfortunately, this is a point which I
could not discuss thoroughly because of the shortage of time.
It dealt with the part which I called specific elimination by
the biocenosis, as shown by the lowest curve in Fig. 4.

In the graphs representing self-purification rate, the
dotted lines represent the "specific elimination" by the bio -
mass. That means self-purification calculated on the basis
of the dry weight of the biomass in the channels, disgegarding
the taxonomic differences between the biomass.

In channel R_1 (10 per cent sewage, previously fed), for
instance, the specific elimination was very low at the beginning,
then increased, and dropped again. In channel R_3 (4 per cent
sewage pre-fed) the absolute magnitude is higher than with
the Sphaerotilus, and the highest specific elimination was
reached in the middle, from 100 to 150 m, where practically
no Sphaerotilus was seen macroscopically, then there was a
slight drop towards the end. Channel R_5 (2 per cent sewage
pre-fed) is relatively clean. The absolute magnitude of the
specific elimination rate of the biomass was relatively low.
Most of these organisms were autotrophic organisms, so this
low value is not surprising; but, comparing it with the
Sphaerotilus channel, it is not much smaller than where the
Sphaerotilus masses were dominant.

This is not easy to interpret, of course, and that is just
one of the points I should like to emphasize: that many more
investigations should be done on this basis, because we are
ignorant to what degree, for instance, so-called autotrophic
organisms in rivers participate in the self-purification and
the elimination of organic components.

In this experiment, glucose was, perhaps, a bad example
because we know that green plants may also absorb glucose

to quite an extensive degree. The present results are, therefore, not at all surprising but similar irregularities and
inconsistencies were also found when we used, for instance,
glutamic acid, and it is my idea that much more remains
to be learned regarding this.

Dr. John Sieburth (Univ. of Rhode Island): I would like
to make a comment in connection with Dr. Mulder's statement.
During some studies on the Sargasso weed and the microflora
of the larger algae, we observed that where the water mass
contained mainly Pseudomonas, arthrobacters and spirilla
were virtually non-existent; the only organisms we could
obtain from the Sargasso species were vibrios, and these
were retained in very large numbers on the older plants; but,
inside the gyre of the Sargasso Sea, where the plants are
very active physiologically and are growing, these organisms
become non-existent and this condition was correlated with
a very marked antibacterial activity of the algae themselves
and, therefore, I think that, when we study relationships of
algae in connection with the micro-flora of waters, we have
to look at both the types of organisms present as well as the
numbers.

Dr. Heukelekian: I am in full agreement with Dr. Wuhrmann about the emphasis, ad nauseam, that we have placed,
in this country, on BOD and dissolved oxygen. In this regard,
we are wasting considerable effort in pointless determinations
and we are just not getting anywhere. However, as alternatives,
as Dr. Wuhrmann pointed out, there are a number of difficulties, such as being forced to use glucose which can be
measured, whereas sewage and other wastes are not such
simple compounds. Furthermore, there are a number of
difficulties when it comes to the estimation and evaluation
of the quantity and the species of the organisms outside of the
attached growths and it is understandable why nobody has
attacked the problem.

Question: It is not quite clear to me, how in the Nile River
study, the truly free-floating or suspended bacteria were
separated from those attached to small particulate matter.

Dr. Wuhrmann: The work cited was that of Jannasch. The
principle of his separation was as follows: He used filtration
through filter paper as a separation method. The assumption
was that the bacteria found in the water-clear filtrate were

those which were living detached from the large particles and, in contrast, that the total count represented mostly the bacteria growing on the soil particles.

10

THE BACTERIOLOGY OF INTERFACES

Charles E. Renn
Department of Sanitary Engineering
The Johns Hopkins University

There's something to be said for choosing a topic like this. You can generate your own seller's market. Everyone knows what an interface is and everyone agrees that our world is full of them. But it's possible to define it as broadly and as grandly as any term of virtue that you can think of. And it sounds really fundamental.

I'll begin by giving my ground rules for interfaces and then I'll go off on an excursion of personal experience. An interface is where conditions change -- to be more specific, where conditions change enough to attract attention. Conventionally, we think of liquid-gas interfaces, like the air-water interface of a pond, or of liquid-solid interfaces, like the wetted surfaces of a glass of water. And we often consider liquid-liquid interfaces as in water-oil emulsions. We have foams, suspensions, emulsions, and other obvious states where the change in characteristics of the components show themselves to the knowing.

We are aware, too, that a variety of significant changes, that themselves have the properties of interfaces, frequently develop as a consequence of the primary condition; sharp gradients in temperature and dissolved gases, together with a variety of micro turbulences, are common at air-water interfaces, for example, and the very familiar and evident Liesegang banding of reaction products and reactants in the gel media surrounding colonies of bacteria and molds. As far as microorganisms are concerned, there is a wide range of differences that can be sensed in the zones of rapid change;

microbiological processes generate these special boundary environments themselves. This puts us on common ground and I shall now get on with my narration.

About thirty years ago when I was a graduate student at Rutgers in the School of Agriculture and its expanding department of soil microbiology, I had the fortune to work with Dr. Walter Kubiena, a Viennese microbiologist who did much to enliven graduate student and faculty life of the campus during those somewhat uncertain depression years. Dr. Kubiena had many ideas and most of them were firmly fixed, a velvet charm and warm humanity covered his personal Gilbraltar. His specialty was the study of the undisturbed soil, and he had developed many clever devices for examining the inner life of soil capillaries and micro voids with minimum dislocation. I served as his photographic assistant and we worked out a practical truce in which I was permitted to disturb the micro environment for photographic purposes as long as I managed to represent conditions as they were without my disruptive intervention. This is the usual dilemma.

By judicious choice of materials I was able to demonstrate one of Dr. Kubiena's favorite theses -- that there were no empty spaces in soil. The alleged voids were filled with bacteria, molds, yeasts, actinomyces, and a variety of associated zoology, root hairs, bacterial gums, gels, and bric-a-brac. One device that I used to advantage was Dr. Starkey's planted microscope slide technique. You simply shoved a clean microscope slide into the soil you were studying. This was temporarily disruptive.

After a week or ten days the slide somehow or other became part of the soil -- at least in our own minds it did. It was no longer disruptive, and it was fair technique to remove it and study the distribution of the microbiological society that adhered to it. By using skillful discrimination bred from long experience, we were able to sort out the kinds of things that were going on in nearby soil voids from what was happening on the surface of the glass slide itself. From my standpoint, that of a young photographer anxious to produce spectacular shots, this was disheartening, for the most interesting pattersns of growth were always in the fresh growth of films that clearly belonged to the slide surface itself. Everyone who has studied with Dr. Starkey has seen these whorls, sheets, plaques, and runaway lines.

Somewhat later, I went with Dr. Waksman as an assistant in marine bacteriology at the Woods Hole Oceanographic
Institution. This was still the Depression and we thought
large thoughts with limited equipment but lots of time. We
had to get educated to some new dimensions in microbiology;
to the concepts of slow changes in systems in which the concentrations of nutrients were very low. The principal difficulty was that of trying to find out what must be going on in
the extremely disperse natural system by following processes
that occurred at an obviously out-scale rate in laboratory
tubes, beakers, and carboys. Our laboratory ocean was
rarely larger than 20 liters.

We secured useful clues from our competitors, mostly
from Dr. ZoBell, of the Scripps Oceanographic Institute at
La Jolla, California. Dr. ZoBell was interested in the
physical distribution of bacteria in the sea and he made useful demonstrations of the fact that marine bacteria were
usually attached to some bigger chunk in what Dr. Krogh,
the Danish physiologist, used to call, "the very thin soup of
the sea." Bacteria in the micron range were riding pickaback
on diatoms fifty to five hundred microns long, and were
carrying on their activities, not in the great vastness of the
sea, but on the surfaces of their rafts. It seemed as though
it were a sensible idea and we spent a lot of time examing
it.

In recalling this period, I remember the profound observations of a team of marine bacteriologists somewhere on the
Continent who were also interested in the problem of distribution. In speaking of bacterial adsorption on marine silts
they noted that "if the silt particle is larger than the bacterium,
then the bacterium will be adsorbed on the silt, but if the silt
particle is smaller than the bacterium the silt will be adsorbed
on the bacterium." This heartens me, the world can still
progress.

Dr. ZoBell made a group of laboratory observations that
stirred up quite a bit of interest and activity in our BOD (biochemical oxygen demand) - conscious sanitary engineering
field. He pointed out that the containing walls in which slow
fermentations of very dilute solutions occurred -- as in
bottled sea water -- were the principal sites of microbiological activity. He demonstrated the development of thin
bacterial films on these surfaces and very satisfactorily

related changes in the ratio of surface to volume in laboratory glassware to the rate at which oxygen was used. It was
his view that the surface site was especially advantageous,
and that supporting interfaces should be considered as a part
of the microbiological environment. As some of you may
remember, this touched off a lot of activity in the re-
examination of BOD techniques, and laboratories all over
our fair land were comparing values secured in systems
ranging from 0.1 ml pipettes to 25 gallon chemical carboys.
There are probably a few doctoral dissertations out of this
melee.

When World War II came, marine bacteriologists became
involved in the study of biological films on surfaces. In
stressful times many professions scramble for demonstrable
utility, and the marine microbiologists picked out the problem
of fouling of ship hulls and other critical structures as their
province. There were two views: (1) that the production of a
primary bacterial film on a sea-wetted surface hastened the
attachment of larger, significant fouling organisms, and (2)
that the production of such a film retarded the attachment of
drag-producing forms. There was one useful finding; the
bacterial film always developed.

About this time, there was considerable misapplication
of knowledge to the technology of waterproofing and the arts
of non-wetting. A wide range of new plastics, the silicones,
and other materials had become available and everyone was
anxious to see how they could be used to make spark plugs
perform better, make clothing airy but water repellent, prevent rust, make boats go faster, air foils stay cleaner, etc.
I became fevered with the possibilities of developing such
materials for improved marine paints -- a non-wetting surface is highly desirable for slow sail boats as well as for fast
hulls. I started with the conviction that it was the bacterial
film that inevitably grew on such surfaces in water that
eventually made them wettable, and destroyed their usefulness,
and I set myself the simple goal of keeping the bacteria from
growing.

That was the beginning of my education. Fortunately, I
already had my advanced degree and could afford it.

I found out, as you would predict, that the surfaces of
non-wetting solids became wetting -- that sterile surfaces
immersed in sterile clean water became wetting almost as
rapidly as the same materials immersed in non-sterile clean

water, and that the wetted surfaces of the first group bore
no evidence of bacterial filming at the time of wetting. This
disheartening finding, which any physical chemist could have
predicted, was offset by my discovery, some years later,
that a group of physical chemists had attempted to solve the
same problem by the same methods of investigation, and
with the same results but at much greater expense. Quite
a pile of advertising copy was put aside.

The limitation is very simple. The water I used wasn't
pure enough and, even if it had been, it wouldn't have stayed
pure enough. Practical water isn't pure enough and the water
that ships sail on isn't pure enough. I don't know of any substantial quantity of water that is sufficiently pure.

If we take a quantity of water, we have to take it in
something and it has to be somewhere. I had a 500 ml glass
tray of water. It had a glass-water interface and a water-
air interface and also an assortment of plastic paint-water
interfaces. In this system, solute materials which tend to
reduce interfacial tension must move to the interfaces. There
are a number of ways in which you can justify this, but the
simplest is that the concentration of surface active materials
at the enclosing interfaces allows energy to escape from the
system. The odds are that materials that reduce surface
tension -- for the greater part, organic materials -- will
occur in greater concentration at the interfaces than in the
solution; the relative interfacial concentration of these
materials rises as the solution concentration declines, so
that the partition is more pronounced and evident in weak
solutions.

Now it becomes clear why microorganisms find interfaces
congenial for their activities. Interfaces are natural organic-
capturing and concentrating devices; with this advantage, there
is no reason, teleologically speaking, why any single-minded
microorganism should wish to pioneer into the vast areas of
low capture probability -- unless, of course, it were able to
carry an organic-capturing interface with it.

I had another go at the bacteriology of interfaces early in
the 40's when I was working on control of Anopheles quad-
rimaculatus. A number of people were trying to make improved larvicidal oils and some were concerned with problems
that grew out of added spreading agents. This was immediately before D.D.T. was introduced and the improvement of
larvicidal oils became a lost art.

We noted that there were many conditions under which
even the best spreading oils failed to spread, and it was
disheartening to observe that these conditions coincided with
high mosquito production. The sites were usually protected
baylets and wooded arms of shallow lakes, during intervals
of gentle on-shore wind. These areas were often difficult
to reach with oiling equipment but they made pleasant places
for quiet wartime reflection and I built them into any research for this purpose. Now and then I'd drop a few drops
of calibrated spreading oil on a convenient water surface
for my conscience's sake.

I noted one feature that struck me as odd. Very frequently, these non-spreading waters showed a shifting
iridescence, a play of rainbow color much like that of a crude
spectral grating. There were no oil slicks, though the water
seemed damped to the riffling of breezes.

One day I had a whim and I took along a box of microscope
cover slips. I stood on shore and skittered them out over the
shallows near shore and floated a satisfactory number. I
retrived some and plopped them as wet mounts on slides;
others I dried. At the laboratory I had a look under the
microscope. I had been fortunate. The floated slides had
captured the pattern of microbial enterprise at the stilled
water surface even more perfectly than the slides that Dr.
Kubiena and I planted some years earlier under Dr. Starkey's
suggestion. The thin, compressed film of rods and cocci
showed patterns that revealed local high concentrations of
interfacially adsorbed organics -- fragments of debris that
had risen to the surface or that had fallen into it, some re-
cognizable, some not. Compression and strain within the
film, produced by wind pressure and surface flow, was
beautifully drawn. It was exciting to come on something so
simple and obvious. In addition, I understood why the spreading oils didn't spread. But that was now a minor matter.

Later, when I became better acquainted with the realities
of earning a living in the sanitary engineering business, I
found these few observations very useful in the solution of a
number of unusual problems. I'll mention these because they
are likely to come to your attention if you operate in this field
long enough and because they illustrate the importance of the
interface as a working microbiological environment. There
are a few type specimens, if you wish to think of them in that
fashion.

First, there is the case of water flowing over fixed surfaces. All such wetted surfaces will always support films
of bacteria and larger organisms that forage on the film --
unless special inhibiting conditions are imposed, such as
disinfectants, or heat. These films are present on the surfaces of tanks, pipes, gauge glasses, heat exchangers,
evaporative coolers, and on the rocks and boulders of clean
stream rapids. The thickness and obviousness of these films
increases as the concentration of organics in the water rises.
We are all familiar with the heavy slimes that appear on
surfaces of trickling filter materials, on channels bearing
waste waters, and on the bottoms of polluted streams. Those
of you who practice the art can readily detect small changes
in the makeup of waste-bearing streams by the feel of stones
under foot.

These microbiological films are contact mechanisms for
purifying waste waters -- they act as biological stripping
systems in trickling filter beds and on the beds of shallow,
rapid streams. They adsorb organic matter from solution
and oxidize it in place while the stripped water whizzes by.
We're coming to the point where we may be able to make
useful predictions of the behavior of such controlled-filmed
surfaces, though we've always thought that we could.

In the past few years, a number of practical problems
rising from biological films and slimes in odd places have
come my way. On two occasions heavy sludges appeared in
pure water tanks. These were large, stainless steel tanks,
used to store demineralized water. In both cases low concentrations of organic materials were present -- in one case
this came from the zeolite bed, in the other it entered
solution from the industrial atmosphere. As the water rose
and fell in the tanks, the bacterial film grew -- it was in-
apparent below the low water lines -- and as it thickened it
sloughed from the smooth metal surface.

More recently, with the general application of air conditioning to whole industrial plants, bacterial slimes have
created problems in the chilled water dehumidifier sections
of recirculated air systems.

In these cases the organics appear to enter solution from
the recirculated air -- vapors of solvents, oil mists, and
other volatiles and aerosols have been involved. A wide
range of bacterial slimes and complex communities are
produced. The slimes sometimes became very heavy. They

range from viscous syrups to rubbery gels in texture and
they cause serious clogging of screens. It is not clear how
much they affect heat exchange surface efficiencies, but it
is obvious that they must alter the behavior of these systems.
    The problem is real and troublesome to maintenance and
plant engineers, who must cope with it because there is no
simple solution so far. Bactericides and bacteriostats have
been screened and a number of companies are active in the
development of odorless, non-toxic agents for specific control of air conditioning slime films.
    The development of heavy bacterial slimes in chilled
water systems is comparable to the dense growth of
Sphaerotilus and kindred bacterial slimes in some waste-
bearing streams in winter. In this case the irrigated surfaces of the stream bottom -- boulders, brush, and other
permanent surfaces subjected to rapid wash -- behave as
initial interfaces, but the heavy developing streamer growth
becomes its own interface.
    One of the most intriguing problems associated with the
role of the interface is that of the bubble in activated sludge
treatment. We now have many improved aeration devices --
we know that little oxygen transfers during the free life of
bubbles in mixed liquor and we've concentrated our efforts
to improving transfer by violent agitation during bubble
formation, using brushes, surface aerators, injectors,
cavitators, and a great variety of devices. All of these do
produce some bubbles, however, and they can be made to
produce more or fewer bubbles.
    Air-water interfaces, the interfaces of bubbles in mixed
liquor, are concentrating devices. This is most strikingly
demonstrated by the affinity of highly surface-active organics,
like detergents, for these surfaces, and the appearance of high
concentrations of these agents in foams. Many other surface-
active materials are undoubtedly concentrated, too. Under
some conditions colloidal materials and bacteria can be
foamed or flotated out. Is the common affinity of surface-
active organics and active bacteria for air-water interfaces
of bubbles a significant mechanism in the successful manipu-
lation of activated sludge treatment? This is an important
question. It costs money to make bubbles and more money
to keep them in suspension. Do we need them?

DISCUSSION

Dr. F. Johnson (Princeton Univ.): Is it really understood, even after all these years, why bacteria will proliferate in bottles? You spoke of the fact that water is not
sufficiently pure, but when you had sea water in a bottle,
you always got enormous reproduction of the bacteria. Can
you enlarge a little bit on that?

Dr. Renn: Of course, when you bring the water in, a
lot of things happen. You remember, a lot of the larger
organisms die. They become nourishment for the bacteria.
When you change the temperature, a lot of things happen to
produce a high mortality, followed by a lot of scavenging,
for one thing.

The surface area is enormous compared to what it is
in the sea. I'm reminded of a contemporary of mine who
was taken with Dr. ZoBell's idea, so much so that he decided he'd get on the bandwagon. He ran BODs in bottles
containing a variety of added surfaces, glass beads, fragments of glass slides, finally he put in some glass wool
and got fantastic BOD values. One of the things he didn't
know was that glass wool is spun with a soap lubricant.

Of course, you can't keep any kind of surface clean
long. The technique we used for the initial work on the
non-wetting of ship's paint was a simple one -- measuring
in the wetting angle tray -- and we found that we could clean
materials so we could get 90 degree wetting -- anything we
wanted. Of course, glass is perfectly wetting. But, by
just leaving it around the atmosphere of the harbor for a
while, it would become non-wetting very frequently. There
was enough hydrocarbon aerosol in the air, and so it
happened.

11

THE PHYSIOLOGY OF THE COLIFORM GROUP

Harold F. Clark and Paul W. Kabler
Division of Water Supply and Pollution Control
Robert A. Taft Sanitary Engineering Center
Cincinnati, Ohio

The utilization of the presence of bacteria as indicators of the sanitary quality of water originated in 1880 with the description, by von Fritsch, of "Klebsiella pneumoniae" and "K. rhinoscleromatis" as microorganisms characteristic of contamination by humans. A short time later, Escherich added his "Bacillus coli" as an indicator of fecal pollution. It is evident, from a careful study of their writings, that they considered human feces as representing dangerous pollution while the feces of other warm-blooded animals were not a hazard to mankind. Apparently, this was the obscure origin of the science of sanitary water bacteriology, and from this source the current "Coliform Group" has developed, with its methods for measurement, its various classifications, procedures, and its complex, but, at times, somewhat controversial systems of interpretation.

Escherich (1), by the use of fermentation reactions in glucose and in milk media, morphology, and motility, divided his B. coli into two species, which he named B. coli-commune and B. lactis-aerogenes. Wurtz (2) recommended the addition of indicators to the culture medium to demonstrate acid production by the coliform group in the fermentation of carbohydrates. Smith (3) established the theoretical basis for the bacteriological examination of water and, on the basis of fermentation of sucrose, divided B. coli-commune (Escherich) into two species, which he named the alpha and beta types of B. coli-communis. A significant contribution was made

202

by Dunham (4) when he devised the inverted vial in liquid
medium for measurement of gas produced by bacterial
fermentation of carbohydrates. There followed a period of
approximately 15 years in which investigators applied all
available physical and biochemical procedures, with special
emphasis on carbohydrate reactions, which resulted in detailed classifications of the coliform group. Space limitations
permit citation of the work of only a minority of the investigators during this time. Ford (5) recommended fermentation
reactions in glucose, lactose, and sucrose; McConkey (6, 7)
described methods for division of the coliform group into
128 possible types and actually isolated 36 types; Bergey and
Deehan (8) expanded the classification to include 16 groups
composed of 256 types; and Jackson (9), being displeased with
all the fine subdivision of the coliform group, proposed retaining the 4 original, basic groups of McConkey (6) by using
sucrose and dulcitol fermentation reactions and adding the
fermentation in raffinose and mannitol to give a total of 16
groups. The Jackson classification was adopted by the Committee on Standard Methods of 1912. Kligler (10) expressed
dissatisfaction with the 1912 "Standard Methods" recommendation and further reduced the number of groups from 16 to 4
by recommending only sucrose and salicin reactions.
     By this time a tremendous quantity of information had been
accumulated on the biochemical and physical characteristics
of the coliform group. From the viewpoint of the taxonomist,
it was a well-classified group with the numerous species and
strain divisions. From a sanitary consideration, however,
the correlation between the sources of coliform bacteria such
as fecal, soils, plants, etc., and their tabulated characteristics left much to be desired for public health interpretation.
Eijkman (11), in dissenting with the current trend, claimed
that such classifications were not serving the public interest
in water quality control; he believed the major objective should
be measurement of fecal content in food and water rather than
estimation of all the coliform bacteria present. He divided the
coliform group into a fecal group that would produce gas from
glucose at 46 C and a non-fecal group that would produce no
change in the medium under the conditions described for the
test. He further defined his "fecal coliform group", which
was positive by the Eijkman test, as the coliform bacteria from
the gut of warm-blooded animals, and the "non-fecal group"
as all coliforms derived from other sources. His test procedure was highly specific for the fecal group (positive test)

and (negative reaction) for the non-fecal group of coliform
bacteria, but was unsatisfactory because of its low sensitivity.

Howe (12) was one of the first investigators to apply methods
of statistical analysis to his coliform data. He reported isolation of 630 strains from human feces that were, according
to his observations, typical E. coli. There was a complete
absence of statistical correlation, in this group of E. coli,
between the presence or absence of motility, fermentation of
dulcitol or mannitol, reduction of nitrates, or indole production.
These data caused Howe to recognize only the sucrose-positive
E. coli-communior and the sucrose-negative E. coli-communis.

Smith (13), in one of his original papers, observed that
"B. coli" produced twice as much hydrogen as it did carbon
dioxide and that "B. aerogenes" produced equal volumes of
hydrogen and carbon dioxide in the fermentation of glucose.
In interpreting these data, Smith had failed to correct differences in solubility of the two gases in the culture medium,
which resulted in the erroneous calculation of the ratios. He
should, however, be credited as the first to suggest the differential characteristic of the hydrogen: carbon dioxide ratio.

THE GAS RATIO (HYDROGEN: CARBON DIOXIDE) DIFFER-
ENTIAL TEST

Harden and Walpole (14), in carefully controlled experiments, demonstrated that the hydrogen: carbon dioxide ratio
was 1:1 for E. coli and 1:2 for Aerobacter aerogenes. It was
some years later when Rogers and his group believed the gas
ratio technique could solve the problem of differentiating the
coliform bacteria of fecal origin from those derived from
plant or soil origin. Rogers et al.(15, 16), using an accurate
and carefully controlled, but complicated and tedious, experimental technique, demonstrated that the fermentation of
glucose by coliform strains isolated from bovine feces produced
approximately equal quantities of hydrogen and carbon dioxide
(1:1 ratio), whereas coliform strains isolated from grains
produced two or more times as much carbon dioxide as they
did hydrogen (1:2 to 1:3 ratios). They concluded that the low -
or high - gas ratios gave an accurate separation between the
coliform strains derived from warm-blooded animal feces and
the coliform group associated with grains. They were equally
certain that the difficulties of the test and the time required
for the procedure made it unadaptable as a routine laboratory

method. It was in the analysis of their data that they observed
an "absolute correlation" between the gas ratios and the terminal concentration of hydrogen ions. Clark and Lubs (17) found
the concentration of hydrogen in the low-gas ratio strains to
be in the range of pH 4.2 to pH 4.6, while the high-ratio strains
under the same conditions produced reactions of pH 5.6 or
greater.

THE METHYL RED TEST

Based on observation of the excellent correlation of gas
ratios and hydrogen ion concentrations, Clark and Lubs
developed the Methyl Red Test. Methyl red indicator solution
was considered a suitable reagent which gave a red color at
pH 4.4, changing through shades of reddish-yellow to yellow
at pH 6.0. Using approximately the same medium as for the
gas ratio technique, a simple procedure involving the color
change of an indicator solution was recommended by the authors
as a practical routine laboratory procedure of equal value to
the complicated gas ratio technique.

The scientific evidence for the validity of the methyl red
test in the separation of the fecal from the non-fecal coliform
group must be based on acceptance of the following assumptions:

1. The short series of coliform strains from bovine feces
   represents, without exception, the fecal coliform types
   found in the feces of all warm-blooded animals, including
   mankind.
2. The coliform group isolated from the grain samples
   likewise represents all coliform bacteria of non-fecal
   origin.
3. The "absolute correlation" between the gas ratios and
   the terminal concentration of hydrogen ions (pH value)
   would exist when the series of tests were extended in
   length to represent a statistically valid series.
4. The methyl red indicator test and the gas ratio test
   are exceptions to the observed variability of all other
   biochemical reactions within the coliform group.
5. The reference samples used as the fecal group and the
   non-fecal group do not vary in geographical distribution,
   climatic conditions, or other environmental factors.

If all these assumptions are true, then the methyl red test
does, in fact, become a single test procedure to distinguish
between the fecal and the non-fecal coliform groups of bacteria,
as was concluded by Rogers and his group and specifically

expressed by Clark and Lubs.

We are not able to accept the above assumptions and therefore reject the idea of the methyl red test being a reference procedure for determining the origin of the fecal and non-fecal coliform groups, although we do hold the opinion that it has considerable value, in a statistical way, along with other tests, in determining the sources of the coliform bacteria. Numerous investigators , including those in our own laboratory, have isolated statistically significant numbers of methyl red-negative strains from human feces, but only rarely (0. 6 per cent) from the feces of other domestic animals. These data suggest that the choice of bovine samples by Rogers et al. was unfortunate. The possibilities cannot be excluded that (1) the gas ratio technique is an accurate measure of the fecal or non-fecal origin of the coliform strains that does not give an absolute correlation with the methyl red test, or (2) the gas ratio technique would yield high ratios on the methyl red-negative fecal coliform strains, which is contrary to Rogers' theory. This suggests an interesting problem for basic research that would add valuable information to a missing portion of the coliform literature.

THE INDOLE REACTION

The decomposition of tryptophan by the coliform group, depending on the enzyme systems present, may produce one or more of the following compounds, in addition to other metabolites: indolepropionic acid, indoleacetic acid, skatole, or indole. Only the property of producing indole from tryptophan has been extensively applied in the classification of the coliform group. Numerous procedures, mainly borrowed from the biological chemist, have been proposed for the detection of indole. The first was used in the early 1880's. Most of the proposed methods gave reasonably adequate sensitivity for the detection of indole, but many were unsatisfactory, owing to their poor specificity which arose from interference by the closely related chemical compounds listed above. Frequently, the interfering substances yielded positive tests in the absence of indole, which resulted in false conclusions. The exact procedure used in the detection of indole must, therefore, be included with the data, and the limitations (specificity and sensitivity) of the methodology must be considered before an attempt is made to interpret the results.

There were at least 11 different methods recommended for indole detection during the period between 1880 and 1920. The 11 procedures reviewed by the authors do not represent a complete search of the technical literature on this subject. The number of methods and reviews of these reports suggests there were considerable differences in opinion among the investigators. Fellows and Clough (18) published an excellent review with references, of the earlier methods for those interested in tracing the development of the various indole reactions used in bacteriology.

Recommended indole test procedure. Exact standardization of the indole test procedure is essential to secure acceptable and comparable data from different laboratories. The indole test described in sec. 1, p. 518, Standard Methods for the Examination of Water and Wastewater (19) is our method of choice. Both the sensitivity and specificity of this procedure can be improved, but changes are not recommended at this time because of its wide usage, standardization, and simplicity, and because of the quantity of data on the coliform group accumulated by this procedure, which is a modification of the original Ehrlich Reaction. It gives a red color with indole and an orange color with skatole, the red color masking the orange when the concentration of indole is relatively larger than the quantity of skatole. The presence of small concentrations of both compounds has been observed to produce a confusing color reaction. It should also be noted that the occurrence in the medium of a pink or red color which is insoluble in amyl alcohol or chloroform, is a reaction indicating indolepropionic and indoleacetic acids. The original Ehrlich reaction gave a violet-blue reaction for skatole in place of the orange color in the Standard Methods test.

Discussion. Numerous methods have been used to detect indole. Indole data should be accepted only in terms of the test procedure used, and rejected when this information is not available, because each procedure varies in sensitivity and specificity. These variations also restrict comments on the indole reaction to the most general considerations. The determination of their applicability in a specific procedure depends on the investigator.

Friever (20) explained indole formation on the assumption that all strains of coliforms were able to produce indoleacetic acid in the metabolism of tryptophan, with some strains able

to produce indole from this compound (indole positive) while
other strains could not (indole negative). Neisser (21) believed
the ability, or inability, to produce indole was a fixed characteristic of the specific strain of coliform bacteria but was
without taxonomic value in species classification. He apparently
agreed with Smirnow that positive strains could lose the indole -
producing ability in certain environments. Smirnow (22) demonstrated that "B. coli" lost its ability to produce indole
when cultured in strong solutions of glucose (3 per cent),
sodium chloride (4 per cent), sodium sulfate (1. 5 per cent),
or phenol (0. 25 to 0. 75 per cent). Fabry (23) confirmed the
phenol report by demonstrating that indole production was
lost by cultivation of Escherichia coli strains on 0. 5 per cent
phenol medium. Kulp (24) emphasized the dependence of the
data on the method used in its detection and he reported that
every strain of bacteria listed in the literature as indole
positive had also been listed as indole negative, with the single
exception of Vibrio cholera. Current indole procedures were
not satisfactory to Holman and Gonzales (25) and Fellows and
Clough (18). They all recommended steam distillation of the
culture as essential for removing the nonvolatile interfering
substances and applying the indole test procedure to the steam
distillate. They even explained, unconvincingly, that this
would involve practically no extra work as a routine laboratory
test.

Interpretation and use. Coliform strains isolated from the
feces of warm-blooded animals are generally over 90 per cent
indole positive. Geldreich et al. (26) reported 94. 9 per cent
indole-positive strains in 4, 512 coliform cultures isolated
(on solid medium) from the fresh feces of humans, cows, sheep,
pigs, and three species of birds. The same investigators
(Geldreich et al., 27) found that 19. 5 per cent of the coliform
group, representing 2, 348 strains isolated from soils, were
indole-positive. These surface soil samples were collected from
various geographical areas in the United States, with each
location having a sanitary inspection which reported "no known
sources of fecal pollution evident in the immediate area. "

Many investigators before the 1930' s used the positive indole test to indicate the fecal origin of the coliform bacteria.
The basis for its acceptance rested on the frequency of the
presence of indole positive strains of coliform bacteria in
locations where fecal pollution was known to exist and the reported infrequency of the positive strains in the absence of

pollution. Its use in recent years has generally been restricted to one of four tests for IMViC types. Currently,
some investigators have suggested the use of a selective
procedure, frequently an elevated incubation temperature
plus the indole positive test, to determine E. coli, type I,
or the fecal coliform group. Procedures in this general
category have been proposed by Delaney, McCarthy, and
Grasso (28), Buttiaux, Samaille, and Pierens (29), Papavassiliou (30), Veger (31), and by others.

Summation. The indole reaction by isolates of coliform
bacteria from feces of warm-blooded animals is generally
positive in excess of 90 per cent. The concept of indole
production as an exclusive characteristic of the fecal coliform
group must be questioned on the grounds that approximately
one-fifth of the coliform bacteria from unpolluted soils can
produce indole.

THE VOGES-PROSKAUER (ACETYLMETHYLCARBINOL) TEST

Voges and Proskauer (32) described a color reaction
occurring on the addition of a few drops of strong solution of
potassium hydroxide to certain bacterial cultures grown in
peptone glucose broth. Some species of bacteria produced
a substance that reacted under these conditions to give a red,
fluorescent color while the other species failed to give a
characteristic reaction. They recommended the test, which
they named the "Voges-Proskauer Reaction," as having diag-
nostic value as a biochemical test in bacterial identification.
Hardin and Walpole (14), in their studies on the fermentation
of glucose by the coliform group, found a crude glycerol that
they identified as 2, 3-butyleneglycol ($CH_3 \cdot CHOH \cdot CHOH \cdot CH_3$). They presented circumstantial evidence indicating that
Aerobacter aerogenes was able to produce, from this compound,
acetylmethylcarbinol ($CH_3 \cdot CHOH \cdot CO \cdot CH_3$), which was in
turn converted to diacetyl ($CH_3 \cdot CO \cdot CO \cdot CH_3$) in the presence of a strong solution of potassium hydroxide. This complex reacted with the peptone, or some fraction of it, to give,
on oxidation by the air, the characteristic pink, fluorescent
color. They explained that the absence of the reaction with
Escherichia coli arose from the inability of this organism to
produce acetylmethylcarbinol from 2, 3-butyleneglycol.

The need for the peptone in the series of chemical reactions
for detecting acetylmethylcarbinol was manifested by negative

reactions with pure acetylmethylcarbinol and potassium hydroxide in the absence of peptone, and positive reactions when
peptone was added. Hardin and Norris (33) showed that the
substitution of arginine, creatinine, dicyanamide, or guanidine
acetic acid for the peptone in the medium would give various
shades of pink color, but the fluorescence was always absent,
emphasizing the need to read both fluorescence and color in
the test. They also demonstrated that carbohydrates such as
fructose, mannose, galactose, arabinose, or adonitol could
be substituted for the glucose. These authors proposed that
the name of the reaction be changed from the "Voges-Proskauer
Test" to the "Acetylmethylcarbinol Reaction" to distinguish it
from the original procedure, which was a reaction for the
hemorrhagic septicemia organism.

Various procedural changes were suggested. West (34)
increased the speed of the reaction without loss of specificity
or sensitivity by passing air bubbles through the alkaline
medium to increase oxidation. Werkman (35) confirmed the
work of Hardin et al. on the chemistry of the reaction and
recommended the addition of a catalyst to increase the oxidation
rate (ferric chloride, 2 per cent, two drops). His most important contribution was, however, the emphasis he placed on
adopting a standardized technique for the reaction. Both Paine
(36) and Williams and Marrow (37) presented evidence indicating
that all members of the coliform group could produce acetylmethylcarbinol during growth but the negative strains could
decompose the compound as rapidly as it was produced.

Recommended test procedure. The procedure for the detection of acetylmethylcarbinol (The Voges-Proskauer Test),
described in sec. 3, p. 519, Standard Methods for the Exami
nation of Water and Wastewater (19), is our method of choice.

Interpretation and use. The production of acetylmethylcarbinol from the fermentation of glucose is not a characteristic peculiar to the coliform group, but may be detected in a
number of species and several genera of bacteria. It is produced by a number of the aerobic spore-producing and non-
spore-producing bacteria found widely distributed in soils.

Durham (38) stated that the acetylmethylcarbinol reaction
would distinguish the negatively reacting E. coli from the
positively reacting A. aerogenes strains. Levine et al. (39,
40, 41), and others, have interpreted a negative reaction as
indicating that the coliform bacteria were probably derived

from fecal sources and that positively reacting strains were probably from grains and unpolluted soils. Others have questioned this interpretation. Originally, the acceptance of the test was based on the high degree of negative correlation where fecal pollution was expected and the high positive correlation in samples believed free from fecal pollution. In later years, the proponents of the test have used their favorite comparative test, for example, the citrate utilization test, to establish its validity, while the critics of the Voges-Proskauer test have used comparative data with the methyl red or the indole reactions. Most of these studies used a limited series of coliform cultures derived from a single geographical area (local samples). All these data should be re-examined and only those accepted in which the coliform strains were derived from known sources.

Stability of the Voges-Proskauer test. Clark, Kabler, and Geldreich (42) demonstrated that Voges-Proskauer positive cultures, maintained on nutrient agar slants from 0.5 to 2.5 years, may lose their ability to produce a positive reaction. In a series of 458 coliform cultures that gave a positive reaction at the time of isolation, 105 strains, or 22.9 per cent, lost this ability to produce a positive reaction. No explanation for this change can now be offered; but, if the theory of Paine, and of Williams and Marrow, is accepted, it may be presumed the change from positive to negative was due to the activation of a latent enzyme system. It should be noted, however, that this explanation is pure speculation offered without proof.

Summation. The Voges-Proskauer test, or acetylmethyl-carbinol reaction, is useful in separation of the fecal from the non-fecal coliform group when the data are interpreted with due regard for statistical probability. The reaction is not infallible. Traditionally, it has been used as a taxonomic characteristic in the identification of the various species of the coliform group.

THE CITRATE TEST

Brown (43) observed that the various members of the coliform group behaved differently when grown on blood agar plates made from citrated blood. He suggested that the presence or the absence of fermentation of the citrate radical could be used as a differential procedure for the separation of "Bacterium coli" from "Bacterium aerogenes." Koser and Rettger (44) had started their investigation of the use of

chemically defined sources of nitrogen and carbon in the
cultivation of the coliform group approximately 2 years before
publication of the Brown report. In a continuation of this
investigation, Koser (45) completed the work on a long series
of the salts of organic acids of lower molecular weight as the
sole source of carbon for the various members of the coliform
group. His work confirmed the suggestion of Brown, in that
he became convinced that the fecal E. coli could not utilize
the carbon of the citrate radical, and that A. aerogenes, in
the absence of any other source of available carbon, grew,
fermented citrate, and produced an alkaline reaction in the
range of pH 8.4 to 9.0. In addition to potassium or sodium
citrate, and adequate source of nitrogen and the other compounds necessary for the metabolism of A. aerogenes are
required.

The commonly used reactions for distinguishing the fecal
from the non-fecal strains within the coliform group were the
methyl red test and Voges-Proskauer test, according to Koser,
but a review of the work during this period indicates the indole
test should also have been included. There was also sufficient
use of the uric acid test to receive some recognition. Koser
(46) attempted to evaluate his citrate test by comparison with
the methyl red, Voges-Proskauer, and uric acid tests. He
avoided the error of many early investigators by attempting
(at least to his own satisfaction) to establish the source of
both the fecal and non-fecal coliform groups. The sources
of the fecal coliform cultures were strains isolated from the
fresh feces of warm-blooded animals, whereas his non-fecal
coliform bacteria were strains isolated from soils where he
could find no evidence of fecal pollution. The conclusions from
this investigation were: (1) citrate positive strains were
characteristic of unpolluted soils, (2) citrate negative strains
were the typical, fecal type of E. coli, and (3) the citrate
reaction gave better correlation with the original sources of
the coliform groups than the other tests included in the study.
The data are reproduced in Table 1. It is unfortunate that
sufficient space was not used in the original publication to
present the data by individual cultures for each of the four
test procedures.

Recommended test procedure. The procedure for detection
of citrate utilization is the sodium citrate test as described in
sec. 4.1 b and 4.2b, p. 519, Standard Methods for the Examination of Water and Wastewater (19). The slant, which indicates

visible growth on the surface accompanied by a color change
to blue of the indicator, is easier to read than the turbidity in
a colorless solution.

Interpretation and use. The presence or absence of
citrate utilization may be of considerable value in distinguishing
between the fecal and the non-fecal types of the coliform group
but it does not have sufficient specificity to be used as a single
test. In the data by Koser (Table 1), the citrate reaction
deviated from the hypothetical results by 9.3 per cent for the
fecal coliform group and 2.8 per cent for the non-fecal types.

TABLE 1: Percentage of negative reactions in various tests on
coliforms from fecal sources and from
non-fecally polluted soils*

Source of coliform strains	Citrate utilization	Uric acid test	Methyl red reaction	Voges-Proskauer test
Fecal strains 118 cultures	90.7	91.5	7.6	7.6
Non-fecal strains, 72 cultures	2.8	40.3	51.4	52.8

*Data from Koser (46). All the above data are expressed as the per-
centage of negative test ractions in each individual test. The author
did not tabulate the data by each test for the individual strains studied.

Summation. The citrate utilization reaction is useful, on
a statistical basis, for the separation of fecal and non-fecal
types of coliforms.

THE IMViC CLASSIFICATION

Various individual biochemical tests such as indole, methyl
red, Voges-Proskauer, or citrate utilization tests had been
proposed as ways to correlate the relationship of the bacterial
strains of the coliform group with their environment. None of
these procedures was entirely satisfactory individually in the
interpretation of the significance of a specific group or of an
individual strain. Parr (47) made a study of the literature
reporting the separation of fecal from non-fecal coliforms,
published between 1924 and 1937 in an attempt to develop an

improved classification for this group. His review indicated
that the investigators during this period used the following
test procedures for separation of the fecal from the non-fecal
types of coliform strains

Voges-Proskauer reaction	22 times
methyl red test	20 "
citrate utilization test	20 "
indole test	15 "
uric acid test	6 "
cellobiose fermentation	4 "
gelatin liquefaction	3 "
Eijkman test	2 "
hydrogen sulfide production	1 time
sucrose fermentation	1 "
alpha-methyl-d-glucoside fermentation	1 "

On the basis of his own experience and on data from published
reports of the majority of other investigators, Parr chose the
indole, methyl red, Voges-Proskauer, and citrate tests as the
combination of the four reactions that would yield the best
classification. The series of four reactions was designated
by the mnemonic "IMViC Test." The classification was
justified by the reasoning that, if the four most commonly
used procedures gave reasonably acceptable results when
each was applied as a single test, the series would give the
greatest possible accuracy when combined. The statistical
proof of this assumption is beyond the scope of this discussion.
This series of four tests gives 16 possible combinations. The
interpretation of these combinations was described by Parr as
follows:

Escherichia group:	consisting of IMViC types + + - - , + - - - and - + - -, which are to be considered of fecal origin.
Aerobacter group:	consisting of IMViC types - - + + , - - + - and - - - +, which probably represent the majority of the soil types.
Intermediate group:	consisting of the remaining 10 possible IMViC types.

The use of the IMViC classification for interpretation of the sources of the coliform group represented a step forward in that it was definitely superior to any of the four tests used singly and was an improvement over previously used methods.

CONDITIONS FOR ACCEPTANCE OF IMViC CLASSIFICATION

Certain assumptions were made before the validity of the IMViC classification of the coliform group could be accepted without reservation.

These assumptions were:

1. Certain IMViC combinations occur only in the fecal environment, other combinations are characteristic of the soil habitat, and so on, for the distribution of the coliform group in nature.

2. Reactions for the indole, methyl red, Voges-Proskauer, and citrate utilization tests are unchanging for each strain of coliform bacteria in its normal habitat.

3. Marked changes in the chemical, physical, or biological environment will not produce any change in the IMViC reaction.

Discussion. There appear to be certain reservations preventing complete acceptance of some of the assumptions listed. Correlation of the data with assumption number 1 was reasonably good when sufficient strains from a single source were examined to give a statistically significant percentage, but unexplained discrepancies occurred when a decision had to be made on the results from a few coliform cultures. The second assumption must be accepted in the absence of any reliable scientific evidence that has demonstrated a change in the IMViC type of any coliform strain while in its natural habitat. In laboratory experiments indole-positive strains have been changed to indole-negative by cultivation on phenol medium, strong glucose solutions, and other chemicals (see indole test). There has been alteration of the positive Voges-Proskauer test to a negative reaction in the maintenance of stock cultures (see Voges-Proskauer test), and there has been temporary loss of typical colony formation, fermentation reactions, and related biochemical characteristics by cultivation on low concentrations of 2-methyl-1, 4-naphthoquinone (0.0025 per cent or less), as demonstrated by

Colwell (48), proving that such changes may occur in an artificial environment. There has been no definite proof presented that any of these changes in the IMViC types occur in nature, but the possibility cannot be excluded from consideration. This is especially true of waters that contain some of the organic compounds from industrial wastes or in waters high in electrolyte content. Thus, the third assumption that the sudden changes in environment will have no effect on the IMViC type of any strain of coliform must, with our present knowledge, be considered as questionable.

Summation. The four reactions designated by Parr were the best available at the time he developed the IMViC classification of the coliform group. The fecal or non-fecal classification of the coliform group yields good results when strains from a single source are examined in sufficient number to be statistically significant. The relationship between sources (fecal, soil, vegetation, etc.) and types has produced a small number of unexplainable results, which makes the interpretation of the significance of a few strains a risky procedure. Experimental demonstration has proved that the indole and Voges-Proskauer reactions may undergo changes in an artificial environment. It is suggested that the possibility of these changes cannot be excluded in certain types of wastewaters.

THE ELEVATED TEMPERATURE TEST

The elevated temperature test for the separation of the fecal from the non-fecal coliform groups was originally proposed by Eijkman. It was concluded on the basis of his findings, that the coliform bacteria derived from the gut of warm-blooded animals produced gas from glucose at 46 C, but the coliform strains from non-fecal sources failed to show growth. This test procedure was widely accepted in Europe and is still an approved method in some areas. The Eijkman reaction, or one of its many modifications, was studied by an impressive list of investigators, but conclusions differed concerning its sensitivity, specificity, and the interpretation of data. Perry and Hajna (49) proposed an elevated temperature test for E. coli that gained little acceptance by the bacteriologists investigating pollution. It should be noted, however, that these latter investigators improved the Eijkman conception by adding bile salts and a buffer system, and by reducing the air incubation temperature to 45.5 C, which improved the sensitivity with but slight loss in specificity. The British bacteriologists

had used 44 C in McConkey's broth for the confirmation of
E. coli, type I.   Most recently, Vaughn et al. (50) recommended a buffer-boric acid-lactose broth for the enrichment
and identification of E. coli, believing that the reduction of the
incubation temperature of 43 C for 48 hr had increased sensitivity of the method and the addition of the boric acid resulted
in inhibition of the growth of the Aerobacter genus for the
maintenance of specificity. We have reviewed the voluminous
literature on the elevated temperature reaction and have
applied the various procedures in the laboratory, with the
following conclusions:

1. The most acceptable temperature for the incubation
    of the fecal coliform group was 44.5 C ($\pm$ 0.5) which
    represented, of necessity, a compromise between
    acceptable sensitivity and specificity for the fecal types.

2. A small percentage of the fecal coliform cultures was
    excluded and an equal percentage of non-fecal coliforms
    was included by incubation at this recommended temper-
    ature.

3. Many of the usual laboratory media for cultivation of
    the coliform group were toxic at this elevated temper-
    ature.

4. Several culture media were acceptable, but use of the
    EC Medium described in the work of Perry and Hajna
    (49) gave the most rapid results, requiring only 24 hr
    incubation, as compared with brilliant green lactose
    bile broth which took 72 hr to give equivalent results.

5. The test can be used only as a confirmatory procedure
    from coliform cultures growing on a nonselective
    medium.

6. The elevated temperature test can not be used on
    microorganisms transferred directly from a selective
    medium (Endo agar or M-Endo MF medium being
    examples) to the EC medium and such cultures must
    be grown on a non-inhibitory culture medium, such as
    a nutrient agar slant or phenol red lactose broth before
    the application of the elevated temperature test pro-
    cedure.

7. The sensitivity and specificity of the test should be
    compared on recently isolated strains from fresh

feces and on coliform cultures freshly isolated from soils that were, after a careful sanitary survey, designated as samples with no known sources of fecal pollution.

8. In the evaluation of results, all coliforms isolated from the feces of warm-blooded animals must be considered as fecal coliform strains and all cultures isolated from unpolluted soils must be considered as non-fecal coliform strains.

Applying the above concepts to their investigation, Geldreich et al. (26, 27) studied coliform group isolates from the feces of a representative number of warm-blooded animals including humans, cows, sheep, pigs, chickens, ducks, and turkeys; from 223 soil samples with no known fecal pollution, collected in 26 states; and from 28 fecally-polluted soil samples collected locally from feed lots or from locations recently flooded with domestic sewage. The bacteriological methods used in these studies consisted of the isolation of 100 strains of coliforms from each fecal sample, purification of the strain on eosin methylene blue agar, examination by the Standard Methods Completed Test and IMViC reactions, and elevated temperature test for production of gas in EC medium within 24 hours when incubated in a constant temperature water bath at 44.5 C ($\pm$ 0.5). The procedure followed for soils was the same except that it was not always possible to isolate 100 strains of coliform bacteria from a 10 gram sample of unpolluted soil. Data from these studies are tabulated in Table 2 and are summarized as follows:

1. Coliform strains derived from feces gave good correlation with the + + - - type, the Parr fecal types (+ + - - , + - - -, and - + - -), the individual tests that make the IMViC classification and the elevated temperature test.

2. Coliform strains isolated from soils (non-fecal sources) gave good correlation with the IMViC type + + - -, with the Parr grouping of fecal types, and with the elevated temperature test, but the attempt to classify the coliform group from soils by the individual reactions was a failure.

3. Polluted soils yielded coliform data that showed good agreement among the + + - - IMViC type, the Parr fecal coliform group, and the elevated temperature

tests, but, owing to the mixture of the soil types of
coliforms in the pollution with the fecal types, individual
reactions, such as the indole test, etc., could not be used.

TABLE 2: Comparison of coliform strains isolated from feces of
warm-blooded animals from unpolluted soils and polluted soils, with
IMViC reactions and the elevated temperature test in EC Medium at
44.5°C (±0.5)

Test	Feces of warm-blooded animals	Soil: unpolluted	Soil: polluted
+ + - -	91.8†	5.6	80.6
+ + - - , + - - -, and - + - -	93.3	8.9	80.7
Indole positive	94.0	19.4	82.7
Methyl red positive	96.9	75.6	97.9
Voges-Proskauer positive	5.1	40.7	97.3
Citrate utilizers	3.6	88.2	19.2
Elevated temperature (FC) positive	96.4	9.2	82.9
Number of cultures studied	8,747	2,348	665

*Data from Geldreich, et al. (26, 27).   †Entries in percentage.

The data are not shown in Table 2, but it was reported in
the original publication that the two most prevalent IMViC
types found in the soil samples from unpolluted sources were
48.1 per cent - + - + type and 18.8 per cent - - + + type for
a total of 66.9 per cent of the coliform strains present.

The data in Table 2 had to be based on the assumptions
that all coliforms present in the guts of warm-blooded animals
were fecal coliforms and all those found in samples of soils
where no known sources of pollution could be identified were
typical soil-type coliforms of non-fecal origin. The IMViC
types found in the feces of humans and chickens were especially
heterogenous in their mixtures, but the types from the cow,
pig, and sheep were relatively uniform, the + + - - type
predominating. The possibility cannot be excluded that some
of the coliform bacteria in the feces of some individuals were

present by accident rather than as normal inhabitants of the
gut. It is also possible that some of the soil samples which
are calculated as unpolluted samples had actually received
small quantities of fecal pollution from domestic or wild
animals. We have had, however, to consider these sources
as "reference samples" for the fecal and non-fecal coliform
groups until better definitions can be offered.

SEPARATION OF FECAL FROM THE NON-FECAL COLIFORM GROUPS

The perfect procedure to distinguish between the coliform
bacteria from a fecal environment and the coliform strains
having as the normal habitat a non-fecal environment has not
been discovered. Criticism of the "reference samples" does
not, however, invalidate the use of discriminatory tests in the
practical solution of pollution problems. We believe that this
separation can be made by using the IMViC types and interpreting the results according to the "Parr classification"
of fecal coliform bacteria or by using the elevated temperature
test, hereafter designated as the "fecal coliform test" or
abbreviated as the "FC Test". Both procedures give essentially equivalent results. The choice depends, therefore,
on technical considerations which greatly favor the FC Test.
IMViC classification should be applied only to a pure culture
of coliform bacteria that has been found positive by the
"Completed Test" as described in Standard Methods (19),
though it has been the practice in many laboratories to type
any colony that produces a typical Escherichia or a fish-eye
Aerobacter colony on an eosin-methylene blue-agar plate.
The completed test is followed by inoculation of the pure
culture in three separate media and application of four biochemical tests, namely: indole, methyl red, V-P (Voges-
Proskauer) test, and citrate utilization. The elapsed time
is generally about 1 week and involves considerable labor in
the laboratory. Abbreviated tests consisting of a combination
of two or three procedures are not acceptable for careful and
accurate work. We do not agree with the recommendation of
Stuart et al. (51) that the indole and V-P tests were adequate
for classification, nor with Griffin and Stuart (52) that
"a similar separation can be made by the citrate and V-P tests."
The EC test, as applied to the multiple tube procedure for the
coliform group, requires the inoculation of one additional tube
of EC medium (Perry and Hajna, 49) for each presumptive

FIGURE 1: Schematic diagram for the detection of the coliform group and the fecal coliform group.

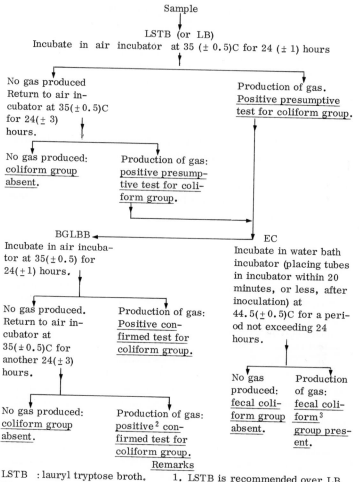

Sample

LSTB (or LB)
Incubate in air incubator at 35 (± 0.5)C for 24 (± 1) hours

No gas produced
Return to air in-
cubator at 35(± 0.5)C
for 24(± 3)
hours.

Production of gas.
Positive presumptive
test for coliform group.

No gas produced:
coliform group
absent.

Production of gas:
positive presump-
tive test for coli-
form group.

BGLBB
Incubate in air incuba-
tor at 35(± 0.5) for
24(± 1) hours.

EC
Incubate in water bath
incubator (placing tubes
in incubator within 20
minutes, or less, after
inoculation) at
44.5(± 0.5)C for a peri-
od not exceeding 24
hours.

No gas produced.
Return to air in-
cubator at
35(± 0.5)C for
another 24(± 3)
hours.

Production of gas:
Positive con-
firmed test for
coliform group.

No gas produced:
coliform group
absent.

Production of gas:
positive[2] con-
firmed test for
coliform group.

No gas
produced:
fecal coli-
form group
absent.

Production
of gas:
fecal coli-
form[3]
group pres-
ent.

Remarks

LSTB : lauryl tryptose broth.
LB : lactose broth.
BGLBB: brilliant green lactose bile broth (2 per cent).
EC : EC medium.

1. LSTB is recommended over LB the presumptive test.

2. A positive confirmed test with a negative fecal coliform (EC). Group test should be examined by the completed test procedure in critical investigations.

3. A positive fecal coliform (EC) group test is equivalent to completed test.

positive lactose (or lauryl sulfate broth) tube, incubation at
44.5 C ($\pm$ 0.5) in a water bath incubator, and the final results
are available within 24 hours. The procedures for the quantitative estimation of the total coliform group and the fecal
coliform group are detailed in Fig. 1.

The fecal coliform group can also be determined by the
membrane filter method. Delaney et al. (28) recommended
for the membrane filter procedure a method involving both
growth and the production of indole. A proposed membrane
filter procedure, soon to be published by the Microbiology
Section, Robert A. Taft Sanitary Engineering Center, proposes
preparation of a membrane, which is then placed on a lactose-
containing medium with aniline blue as an indicator, followed
by incubation at 44.5 C ($\pm$ 0.5) for 24 hours, and counting all
the blue colonies, which are the fecal coliform colonies. The
total coliform colony count can be made by the usual procedure
for membrane filter technique.

SUMMARY

Bacterial species were discovered in 1880 that were believed to be characteristic of the bacterial flora of human feces.
These microorganisms were important in health and sanitation
as indicators of fecal pollution in water and food. Microorganisms with similar morphological and biochemical characteristics
were discovered in soils. Questions arose as to which species
represented fecal pollution and which were native to soil, vegetation, etc. All these species with similar characteristics
became known as the "coliform group" after passing through
a number of transitional names and classifications. Early
investigators used all known physical and biochemical tests,
with considerable emphasis on the fermentation of carbohydrates,
to separate the coliform group into various species. These
data produced detailed subdivision of the coliform group into
genera and species, but had little significance, from a public
health point of view, because it was impossible to secure
agreement on the biochemical differences between coliforms
from a fecal environment and those from non-fecal habitats.
Certain significant contributions had been made during this
time by Wurtz by the addition of an indicator of acid production
to the medium, the inverted vial for gas production by Dunham,
a theoretical basis for the bacteriological examination of water
by Smith, and development of technical methods for use in
sanitary bacteriology by numerous investigators.

One important objective of those concerned with water pollution continued to be the elucidation of the relationship between members of the coliform group and their natural environment. Rogers and his group believed that the fecal group of coliforms and the coliforms indigenous to grains could be separated by the hydrogen:carbon dioxide gas ratio and, from their experimental data, developed the methyl red test. Other commonly used tests, accompanied by improvement in technique, were the Eijkman test (in Europe), indole, Voges-Proskauer, and citrate tests. Numerous other procedures were used infrequently by other investigators. Each of these procedures was believed by the respective investigators to distinguish adequately between the fecal and non-fecal groups of coliform bacteria. Parr proposed the use of the combination of the indole, methyl red, V-P, and citrate tests as the IMViC test and defined the Escherichia group of fecal origin, the Aerobacter group as representive of soils, and the Intermediate group consisting of the 10 remaining types of no defined origin.

The elevated temperature test was modified to a confirmatory procedure to identify the fecal coliform group. This procedure was compared with the IMViC reaction on coliform bacteria from numerous sources. The elevated temperature test for distinguishing between fecal and non-fecal coliform bacteria gave results comparable to any known method, including the IMViC typing procedure. It was superior to other procedures in simplicity of technical procedure. The perfect test for distinguishing between the coliform strains of fecal and non-fecal origin has not been developed. This may be due to the difficulty of obtaining coliform bacteria from known sources for evaluation of the test procedure, to limitation of methods, or to lack of biochemical uniformity among the coliform groups. This criticism is, however, only of investigational importance in the research laboratory, since the methodologies for distinguishing these two groups are adequate for pollution investigation and the identification of fecal pollution in waters.

LITERATURE CITED

1. Escherich, T. 1885. Die Darmbakterien des Neugeborenen und Säuglings. Fortschr. der Med., 3:515.
2. Wurtz, R. 1892. Note sur deux caracteres differential entre le bacilli d'Eberth et le B. coli commune. Arch. de med. exp., 4:85.

3. Smith, T. 1895. Notes on Bacillus coli-communis and related forms, together with some suggestions concerning the bacteriological examination of drinking water. Am. J. Med. Sci. 110:283.
4. Dunham, F. E. 1898. A simple method for demonstrating the production of gas by bacteria. Brit. Med. J. 1:1387.
5. Ford, W. W. 1901. Classification of intestinal bacteria. J. Med. Res. 6:211.
6. McConkey, A. 1905. Lactose-fermenting bacteria in feces. J. Hyg. 5:333.
7. McConkey, A. 1909. Further observations on the differentiation of lactose-fermenting bacilli, with special reference to those of intestinal origin. J. Hyg. 9:86.
8. Bergey, D. H., and S. J. Deehan 1908. The Colon-aerogenes group of bacteria. Jour. Med. Res. 19:175.
9. Jackson, D. C. 1911. Classification of the Bacillus Coli group. J. Inf. Dis. 8:241.
10. Kligler, I. J. 1914. Studies on the classification of the colon group. J. Inf. Dis. 15:187.
11. Eijkman, C. 1904. Die Gärungsprobe bei 46° als Hilfsmittel bei der Trinkwasseruntersuchung. Centr. Bakteriol. Parasitenk., Abt. I, orig. 34:742.
12. Howe, E. C. 1912. A biometric investigation of certain non-spore-forming intestinal bacteria. Science 35:225.
13. Smith, T. 1895. Ueber den Nachweis des Bacillus coli communis im Wasser. Centr. für Bakt. 18:494.
14. Hardin, A. and S. G. Walpole 1905-06. Chemical reaction of B. lactis aerogenes (Escherich) on glucose. Production of 2,3-butylene-glycol and acetylmethylcarbinol. Proc. Roy. Soc. B. 77:399.
15. Rogers, L. A. and W. M. Clark, A. C. Evans. 1914. The characteristics of bacteria of the colon type found in bovine feces. J. Inf. Dis. 15:100.
16. Rogers, L. A. and W. M. Clark, A. C. Evans. 1915. The characteristics of bacteria of the colon type occurring on grains. J. Inf. Dis. 17:137.
17. Clark, W. M. and H. A. Lubs. 1915. The Differentiation of bacteria of the colon-aerogenes family by the use of indicators. J. Inf. Dis. 17:160.
18. Fellows, C. R. and R. W. Clough. 1925. Indole and skatole determination in bacterial cultures. J. Bact. 10:105-133.
19. Standard Methods for the examination of water and waste-

water. A. P. H. A. New York City, N. Y. 11 ed.

20. Frieber, W. 1922. Beiträge zur Frage. Cent. f . Bakt. I Abt. 87:254-277.

21. Neisser, M. 1921. Ueber Indol-phenolbildung durch Bakteria. Munch. Med. Wch. 68:1384-85.

22. Smirnow, M. R. 1916. Biological variation of bacteria. I. Induced variation in the cultural characteristics of B. coli. J. Bacteriol. 1:385.

23. Fabry, P. 1922. Note sur le bacilli coli modifie, ne praduisant plus d'indole. Compt. rend. Soc. de Biol. 87:113-115.

24. Kulp, W. L. 1925. Indole studies. J. Bacteriol. 10:459-471.

25. Holman, W. L. and F. L. Gonzales 1923. A Test for indole based on the oxalic acid reaction of Gnezda. J. Bacteriol. 8:577-583.

26. Geldreich, E. E., R. H. Bordner, C. B. Huff, H. F. Clark and P. W. Kabler. 1962. Type distribution of coliform bacteria in the feces of warm-blooded animals. J. Wat. Poll. Cont. Fed. 34:295-301.

27. Geldreich, E. E., C. B. Huff, R. H. Bordner, P. W. Kabler, and H. F. Clark. 1962. The faecal coli-aerogenes flora of soils from various geographical areas. J. Appl. Bacteriol. 25:87-93.

28. Delaney, J. E., J. A. McCarthy, and R. J. Grasso. 1962. Measurement of E. coli Type I by the membrane filter. Water and Sew. Works, 109:289-294.

29. Buttiaux, R., J. Samaille, and Y. Pierens. 1956. Identification of coliform bacteria isolated from water. Eijkman test and production of indole at 44 C. Ann. Inst. Pasteur (Lille), 8:137-149.

30. Papavassiliou, J. 1958. The rapid identification of Escherichia coli I by the production at 44 of both indole and gas from lactose. J. appl. Bacteriol. 21:104-108.

31. Veger, J. 1962. Single tube identification of coliform organisms in the bacterial investigation of drinking waters. Cheskoslov. Hyg. (Prague), 7:28-34.

32. Voges, O. and B. Proskauer. 1898. Beiträge zur Ernährungsphysiologie und zur differential Diagnosis der Bakterien der hemmorrhagischen Septicämie. Zeit. f. Hyg. 28:20.

33. Hardin, A. and D. Norris. 1911-12. The bacterial production of acetylmethylcarbinol and 2, 3-butylene-glycol

from various substances. Proc. Roy. Soc. (B), 84:492.
34. West, F. D. 1909. Notes on the Voges and Proskauer reaction for Bacillus coli communis. Amer. J. Pub. Hyg. 19:227.
35. Werkman, C. H. 1930. An improved technique for the Voges-Proskauer test. J. Bacteriol. 20:121.
36. Paine, F. S. 1927. The destruction of acetylmethyl-carbinol by members of the colon-aerogenes group. J. Bacteriol. 13:269.
37. Williams, O. B. and M. B. Marrow. 1928. The bacterial destruction of acetylmethylcarbinol. J. Bacteriol. 16:43.
38. Durham, H. E. 1901. Some theoretical consideration on the nature of agglutinins, together with further observations upon Bacillus typhi abdominalis, Bacillus enteritidis, Bacillus coli communis, Bacillus lactis aerogenes and some other bacilli of allied character. Jour. Exp. Med. 5:353.
39. Levine, M. 1916. The correlation of the Voges-Proskauer and methyl red reactions in the colon-aerogenes group of bacteria. Jour. Inf. Dis. 18:358.
40. Levine, M., J. C. Weldin, and B. R. Johnson. 1917. The Voges-Proskauer and correlated reactions of the coli-like bacteria. Jour. Inf. Dis. 21:39.
41. Levine, M. 1918. A statistical classification of the colon-cloacae group. J. Bacteriol. 3:253.
42. Clark H. F., P. W. Kabler and E. E. Geldreich. 1963. Laboratory records; unpublished data. Microbiology, Taft San. Eng. Cen.
43. Brown, H. C. 1921. Observations on the use of citrated medium. Lancet, 1:22.
44. Koser, S. A. and L. F. Rettger. 1919. Studies on bac-terial nutrition. The utilization of nitrogenous compounds of definite chemical composition. J. Inf. Dis. 24:301.
45. Koser, S. A. 1923. Utilization of salts of organic acids by the colon-aerogenes group. J. Bacteriol. 8:493.
46. Koser, S. A. 1924. Correlation of citrate utilization by members of the colon-aerogenes group with other differential characteristics and with habitat. J. Bacteriol. 9:59.
47. Parr, L. W. 1938. Coliform intermediates in human feces. J. Bacteriol. 36:1.
48. Colwell, C. A. 1946. Small colony variants of Escherichia coli. J. Bacteriol. 52:417.

49. Perry, C. A. and A. A. Hajna. 1944 Further evaluation of EC medium for the isolation of coliform bacteria and Escherichia coli. Amer. Jour. Pub. Health. 34:735.
50. Vaughn, R. H., M. Levine and H. A. Smith. 1951. A buffered boric acid lactose medium for enrichment and presumptive identification of Escherichia coli. Food Res. 16:10.
51. Stuart, C. A., A. M. Griffin and M. E. Baker. 1938. Relationship of coliform organisms. J. Bacteriol. 36:410.
52. Griffin, A. M. and C. A. Stuart. 1940. An ecological study of the coliform bacteria. J. Bacteriol. 40:83.

DISCUSSION

Mr. J. Zajic (Kerr-McGee Oil Ind.): Have immunological methods been used to differentiate between these groups; more specifically, has the fluorescent antibody technique been applied in any of your studies?

Mr. Clark: We have not used the immunological techniques in the separation of the coliforms. One of the reasons that we have avoided it is that there are at least 256 serological types in the coliform group. This creates the same sort of difficulty that we ran into with MacConkey's 128 types or Bergey's and Deehan's 256 types on classification by permutation reactions. There have been no definitive serological studies which have shown that one can separate human strains from those of other warm-blooded animals or that one could separate the fecal from the non-fecal strains. The greatest importance of serological typing is in its use with the pathogenic E. coli, such as Type 05, 011, 055, and so forth.

Typing has been carried out further in England by Smith and Crabb (1956) with phage types instead of serological types. They compared a series of 10 calves suffering from scours and another 10 normal calves from another pasture. They found 33 phage types in both calves, of which 31 were common to both.

The fluorescent antibody method is an application of serological technique. If the serological technique is not basically sound, then the fluorescence method would not be either. (Smith, H. W., and W. E. Crabb. 1956. The typing of Escherichia coli by bacteriophage: its application in the study of the E. coli population in the intestinal tract of healthy calves and calves suffering from white scours. J. Gen. Bacteriol. 15:556-574) .

Dr. S. R. Green (Wallerstein Co.):   I noted that you
indicated the V-P test was not very reliable and, also, that
when one cultivated the Aerobacter on nutrient agar the production of acetylmethylcarbinol was either decreased or
lacking, at times. Since we know that citrate is very in-
fluential in producing diacetyl with the lactic acid bacteria,
I wonder whether: (1) one could add citrate to the nutrient
agar, and (2) the introduction of citrate into the V - P test
may not give a better response. In other words, if there
were a low citratase activity, perhaps it could be activated.

Mr. Clark: Hardin and Walpole, who made a very careful
study in England, tried using citrate and found that they did
not get the acetylmethylcarbinol. That is the best I can give
you for an answer.

Dr. ZoBell (Scripps Inst. Oceanogr.): Although Dr. Clark
and Kabler are to be complimented upon the succinct summary
of the physiology of the coliform bacteria, it seemed my duty
to point out that more than 98 per cent of the water of the world
is in the sea, which is the home of large numbers of animals.
Exclusive of insects, more than 80 per cent of all known animal
species live in the sea, including large numbers of warm-
blooded types such as whales, porpoises, dugongs, manatees,
sea otters, polar bears, fowl, just to mention a few among
many others -- all of which serve as homes for large numbers
of coliform bacteria, or at least bacteria which have some of
these characteristics, such as the ability to ferment lactose
with the production of gas, to produce indole, are methyl-red
positive, utilize citrate, etc.

I think these will have to be added to the numerous strains
already enumerated. However, in a quarter of a century of
searching for them ourselves, we have yet to find a positive
Eijkman test for coliform organisms from the sea. None will
grow at temperatures higher than 40 C; but, by the usual
criteria other than growth temperature and a few other minor
characteristics which distinguish them from human fecal
coliforms, there is a vast reservoir of coliform organisms
in the sea which should be considered, I believe, in such
summaries.

Mr. Clark: Regarding the classification of the coliform
group, I did not, perhaps, make myself clear. I would like
to reduce it to a working classification of only two groups of
organisms: those of fecal origin and those of non-fecal origin.

The shortness of time for this report has made me omit
perhaps most of the information we have on the coliform group.
We have made some studies on sea waters. We have found
Eijkman-positive tests or EC-positive tests with fecal coliforms
which were present in sea water where sewage effluents were
falling into the sea.

I do not think one should find EC-positive strains in sea
water unless there was fresh fecal pollution. The point I
want to emphasize is that growth at elevated temperature is
characteristic of the association with warm-blooded animals,
not the other coliform properties. There are any numbers of
coliforms. There are the coliforms groups having maximum
growth temperatures of from 15 C up to 45 C. I have confined
my discussion, in the interest of brevity, to those organisms
which are characteristically found in fresh water, which we
consider to be of public health significance, and which may be
isolated at 35 C.

Mrs. Lubove Schnable (Douglass College): Have there
been tests designed to correlate specific IMViC patterns with
genetic exchange mechanisms?

Mr. Clark: I cannot give you an answer. I have no information.

12

THE ACTINOMYCETES

Hubert Lechevalier
Institute of Microbiology
Rutgers — The State University

Actinomycetes are bacteria. Certain living organisms
only reluctantly fit into human classification systems. Such
is the case with the myxomycetes of the mycologists, which
the protozoologists prefer to think of as mycetozoa. The
actinomycetes also have such a dualistic nature. Microbiological history is studded with disputes aimed at settling
the question of whether the actinomycetes should be considered bacteria or fungi. It is not quite clear whether these
discussions between bacteriologists and mycologists were
aimed at reserving the right of investigating these minute
filamentous and branching organisms to one or the other
group or simply at trying to be rid of them. At first, the
arguments were purely Byzantine in nature and not over-
loaded with scientific fact. As time passed, and as new tools
were introduced in the study of microorganisms, it became
apparent that actinomycetes could not be considered as anything else but bacteria.

The relationship between actinomycetes and fungi is of a
purely superficial nature. Like the fungi, the actinomycetes
form both hyphae with true branching and various types of
spores of dissemination. As far as we know at present, they
do not form endospores comparable to those of Bacillus or
of Clostridium.

The relationship between actinomycetes and true bacteria,
on the other hand, is profound. There is a basic relationship in size. Both bacteria and actinomycetes have a

cellular diameter on the order of one micron. So minute are
the filaments of actinomycetes and the cells of bacteria that truly satisfying cytological investigations had to wait for the development of the electron microscope. With this powerful tool, the
obvious relationship in cellular size was fortified by the now
evident relationship between cellular contents. One of the most
striking differences between the cellular content of fungi and
that of actinomycetes, is the absence of any membrane around
the nuclear material of actinomycetes, a feature which is strikingly similar to that of true bacteria.

Since the work of Twort and d'Herelle, it has been known
that viruses attack bacteria. The considerable literature which
has accumulated since that time reveals that bacteriophages
have turned out to be one of the microbiologist's pet tools for
physiological and genetic investigations. The electron microscope has revealed that the individual bacteriophage particles
have an intricate morphology of their own. Actinomycetes are
also hosts to phages of their own. The actinophages are similar
to bacteriophages both in their action and in their morphology.
The fungi, on the other hand, seem to be immune to the action
of such viruses, with the exception of some yeasts which have
been recently reported to be susceptible to the action of a "zymophage" (22). We have to wait for further developments in this
field to evaluate the relationship between bacteriophages, actinophages and zymophages. Superficially at least, the existence
of actinophages points to a close relationship between true bacteria and actinomycetes.

Antibiotics, which at first may have been considered as od-
dities in the biological world, developed into important chemotherapeutic agents and biochemical tools. It has been known for
many years that antibiotics have typical antimicrobial spectra.
Some antibiotics, for instance, are active only against Gram-
positive bacteria, whereas others are effective only against
fungi. Even very similar antibiotics with very similar spectra
can be differentiated on the basis of minute but characteristic
differences which are there for those who want to look for them
(20). Thus, it is possible to group all antibiotics according to
such spectra (41). This has proved useful in establishing the relationship of the actinomycetes to the bacteria even more firmly, since they are sensitive to strictly antibacterial antibiotics
and resistant to strictly antifungal antibiotics.

All these arguments in favor of the bacterial nature of actinomycetes are further strengthened by the study of the composition of the cell wall. Nickerson and co-workers, for example,

showed that the mucoid nature of the cell walls of actinomycetes
indicated they were similar to those of certain Gram-positive
bacteria. Differences were noted among various genera of actinomycetes. For example, most Streptomyces tested were
lysed by lysozyme, whereas the Mycobacteria and Nocardia and
a small number of Streptomyces were not lysed by this enzyme
(33). These studies clearly differentiate the walls of actinomycetes from those of fungi (12).

   A further difference between fungi and actinomycetes was
noted by A.R. Prévot, of the Pasteur Institute, who remarked
that there are strictly anaerobic forms among the actinomycetes,
as there are among the true bacteria, but that such forms are
unknown among the fungi.

   Actinomycetes can be isolated from natural substrates with
poor culture media. From the previous discussion, one might
correctly conclude that actinomycetes will not be isolated from
natural substrates on media suitable for the selective isolation
of fungi. Being bacteria, they will grow on media that are also
suitable for the growth of other bacteria. Since, in general, actinomycetes are slow-growing organisms, they are overrun by
fast-growing bacteria on such media. Media selective for the
isolation of actinomycetes are not, necessarily, the media on
which they grow best. It is enough that they grow to form visible
and isolated microcolonies. Once isolated in pure culture, actinomycetes can be transferred for morphological or physiological studies to media which permit more luxuriant growth. The
selective isolation of actinomycetes is, thus, helped by the fact
that they manage to grow — slowly, of course, but to grow — on
media which are so poor that they are disdained by most respectable, true bacteria. This fact is illustrated by their ability
to grow in water agar; that is, tap water solidified with agar.
The impurities in the two constituents of this lean medium are
enough to permit growth of actinomycetes while discouraging
that of most true bacteria and fungi. Another medium which had
been found quite satisfactory contains arginine, glycerol, and a
mixture of salts (10). The medium used for isolation of actinomycetes is only one of the methods advocated for increasing the
experimenter's chances of isolating these finely filamentous organisms. Before plating-out, the samples of natural substrates
can be treated in various ways in order to increase the proportion of actinomycetes in the sample. The relative value of these
various methods has been questioned by El-Nakeeb and Lechevalier (10), who concluded that a calcium carbonate treatment
of samples, previously advocated by Tsao and co-workers (37),

was the best of the methods suggested. It seems that such a method could be modified to suit the special purpose of isolating actinomycetes from water samples.

Actinomycetes are bacteria with fungal morphology. Actinomycetes, from a morphological point of view, can be divided into two groups of uneven size. The larger group contains those actinomycetes not forming sporangia, and the smaller, select group, those producing such structures. Further subdivisions may be made depending on oxygen requirement and according to the type and location of the conidia formed.

In general, actinomycetes growing on a solid medium form a substrate, or primary, mycelium growing into or on the agar and may form an aerial, or secondary, mycelium growing away from the agar into the air. Accordingly, from a morphological point of view, it is possible to make a distinction depending on whether a certain type of spore is produced on the aerial mycelium or on the substrate mycelium. In addition, certain sporogenic structures of the primary mycelium may be observed, both on the surface of the agar and deep in the agar medium, while others may be formed only deep in the solid medium. A number of slide methods have been described in the literature for the study of the morphology of actinomycetes. Our own experience has been that it is difficult to surpass the effectiveness and simplicity of a direct examination of agar plates under ordinary bright field microscopy. The only special pieces of equipment necessary, apart from much patience, are a long focus condenser, which permits one to set up Koehler illumination at any level of the culture examined, and a powerful source of light equipped with proper filters. We keep away from liquid culture methods, such as hanging drop techniques, since they do not permit one to exploit the differences between substrate and aerial mycelia. We like to complete our in situ examinations by using water mounts in which we use stains sparingly. We never use dry fixed preparations. Even though actinomycetes are bacteria, their fungal morphology requires the use of the methods preferred for the study of the morphology of fungi.

The various form genera of actinomycetes known so far can be reviewed by examining the following illustrated key:

Illustrated Key to the Form Genera of Actinomycetes

In the schematic illustrations, the white portion represents the aerial mycelium, the cross-hatching identifies the substrate mycelium which is on the surface of the agar, and the dark filaments and spores represent the part of the culture located in the agar.

I. - No sporangia formed   ACTINOMYCETACEAE

    A. - Anaerobic or microaerophilic. No conidia formed.

                    1. Actinomyces Harz, 1877

    B. - Usually aerobic. May form conidia.

        a. - Conidia single.

            aa. - No aerial mycelium; some forms are anaerobic.

                    2. Micromonospora Orskov, 1923

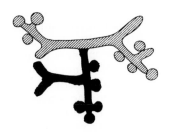

bb. - Aerial mycelium formed.

3. <u>Thermoactinomyces</u>
   Tsiklinski, 1899

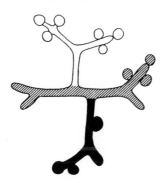

b. - Longitudinal pairs of conidia on the aerial mycelium.

4. <u>Waksmania</u> Lechevalier and
   Lechevalier, 1957

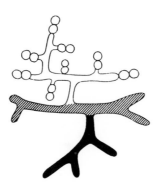

c. - Conidia single or in short chains on substrate and
aerial mycelia.

> 5. <u>Micropolyspora</u> Lechevalier,
> <u>S</u>olotorovsky and McDurmont,
> 1961

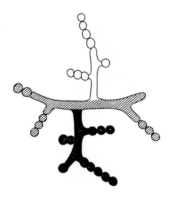

d. - Conidia, when formed, are in chains on the aerial mycelium.

    aa. - Mycelium breaking up in short segments; conidia not always formed.

        6. <u>Nocardia</u> Trevisan, 1899

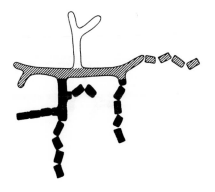

bb. - Mycelium not breaking up; conidia formed.

7. <u>Streptomyces</u> Waksman and
Henrici, 1943

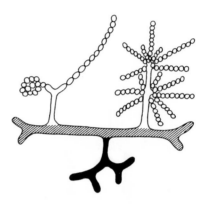

II. - Sporangia formed.   ACTINOPLANACEAE

A. - Aerial mycelium usually not formed. Sporangiospores
motile.

8. Actinoplanes Couch, 1950

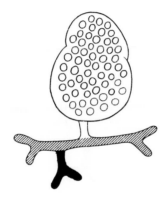

B. - Aerial mycelium abundant. Sporangiospores non-
      motile.

    a. - Spherical sporangia containing many spores.

                  9. <u>Streptosporangium</u> Couch,
                          1955

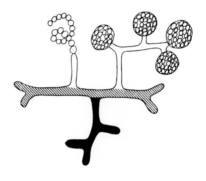

b. - Sporangia containing a single straight chain of
sporangiospores.

10. <u>Microellobosporia</u> Cross,
Lechevalier and Lechevalier,
1963

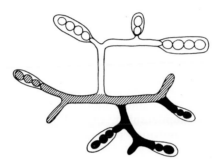

This classification may look neat on paper but, in practice,
there are numerous complications. For example, some <u>Strepto-</u>
<u>myces</u> may form their chains of spores only on certain media
and some variants of them may be indistinguishable from
<u>Nocardia</u>. On the other hand, some <u>Nocardia</u> may produce not
only sterile aerial mycelium but also chains of spores in every
respect similar to those of the most respectable <u>Streptomyces</u>.
In this domain, the study of the chemical composition of the cell
wall may be of great help, since the composition of the cell wall
of the two groups seems to differ.

Hoare and Work (15) studied the distribution of diamino-
pimelic acid isomers in true bacteria and actinomycetes. In the
strains of aerobic actinomycetes studied by these authors appreciable amounts of the LL isomer were detected only in members of the genera <u>Streptomyces</u> and <u>Micromonospora</u>. This

isomer was absent in <u>Nocardia</u> and <u>Mycobacteria</u>. The most
detailed studies in this field have been carried out during the
past few years by Cummins and his co-worker Harris (9). One
can summarize the results obtained by these workers with
aerobic actinomycetes as follows: 1) Both <u>Streptomyces</u> and
<u>Nocardia</u> cell walls contained amino sugars. Glucosamine and
muramic acid were always present. Galactosamine was present
only occasionally. 2) Cell walls of <u>Nocardia</u> contained arabinose
and galactose. Occasionally they also contained glucose or
mannose. Usually the cell walls of <u>Streptomyces</u> contained no
sugars. Occasionally glucose or galactose or both were present.
3) The cell walls of both <u>Nocardia</u> and <u>Streptomyces</u> contained
alanine and glutamic acid, however glycine and LL-diaminopi-
melic acid were found only in the cell walls of <u>Streptomyces</u>.
DL-diaminopimelic acid was always found in <u>Nocardia</u> and
sometimes in <u>Streptomyces</u>. 4) The cell walls of <u>Nocardia</u> were
similar to those of <u>Mycobacteria</u> and <u>Corynebacterium</u>.

The various form genera included in the above key are
those considered important by the author. Other forms have
been described, sometimes poorly, during the past few years
and it seems unnecessary to include them in this broad and general survey. For details on the various species of actinomycetes
which have been described, one can refer to the second volume
of "The Actinomycetes" by Waksman (40).

<u>Actinomycetes are widely distributed in nature</u>. The great-
est natural reservoir of actinomycetes is soil, but they can be
found almost anywhere, at least as casual contaminants.

a) <u>Actinomyces</u>: As we have noted, some actinomycetes do
not form any type of conidia and are anaerobic. These, referred
to as <u>Actinomyces</u> in the classification of Waksman, have been
considered for many decades as inhabitants of the oral cavity
of animals. Even though they are rarely troublesome, they may
cause dramatic infections, called actinomycoses. The two main
types of these organisms are the so-called bovine and human
types. Actinomycoses also occur in carnivores but are rare
(25). In 1951, Hvid-Hansen changed this classically accepted
ecological concept by reporting that some anaerobic actinomycetes could be isolated from ground waters rich in hydrogen
sulphide (17). These waters were not rich in organic substances
and the organisms isolated by Hvid-Hansen, such as <u>A. israeli</u>,
required organic matter. Their occurrence in these waters
might be explained by a possible association with some nutritionally less fastidious organism that might furnish the <u>Acti-
nomyces</u> with a minimum amount of acceptable food. These

findings were substantiated by the work of Beerens and Hvid-
Hansen (3) and that of Kalakutskii, in Moscow, who also isolated
some anaerobic Actinomyces, which he called anaerobic Proactinomyces, from water. In addition, he isolated them from
air which had been recently contaminated by the presence of
people. In contrast, he was not able to isolate any such organisms from soil (18). It seems likely, however, that they would
also be isolated from soils recently contaminated by human beings or animals since it is unlikely that Actinomyces would die
instantly upon touching the ground. As a matter of fact these
organisms have been reported to be present in farm yard manure (17).

b) Micromonospora and Thermoactinomyces: In this group,
we find a few anaerobic species. At least two such anaerobic
organisms have been isolated from the intestine of termites
(16, 30). Aerobic forms of these organisms can be found in soil,
as can be seen from Table 1, but they have often been reported
to be present in the mud of lakes and ponds. This may not be a
proof that micromonosporas are normal water inhabitants, but
may simply mean that among the soil actinomycetes that reach
the bottom of water bodies, they are the best adapted for survival, if not growth, at low temperature and in presence of little
oxygen. This will be discussed in more detail when we come
back to the problem of actinomycetes in water. Thermoactinomyces, like thermophilic Streptomyces, are most common in
composts, and in manure piles.

c) Waksmania: Most of the strains of Waksmania isolated
thus far have been found in soils (26). Table 1 gives an idea of
the frequency of occurrence of these organisms in various soil
samples. One strain of Waksmania has been isolated from a
patient suffering from pericarditis. The patient had probably
become infected by means of a stab wound inflicted by a soiled
knife (23). Thermophilic forms of these organisms have been
isolated from various manure piles, and they have been called
Thermopolyspora bispora (14).

d) Micropolyspora: As can be seen in Table 1, some strains
of Micropolyspora can be found in soil. Other strains have been
isolated from human sputa (21), the nose exudate of a leprous
patient and from the lung of a calf that had died of pneumonia
(2).

e) Nocardia and Streptomyces: These organisms are abundantly distributed in soil, and some are pathogenic to animals
and plants. In animals they can cause visceral infections such
as the human nocardiosis caused by N. asteroides and bovine

Table 1. Distribution of the "rare" forms of
actinomycetes in 16 soil samples.

Soil samples plated out on three different media.

About 5000 colonies of actinomycetes were examined. Those showing
interesting morphology were subcultured on various media to check the
identification of the form genus. Incubation mostly at 36° C.

Soils	Form genera (no. of colonies)						
	Micropolyspora	Micromonospora	Waksmania	Actinoplanes	Streptosporangium	Thermoactinomyces	Microellobosporia
CULTIVATED							
Garden I	0	1	0	1	0	0	0
Garden II	0	3	1	0	1	0	0
Greenhouse I	3	4	1	0	0	4	0
Greenhouse II	2	3	1	0	0	0	0
Planter	5	3	3	0	2	3	0
Hedge soil	0	4	0	0	2	0	0
Cultivated tree	3	7	1	2	0	0	1
Mustard field	10	5	0	1	0	0	0
Cow beet field I	0	5	0	0	0	0	0
Cow beet field II	5	7	1	5	0	1	0
Wheat field	0	4	0	0	0	0	0
UNCULTIVATED							
Grassland I	0	13	0	0	0	0	0
Grassland II	0	2	0	1	0	0	1
Riverbank	0	7	1	0	0	0	0
Forest edge	0	2	0	0	0	0	0
Deep forest	0	0	0	0	0	0	0
TOTALS	28	70	9	10	5	8	2

"farcy." They can also cause, as does the anaerobic Actinomyces, subcutaneous and bony tumefactions with the formation
of fistulae and grains. These mycetomae may be caused by
N. asteroides, N. brasiliensis, S. madurae, S. pelletieri and
S. somaliensis (31). Some of these organisms, such as N. asteroides (24) have been isolated from soil, and there is no reason to believe that they could not survive in natural water, at
least for a brief period of time. These two groups of organisms
which form the bulk of the soil actinomycetes are also responsible for some plant diseases. The best known of these diseases
is potato scab, which is caused by S. scabies.

The total counts of actinomycetes and their relative importance in the soil microflora depends on a number of factors,
such as the season of the year, the depth in the soil, the type of
soil, its state of dryness, its aeration, its pH, etc. These factors are considered in some detail in Waksman's books on actinomycetes (38, 39). Let us stress merely that actinomycetes,
in general, do not like to have their feet wet, that they prefer a
neutral or slightly alkaline pH to an acidic one and that, since
most of them are aerobic, they are numerous in well-aerated
soils.

Soil actinomycetes can also find their way into various
products and be a nuisance (38, 39). Some spoil milk products
while others have given headaches to cocoa manufacturers. Not
satisfied with attacking our foods, they also use as food other
things that we would like to utilize in some other way, such as
rubber and wool. This last property has been exploited by using
actinomycetes as a source of keratinase which could conceiv-
ably be used for the preparation of leather (28).

f) Actinoplanaceae: Couch found species of Actinoplanes
widely distributed in a number of soil samples coming from all
over the world (6). Since Actinoplanes have motile sporangiospores, it would not be surprising if at least some of them were
to be found in natural waters. Couch isolated the type species
of Streptosporangium from a garden soil (7). Later, members of
this genus were isolated from acid forest soils in the Netherlands, among others (5), from a number of Japanese soils that
were mostly acidic (27) and from samples of asiatic and Russian
soils (34). The three strains of Microellobosporia isolated thus
far also came from soil (8). The distribution of these sporangi-
um-forming organisms in a survey of soil samples which had
been carried out specifically to detect the less common forms
of actinomycetes, will be found in Table 1.

Actinomycetes are only a minor part of the marine micro-

flora. In the sea, actinomycetes are only a minor component of
the bacterial flora, which is mainly composed of Gram-negative
bacteria. However actinomycetes have been considered by
ZoBell as being widely distributed in the marine environment
(42). He observed species of Streptomyces (which he calls Actinomyces) growing on dead marine algae and in bottom deposits. He and Upham (43) described two new species of Streptomyces called S. marinolimosus and S. halotrichis. ZoBell
also noted that many actinomycetes could be seen growing on
contact slides buried in the sea. Often, species of Mycobacteria,
Nocardia and Micromonospora, which are present in the sea,
have been isolated by enriching marine samples with hydrocarbons. Such compounds can be used as a selective source of
carbon for actinomycete isolation.

The question has not yet been settled whether these are
truly marine actinomycetes or whether those which can be isolated from the sea are only land forms surviving for a while in
this salty medium. Grein and Meyers (13) noted that more actinomycetic colonies could be isolated from marine samples if
the medium had only 25 to 50 per cent of the salinity of sea
water, than if the isolation medium had the full salinity of the
sea. This observation would tend to indicate that at least a part
of the marine actinomycetic flora is of a purely transient nature. In interpreting these data, one should remember that soil
actinomycetes are already quite tolerant to rather high doses
of salt. Grein and Meyers noted the high salt tolerance of strains
of the ubiquitous Streptomyces griseus group. The salt tolerance
of soil actinomycetes has been studied by Klevenskaya (19) who
found that the limiting salt concentration for the growth of a
number of strains of Streptomyces varied, for NaCl, between
1.5 per cent and 7 per cent. This author also noted that actinomycetes were prevalent in saline soils. On this basis, one might
postulate that saline soils could be the breeding farm on which
salt tolerant strains are selected. When these eventually make
their way to the sea, they at least survive long enough to be
plated out by the marine microbiologist, and, most likely, they
also play a role in the decomposition of organic matter in the
sea.

Actinomycetes can cause undesirable odors in fresh water
bodies. We have already mentioned that actinomycetes can be
found in lakes and rivers. Streptomyces, Nocardia and Micromonospora are the genera most commonly encountered from
these fresh water sources, just as they are the genera most
commonly found in soil. It seems however, that some micro-

monosporas may even be normal inhabitants of fresh water sediments, since Erikson (11) found them to be "admirably adapted for life under the conditions obtaining at the bottom of Lake Mendota" and they occur there in numbers proportionally greater than in soil. Of importance was their ability to decompose chitin, cellulose and lignin, all substances to be found at the bottom of fresh water bodies. Waksman has reviewed literature on the distribution of actinomycetes in aqueous environments (38, 39).

The importance of actinomycetes as sources of undesirable tastes and odors has been stressed recently by Silvey and Roach (32). Probably from prehistoric times, those tilling the soil have noted that freshly plowed earth had a special odor. In 1891, Berthelot and André (4) noted that the substance in soil responsible for the "earthy" odor could be extracted from soil by steam. Soon it became clear that microorganisms were responsible for the production of such odors and Adams (1) linked the odor to the presence of actinomycetes, which he then, in 1929, referred to as Streptothrix. He wrote: "...The mud from a canal originating from the Nile often had this odour and contained large numbers of streptothrix-like organisms. When this mud was added to non-tasting water, followed by filtration, the water acquired the earthy taste of the mud. Similarly, if the water and the mud, in separate vessels, was placed under a bell-jar, the water absorbed the odour and gave rise to the taste." And the author added mournfully: "Although many experiments have been undertaken dealing with the prevention and removal of this particular taste, the results are not very encouraging...."

The odoriferous substance produced by actinomycetes was studied by Thaysen (35) and Thaysen and Pentelow (36). The odoriferous extract of these authors was partly soluble in ethyl alcohol and soluble in ether. It was an organic compound and possibly an amine. At high concentrations it had a manurial odor. When diluted, and at a slightly alkaline pH, the odor became earthy. These authors described some very clear experiments by which they showed that a live fish placed in a water containing minute amounts of the odoriferous substance would pick up and store the substance in its flesh. This accumulation, undesirable for a gourmet, was rapid and took place either through the gills or the mouth, but not the skin. Although the picking up of the taint was rapid, its elimination was slow. The latter was accomplished by keeping the fish alive for a few days in untainted running water.

The most complete study on the nature of this odoriferous

substance has been carried out by Romano and Safferman (29) who worked at the Robert A. Taft Sanitary Engineering Center in Cincinnati, Ohio. They obtained an odoriferous concentrate from a culture of Streptomyces. Their method was as follows: 1) preparation of odoriferous broths, 2) removal of the odor by distilling 10 per cent of the culture medium volume, 3) extraction of the odoriferous component with ether or adsorption on activated carbon and elution with chloroform. Their studies were hindered by the lack of precise assay methods. Romano and Safferman remarked that the odoriferous substance produced by the strain of Streptomyces that they studied could be removed with 10 mg per l of activated carbon. It remained to be seen if the same treatment would be effective in removing odoriferous substances produced by other types of actinomycetes.

CONCLUSION

The minute, filamentous organisms that we have discussed can form some exceedingly intricate patterns of sporulation and they thus can be a joy to the morphologist. They may also be, in some cases, the despair of the food technologist or the water engineer. They have not yet yielded all their secrets to us, be it from the point of view of their ecology, or that of their biochemistry, but their greatest claim to fame has been that some of them produce most of the potent chemotherapeutic agents known as the antibiotics (41). Dr. Waksman, who directed the work at Rutgers which catapulted the actinomycetes into the antibiotic limelight, worked with them for many long years while they were still only an unglamorous and neglected sector of the soil microflora. But now that the actinomycetes have become renowned for the good they can do, we realize how truly dualistic they are. For their capacity for good will always be balanced, for the sanitary engineer among others, by their potential for mischief.

ACKNOWLEDGMENT

The work reported in Table 1 was supported by Public Health Special Fellowship No. E.F. 13,313.

LITERATURE CITED

1. Adams, B. A. 1929. Odors in water of the Nile River. Water and Water Eng. 31:327-329.

2. Austwick, P. K. C. Personal communication.

3. Beerens, H. and N. Hvid-Hansen. 1952. Présence dans les eaux sulfureuses françaises de bactéries réductrices de sulfate et d'une variété protéolytique d'Actinobacterium israëli: A. israëli var. liquefaciens nov. sp. Compt. Rend. Acad. Sci. 234:480-482.

4. Berthelot, M. and G. André. 1891. Sur l'odeur propre de la terre. Compt. Rend. Acad. Sci. 112:598-599.

5. Brummelen, J. van and J. C. Went. 1957. Streptosporangium isolated from forest litter in the Netherlands. Antonie van Leeuwenhoek 23:385-392.

6. Couch, J. N. 1954. The genus Actinoplanes and its relatives. Trans. N.Y. Acad. Sci. 16:315-318.

7. Couch, J. N. 1955. A new genus and family of the Actinomycetales, with a revision of the genus Actinoplanes. J. Elisha Mitchell Sci. Soc. 71:148-155.

8. Cross, T., M. P. Lechevalier, and H. Lechevalier. 1963. A new genus of the Actinomycetales: Microellobosporia gen. nov. J. Gen. Microbiol. 31:421-429.

9. Cummins, C. S. 1962. Chemical composition and antigenic structure of cell walls of Corynebacterium, Mycobacterium, Nocardia, Actinomyces and Arthrobacter. J. Gen. Microbiol. 28:35-50.

10. El-Nakeeb, M. A. and H. A. Lechevalier. 1963. Selective isolation of aerobic actinomycetes. Appl. Microbiol. 11:75-77.

11. Erikson, D. 1941. Studies on some lake-mud strains of Micromonospora. J. Bacteriol. 41:277-300.

12. Foster, J. W. 1949. Chemical activities of fungi. Academic Press, Inc., New York.

13. Grein, A. and S. P. Meyers. 1958. Growth characteristics and antibiotic production of actinomycetes isolated from littoral sediments and materials suspended in sea water. J. Bacteriol. 76:457-463.

J. Bacteriol. 76:457-463.

14.   Henssen, A. 1957. Beiträge zur Morphologie und Systematik der thermophilen Actinomyceten. Archiv. für Mikrobiol. 26:373-414.

15.   Hoare, D. S. and E. Work. 1957. The stereoisomers of aε-diaminopimelic acid. II. Their distribution in the bacterial order Actinomycetales and in certain Eubacteriales. Biochem. J. 65:441-447.

16.   Hungate, R. E. 1946. An anaerobic cellulose-decomposing actinomycete, Micromonospora propionici. J. Bacteriol. 51:51-56.

17.   Hvid-Hansen, N. 1951. Anaerobic actinomyces (Actinomyces israeli) in ground water. Acta Path. Microbiol. Scan. 29:335-338.

18.   Kalakutskii, L. V. 1960. Study of anaerobic Proactinomyces. I. Isolation of pure cultures from nature. Microbiology (a translation of Mikrobiologiya) 29:59-63.

19.   Klevenskaya, I. L. 1960. Growth of soil actinomycetes in media of varying osmotic pressure. Mikrobiologiya, 29:215-219.

20.   Lechevalier, H. 1960. Comparison of the in vitro activity of four polyenic antifungal antibiotics. Antibiotics annual 1959-1960, pp. 614-618. Antibiotica, Inc., New York.

21.   Lechevalier, H. A., M. Solotorovsky and C.I. McDurmont. 1961. A new genus of the Actinomycetales: Micropolyspora gen. nov. J. Gen. Microbiol. 26:11-18.

22.   Lindegren, C. C. and Yong Nyu Bang. The Zymophage. Antonie van Leeuwenhoek 27:1-18.

23.   Louria, D. B. and R. E. Gordon. 1960. Pericarditis and pleuritis caused by a recently discovered microorganism, Waksmania rosea. Am. Rev. Resp. Dis. 81:83-88.

24.   McClung, N. M. 1960. Isolation of Nocardia asteroides from soils. Mycologia 52:154-156.

25.   McGaughey, C. A. 1952. Actinomycosis in carnivores: A review of the literature. Brit. Vet. J. 108:89-92.

26.   Nonomura, H. and Y. Ohara. 1960. The isolation and classification of the genus Microbispora. J. Ferment.

Technol. 38:401-405.

27.   Nonomura, H. and Y. Ohara. 1960. The isolation and classification of the genus Streptosporangium. J. Ferment. Technol. 38:405-409.

28.   Noval, J. J. and W. J. Nickerson. 1959. Decomposition of native keratin by Streptomyces fradiae. J. Bacteriol. 77:251-263.

29.   Romano, A. H. and R. S. Safferman. 1963. Studies on actinomycetes and their odors. J. Am. Water Wks Assoc. 55:169-176.

30.   Sebald, M. and A. R. Prévot. 1962. Étude d'une nouvelle éspèce anaèrobie stricte Micromonospora aceto-formici n. sp. isolée de l'intestin postérieur de Reticuli-termes lucifugus var. saintonnensis Ann. Inst. Pasteur 102:199-214.

31.   Segretain, G., E. Drouhet and F. Mariat. 1958. Diag-nostic de laboratoire en mycologie médicale. Editions de la Tourelle. St. Mandé.

32.   Silvey, J. K. and A. W. Roach. 1956. Actinomycetes may cause tastes and odors in water supplies. Public Works 87:103.

33.   Sohler, A., A. H. Romano, and W. J. Nickerson. 1958. Biochemistry of the Actinomycetales. III. Cell wall compo-sition and the action of lysozme upon cells and cell walls of the Actinomycetales. J. Bacteriol. 75:283-290.

34.   Taig, M. M., S. M. Rudaya, and N. K. Solovieva. 1962. Cultures of actinomycetes of the Actinoplanaceae Family. Antibiotiki 7:483-491.

35.   Thaysen, A. C. 1936. The origin of an earthy or muddy taint in fish. I. The nature and isolation of the taint. Ann. Appl. Biol. 23:99-104.

36.   Thaysen, A. C. and F. T. K. Pentelow. 1936. II. The effect on fish of the taint produced by an odoriferous spe-cies of Actinomyces. Ann. Appl. Biol. 23:105-109.

37.   Tsao, P. H., C. Leben, and G. W. Keitt. 1960. An en-richment method for the isolation of actinomycetes that produce diffusible antifungal antibiotics. Phytopathology 50:88-89.

38.   Waksman, S. A. 1950. The actinomycetes. Their nature, occurrence, activities, and importance. Chronica Botanica Co. Waltham, Mass.

39.   Waksman, S. A. 1959. The actinomycetes, Vol. I, Nature, occurrence and activities. The Williams and Wilkins Co., Baltimore, Md.

40.   Waksman, S. A. 1961. The actinomycetes, Vol. II, Classification, identification, and description of genera and species. The Williams and Wilkins Co., Baltimore, Md.

41.   Waksman, S. A. and H. A. Lechevalier. 1962. The actinomycetes, Vol. III, Antibiotics of actinomycetes. The Williams and Wilkins Co., Baltimore, Md.

42.   ZoBell, C. E. 1946. Marine microbiology. Chronica Botanica Co., Waltham, Mass.

43.   ZoBell, C. E. and H. G. Upham. 1944. A list of marine bacteria including descriptions of sixty new species. Bull. Scripps Inst. Oceanogr. Tech. Ser. 5:239-292.

DISCUSSION

Dr. Pramer (Rutgers University): If I recall correctly, there was a report by Japanese investigators of autotrophic development of streptomyces. Has this been confirmed? If so, would you include this, too, as a characteristic indicating that actinomycetes are more closely related to bacteria than fungi?

Dr. Lechevalier: There have been such reports for a long time. Not only Japanese workers recently, but also a German, Peter Hirsch, has also maintained that many actinomycetes are autotrophic.

So far, I have not studied them. I have no opinion on the subject.

Mr. Morris B. Smith (Toms River Chemical): What is the influence of the actinomycetes in soil on the degradation of organic material? Would you speculate upon the influence of their presence in aquatic media on biodegradation, particularly with regard to the possibility of antibiotic production by some of these actinomycetes and its role in degradation?

Dr. Lechevalier: I'm not quite convinced that antibiotics play a role in soil; at least, if they do it is on a micro environmental level. In the aquatic environment the dilution factor probably becomes tremendous and I cannot envision much of a role.

Chairman Seeley (Cornell Univ.): Dr. ZoBell, do you wish to make comments about actinomycetes in the ocean?

Dr. ZoBell: We regularly find what we believe to be certain genera of the actinomycetes in the sea. Certainly, they are in the minority; they are not common. I doubt very much if they play an important role in producing antibiotics to the extent that they may influence the microflora, because, of dilution. In other words, there are so few of them that their effects probably would be diluted out by the vast volumes of water.

Dr. Martin Alexander (Cornell Univ.): I think it is commonly accepted that the phylogenic transition of the actinomycetes and the true bacteria is through the coryneforms and the mycobacteria. What group of fungi, do you think, are most closely related phylogenetically to the actinomyces?

Dr. Lechevalier: Considering the actinoplanes one might suspect that the chytrids would be the closest group. That is about all I could think of for the moment.

Dr. Gladys Baker (Vassar College): I wanted to comment that, during Flathead Lake studies, we isolated actinoplanes from water and mud.

Dr. Lechevalier: Did you publish it?

Dr. Baker: No.

13

ARTHROBACTER

E. G. Mulder
Laboratory of Microbiology
Agricultural University
Wageningen, The Netherlands

Arthrobacter is an aerobic, pleomorphic microorganism belonging to the Corynebacteriaceae. In a young stage cells of this organism generally occur as rods of irregular form and variable length, sometimes developing filaments and true branching. Upon aging, the rod-shaped cells turn to coccoid forms.

Bacteria of this type were described by Conn and Dimmick in 1947 (11) under the name of Arthrobacter globiformis and earlier by Conn as Bacterium globiformis (9). H. L. Jensen (15) made an extensive study of this group of organisms and about thirty years ago he described them as soil corynebacteria. It was shown by him that these bacteria are closely related to Mycobacterium and Nocardia (see also Clark, 8).

Extensive investigations concerning the morphology and physiology of Arthrobacter have been carried out by Lochhead and Katznelson and their collaborators (4, 6, 7, 18, 19, 20, 28, 29). Several authors have studied the phenomena occurring during the life cycle of Arthrobacter species (3, 6, 17, 23, 24, 27, 28, 29, 30, 31, 32); others have reported on the nutritional requirements of this group of bacteria (7, 18, 19, 20, 21, 23).

The author and his collaborators (Mrs. Adamse, Antheunisse, van der Struik and Wieringa) have isolated large numbers of Arthrobacter strains from arable and grassland soils. A second group of strains was isolated from activated sludge and a third group from soft cheese. Morphological and physiological characters of these strains were studied.

METHODS

The method employed for the isolation and identification of Arthrobacter strains is as follows. A suspension in physiological saline solution of the material to be tested is shaken for 5 min, diluted in the same solution, and plated on an agar medium of the following composition: $Ca(H_2PO_4)_2$, 0.25; K_2HPO_4, 1; $MgSO_4 \cdot 7H_2O$, 0.25; $(NH_4)_2SO_4$, 0.25; casein, 1; yeast extract, 0.7; glucose, 1; and agar (Davis), 10 g per liter of tap water (pH 7.0). After five days incubation at 25 C, uncontaminated colonies are transferred to slants of the same composition and after 7 days incubation at 25 C the cells are tested microscopically. When cocci are present, the culture is transferred to slants containing 7 g yeast extract and 10 g glucose per liter. On such a medium, Arthrobacter cocci germinate and give rise, within 24 hr, to a mixture of germinating cocci and rods of variable length, sometimes branched or occurring in V-position ("snapping") or palisade position.

The mineral nutrient medium employed for certain nutritional tests had the following composition: K_2HPO_4, 1; $MgSO_4 \cdot 7H_2O$, 0.3; $CaCl_2 \cdot 2H_2O$, 0.05; $FeCl_3 \cdot 6H_2O$, 0.01 g per liter; $CuSO_4 \cdot 5H_2O$, 0.1; $ZnSO_4 \cdot 7H_2O$, 0.1; $MnSO_4 \cdot 7H_2O$, 1.0; Na_2MoO_4, 0.01; and H_3BO_3, 0.01 mg per liter of medium. The pH of this medium was 7.0.

MORPHOLOGY

Morphological characteristics were mainly studied with two strains of Arthrobacter globiformis, 1 and 166, isolated from soil. Further, with two strains of Arthrobacter isolated from soft cheese, 252 and 268, and with a number of cultures of Cellulomonas, Brevibacterium linens, and Mycobacterium phlei, organisms which, at least morphologically, are similar to Arthrobacter.

Effect of nutrient conditions and age. The nutrient supply and the age of the cultures have been found to exert a pronounced effect on cell morphology. Cultivated for 24 hr at 30 C on a rich nutrient agar containing 0.7 per cent yeast extract and 1 per cent glucose, Arthrobacter globiformis, strain 1, formed long, irregular, sometimes branched rods (Pl. I, Fig. 1). Two days later, most rod-form cells had turned to large,

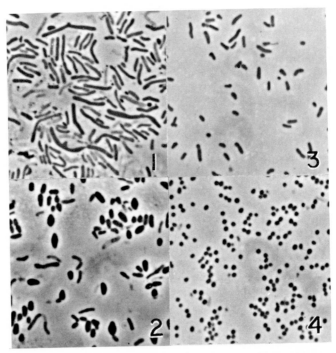

Figs. 1 to 4—Arthrobacter globiformis, strain 1, after an incubation time of one day (Figs. 1 and 3) and three days (Figs. 2 and 4) on a rich (left) and a poor (right) agar medium; 1625 x.

oval cells, called cystites by Jensen (Pl. I, Fig. 2). On a poor medium (soil extract agar containing 0.1 per cent yeast extract and 1 per cent Davis agar) short, rod-form cells were present after a 24 hr incubation time at 30 C. Two days later, these cells had turned entirely to coccoid cells (Pl. I, Fig. 3 and 4).

Strain 166 of A. globiformis gave results similar to those with strain 1 (Pl. II, Fig. 5, 6, 7 and 8).

Germination of coccoid cells. The germination of cocci upon transfer of the cultures to a fresh nutrient medium is a characteristic typical of Arthrobacter. The cells swell and, after a few hours, form germination tubes which develop to rod-form cells. Large cocci (cystites), such as those occurring in cultures grown in rich media, often form two or even three germination tubes (Pl. IV, Fig. 17). These germination tubes develop into normal rods. Release of small oval cells

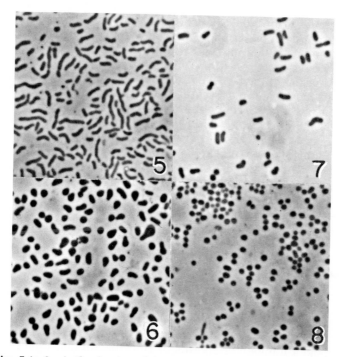

Fig. 5 to 8- <u>Arthrobacter globiformis</u>, strain 166, after an incubation time of one day (Figs. 5 and 7) and three days (Fig. 6) and two days (Fig. 8) on a rich (left) and a poor (right) agar medium; 1625 x.

from the germination tubes, as described by Chaplin (6) in <u>A. pascens</u>, was not observed in strains 1 and 166 of <u>A. globiformis</u> employed in the present study. Under certain conditions, large yeast-like cells may occur in germinating suspensions of cystites (Pl. IV, Fig. 18). These bodies, which were found to be unable to proliferate, presumably are swollen cystites.

    <u>Formation of coccoid cells</u>. Coccoid cells can be formed from rods in two different ways, viz, (a) by gradual shortening of dividing rods, and (b) by simultaneous formation of a number of septa in filamentous cells. The first mechanism may be observed when coccoid cells are transferred to a poor medium, e.g., soil extract containing a small amount of yeast extract. Figures 9 to 16 (Pl. III) show the sequence of events in a slide

culture of A. globiformis, strain 166, growing in soil extract
agar supplied with 0.05 per cent yeast extract. It will be seen
that, after the germination of the cocci, the resulting short
rods, often occurring in V-position ("snapping"), after a few
divisions have returned to the coccus form. However, this
transformation did not prevent the cells from dividing. The
latter observation demonstrates that Arthrobacter cocci do not
represent merely resting cells ("arthrospores") but can also
be slowly dividing cells. This may happen under unfavorable
growing conditions (lack of carbon compounds, biotin deficiency
and, presumably, low pH, low oxygen supply, etc.). The occurrence of Arthrobacter in soil and activated sludge in the coccoid stage presumably depends on the prevalence of such adverse conditions.

The formation of coccoid cells by degradation of filamentous cells is less easily realized under slide-culture conditions.
It was found to occur in a culture of A. globiformis, strain 1,
growing in a mineral nutrient medium supplied with 0.7 g
NH_4NO_3, 3.6 g casamino acids and 3.5 g yeast extract per
liter.

Morphology of Brevibacterium linens, Mycobacterium
phlei, and Cellulomonas biazotea. A comparison was made between the morphology of Arthrobacter strains from different
origins and a number of strains of Brevibacterium linens, Cellulomonas biazotea, and Mycobacterium phlei obtained from
type-culture collections in the U.S.A. and Europe. A striking
similarity in morphology was found to occur (Plates I, II, IV,
and V). This similarity raised the question as to the physiological characteristics of the latter organisms and the Arthrobacter strains from different origins. Therefore a number of
physiological properties has been estimated (Gram stain,
utilization of various carbon compounds, and nitrogen and
vitamin requirements).

PHYSIOLOGY

Gram stain. According to Conn and Dimmick (11), soil
arthrobacters would be Gram-negative in the rod form and
Gram-positive in the coccus form. Mr. Antheunisse, in the
author's laboratory, has tested a large number of Arthrobacter
strains of different origins, in both the rod and the coccus
form, for the Gram stain. The rods had been grown for 24 hr

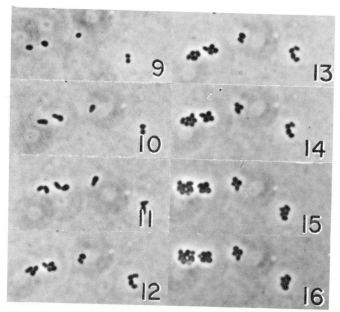

Figs. 9 to 16—<u>Arthrobacter globiformis</u>, strain 166, on a poor agar medium (slide culture) photographed after an incubation time of 1, 4.5, 7.5, 11.5, 13.5, 18.5, 23.5, 34 hrs., respectively; 1625 x.

at 30 C on yeast extract agar (0.7 per cent yeast extract) supplied with 1 per cent glucose; the cocci for 8 days at 30 C on casein agar (0.1 per cent casein). For comparison, a number of plant pathogenic corynebacteria, <u>Brevibacterium linens</u>, <u>Cellulomonas</u>, <u>Microbacterium</u>, and <u>Mycobacterium</u> were included in this investigation.

No clear-cut differences were found between both cell types (Table 1). The major part of the soil arthrobacters was found to be Gram-negative or Gram-variable in the rod stage. A shift from Gram-negative in the rod form to Gram-variable in the coccoid form was found in a number of cases, but the reverse was also found to occur frequently. Similar results were obtained when organisms of the same culture were stained in the rod and the coccus stages.

The strains isolated from activated sludge reacted like the majority of the soil strains except those with phenol-decomposing capacity, which were, for the greater part, Gram-positive in both the rod and the coccus stages.

Table 1. Gram stain of arthrobacters

Source	Total	Number of strains					
		As rods			As cocci		
		Gram +	Gram var.	Gram −	Gram +	Gram var.	Gram −
Sandy soil	45	6	18	21	3 / 2	2 / 5 / 14	1 / 11 / 7
Clay soil	24	0	6	18		2	6 / 16
Peaty soil	10	5	2	3	4 / 1	1 / 1 / 1	2
Grassland soil	15	6	4	5	6	3 / 1	1 / 4
Tropical soil	17	4	7	6	4 / 3	2 / 1	2 / 5
Milk	4	2	2	0	2 / 2		

Cheese	46	39	7	0	36	3	3
Activated sludge	9	1	3	5	4	3	4
Phenol-decomposing activated sludge	5	4	1	0	1	1	1
Plant-pathogenic corynebacteria[a]	8	8	0	0	8		
Cellulomonas[a]	2	0	0	2	2		
Mycobacterium phlei[a]	1	1	0	0	1		
Microbacterium[a]	2	1	1	0	1	1	
Brevibacterium linens	3	3	0	0	3		

[a] Obtained from existing collections.

The majority of the Arthrobacter strains isolated from cheese was Gram-positive in both the rod and coccoid form. The phytopathogenic Corynebacterium species and the representatives of Brevibacterium linens, Microbacterium, and Mycobacterium phlei were Gram-positive; those of Cellulomonas, Gram-negative.

Nutritional requirements. Utilization of carbon compounds. The effect of different carbon compounds was tested on agar media containing 0.1 or 0.15 per cent yeast extract and 0.5 per cent of the compounds to be tested. From the results (Table 2), it will be seen that Arthrobacter strains isolated from soil and those from activated sludge had a strong ability to decompose carbohydrates such as various sugars and starch, as well as citrate, glutamic acid, and proteins. Their lipolytic activity, in general, was weak.

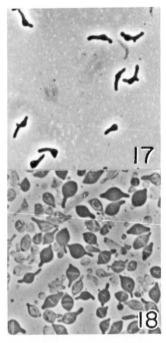

Figs. 17 and 18—Arthrobacter globiformis, strain 166. Fig. 17 germinating coccoid cells. Fig. 18 yeast-like cells.

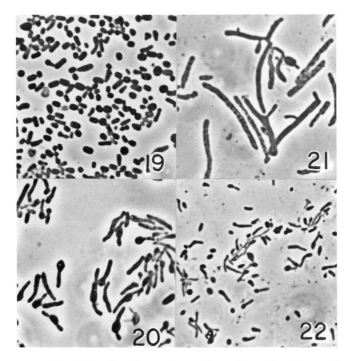

Figs. 19 to 21—<u>Mycobacterium phlei</u>. Fig. 19, after an incubation time of eight days on casein agar. Fig. 20, five hours, and Fig. 21, twenty-four hours after transfer of cells from Fig. 19 to an agar medium containing 0.7 percent yeast extract and 1 percent glucose; 1625 x. Fig. 22—<u>Cellulomonas biazotea</u>. Germinating cocci and rod-form cells; 1625 x.

<u>Arthrobacter</u> strains isolated from cheese were much less active in decomposing carbon compounds than those from soil and activated sludge; sucrose, glycerol, and starch were not utilized by the majority of these strains.

<u>Nitrogen and vitamin requirements</u>. The utilization of different nitrogen compounds and the vitamin requirement are important characters in the classification of <u>Arthrobacter</u> strains. According to Conn and Dimmick (11), the soil arthrobacters would be able to utilize inorganic nitrogen compounds in the absence of vitamins. This statement was not always confirmed by other authors. Taylor (31), in Canada, found that only 17 of 106 soil arthrobacters were able to grow on nitrate nitrogen; the others required yeast extract. It is undecided whether the effect of the latter substrate

Table 2. Utilization of carbon compounds by arthrobacters

Source	Number of strains	Percentages of strains utilizing								
		Glucose	Sucrose	Lactose	Glycerol	Citrate	Starch	Glutamic acid	Tween-80	Gelatine
Sandy soil	40	100	95	93	98	98	73	86	13	86
Clay soil	25	100	100	100	100	100	84	76	8	76
Peaty soil	12	75	50	25	34	50	17	17	17	50
Permanent grassland	18	89	83	39	83	83	6	83	6	61
Cheese	46	87	7	30	11	93	22	43	7	33
Activated sludge	10	100	80	90	100	100	80	100	0	90

depended on the presence of organic nitrogen compounds or of vitamins.

Earlier investigations on the soil corynebacteria by Jensen (15) revealed that certain strains of this group were able to utilize inorganic nitrogen compounds; others, however, required peptone.

Morris (21), and Chan and Stevenson (4) obtained a good growth of Arthrobacter globiformis with inorganic nitrogen when biotin was present. These results were confirmed by Veldkamp (33, 34), working in the author's laboratory.

We have made an extensive study of the nitrogen requirements of a large number of Arthrobacter strains of different origins. For these investigations, use was made of the mineral nutrient medium, supplied with 0.25 g nitrogen in the form of ammonium nitrate or casamino acids, and 5 g glucose per liter; pH 7.0. The comparison was made both in the absence and presence of vitamins, particularly biotin.

The results of these experiments, presented in Table 3, show that almost all of the Arthrobacter strains from soil were able to utilize inorganic nitrogen, either without vitamins or in the presence of biotin (5 μg per liter). A number of strains from peaty soil and from tropical soils, however,

Table 3. Utilization of nitrogen and vitamins

Source	Number of strains	Number of strains growing on				
		NH$_4$NO$_3$			Amino acids	
		No vitamins	Biotin	Vitamin mixture	No vitamins	Vitamin mixture
Sandy soil	45	21	20		1	2
Clay soil	25	9	16			
Peaty soil	10	2		5		3
Grassland soil	16	8	8			
Tropical soils	16	2	7	7		
Milk	4					4
Cheese	46	10	3	11	14	8
Activated sludge	10	1	9			
Phenol-decomposing activated sludge	5	5				
Plant-pathogenic corynebacteria [a]	8			2		6
Cellulomonas [a]	2			2		
Mycobacterium [a]	1	1				
Microbacterium [a]	2			1		1
Brevibacterium linens [a]	2			1	1	1

[a] Obtained from existing collections.

required a vitamin mixture. With the latter mixture the following vitamins were supplied: biotin, 2; folic acid, 20; riboflavin, 100; thiamine, 100; pyridoxine, 100; nicotinic acid, 100; pantothenic acid, 100; p-aminobenzoic acid, 100; and vitamin B_{12}, 1 μg per liter of nutrient medium. So far, it is undecided on which of the added vitamins the beneficial effect of the mixture depended.

The Arthrobacter strains isolated from activated sludge reacted like the soil strains; they were able to utilize inorganic nitrogen either in the absence of vitamins or in the presence of biotin.

Of the 46 cheese strains, 13 had the same nitrogen and vitamin requirements as the soil strains, 11 utilized ammonium nitrate when a vitamin mixture had been added, and 22 required casamino acids, either without or in the presence of added vitamins. The four strains isolated from milk had the

same requirements as the latter group. The strains of Cellulomonas, Mycobacterium, and Microbacterium, for the greater
part, were able to utilize inorganic nitrogen in the presence of
vitamins. Two of the 8 phytopathogenic corynebacteria behaved
similarly to the latter group, the other 6 required both casamino
acids and vitamins.

In a subsequent experiment the casamino acid mixture was
replaced by separate amino acids. The nutrient solution used
in this experiment contained, in addition to the basal mineral
nutrient medium, 5 g glucose and 250 mg N in the form of
either ammonium nitrate or glutamic acid. Approximately half
of the 31 strains requiring casamino acids was able to use inorganic nitrogen when L-methionine had been added in an amount
of 40 mg per liter. The majority of these strains grew on ammonium nitrate and methionine without vitamins, but some required vitamins. Most of the remaining strains made good
growth on glutamic acid as the nitrogen source either without
vitamins and methionine or in the presence of one or more of
the latter compounds.

Some further physiological characters of Arthrobacter.
Formation of polysaccharides. Soil arthrobacters are able to
produce large amounts of polysaccharides (22). This was
shown in Warburg experiments in which washed cells of A.
globiformis, strain 1, either cocci or rods, suspended in phosphate buffer (0.04M), were supplied with glucose. When the
latter had been taken up by the cells, and the respiration rate
had fallen to the endogenous level, no more than 20 to 25 per
cent of the theoretical amount of oxygen required for the respiration of the added glucose had been consumed. In coccoid
cells this value was higher than in rods (Fig. 23). Since the
formation of organic acids was slight, it was assumed that the
glucose had been converted to some reserve material, presumably polysaccharides. In a similar experiment (Fig. 24),
upon analysis of the cells, Mr. Zevenhuizen found more than
50 per cent of the added glucose accounted for as polysaccharides. In a subsequent experiment it was found that both intra-
and extra-cellular polysaccharides had been synthesized.

Excretion of amino acids. An important character of
several Arthrobacter strains is their capacity to excrete large
amounts of amino acids. This phenomenon was studied in our
laboratory by Dr. Veldkamp (33, 34). Arthrobacter strains requiring biotin for growth excreted approximately 0.5 mole
glutamic acid per mole of glucose consumed when the biotin
content of the medium was sub-optimal. Under such conditions

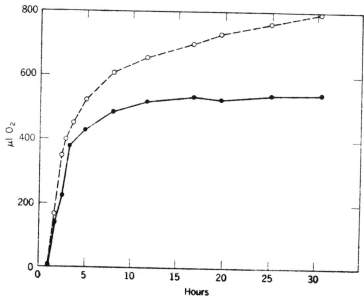

Fig. 23—Oxygen consumption by suspensions of washed coccoid
and rod-form cells of Arthrobacter globiformis, strain 166, upon
the addition of 2.9 mg glucose (endogenous values subtracted).
Complete oxidation of glucose requires 2200 $\mu\ell$. oxygen.
o⎯⎯⎯⎯⎯⎯⎯o rods, o-------------o cocci.

the synthesis of cellular material was depressed (Fig. 25); the
bacteria occurred in the coccoid form.

The effect of biotin on production of glutamic acid has been
observed earlier by Chao and Foster (5) and by Shiio et al. (26).
The former used a Bacillus species, the latter a Brevibacterium. It may be stressed that Brevibacterium linens was recognized in the present study as an organism resembling Arthrobacter very closely. Yet another bacterium, used for producing glutamic acid commercially, Micrococcus glutamicus
(Kinoshita, 16), is, presumably, also identical or closely related to Arthrobacter.

BACTERIOPHAGES

For the isolation of bacteriophages of Arthrobacter, a
mixture of twelve Arthrobacter strains, grown for 24 hr in a
nutrient medium containing mineral salts, yeast extract, and

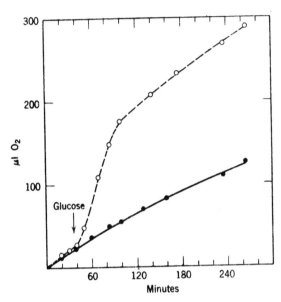

Fig. 24—Oxygen consumption by a washed suspension of Arthrobacter globiformis cells, strain 1, upon the addition of 2.0 mg glucose. Complete oxidation of glucose requires 1500 $\mu\ell$. oxygen. o————o endogenous values, o————o glucose added.

glucose (0.3 per cent), was added to garden soil, incubated for 48 hours at 25 C, filtered through filter paper, and, subsequently, through a Chamberland filter. The filtrate was added to the separate strains which had been growing for 24 hr in the yeast extract glucose medium. With one of the strains, some clearing of the bacterial suspensions was obtained. After repeating the filtration and inoculation four times, an active phage suspension was obtained which gave complete clearing of the bacterial suspension within 2 days.

Two types of plaques were obtained on arthrobacter-containing plates, viz, large ones of 4 mm and small ones of a 2 mm diameter (Pl. VI, Fig. 26 and 27) corresponding with two types of bacteriophage, AR 4L and AR 4S. Each type had a different reproduction time (Fig. 28). Bacteriophages of Arthrobacter strains have been described earlier by Conn and collaboraters (10) who tried to use them for the classification of a number of soil bacteria. Gillespie (12) isolated two types of bacteriophage of A. globiformis, one producing small plaques and one forming large plaques. These phages may have been similar to those described in the present study.

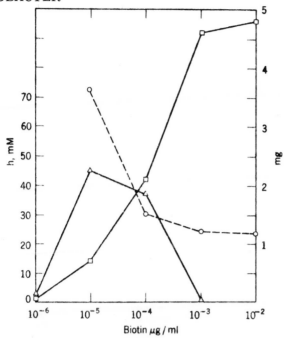

Fig. 25—Effect of biotin on growth (dry weight, mg per ml), on the production of glutamic acid and on time required for the consumption of glucose by Arthrobacter globiformis, strain 23. The cultures were analysed when the glucose had been consumed (see Veldkamp, 33, 34) o------------o time (hours, h) required for the consumption of glu- cose, ——————— dry weight of cells (mg per ml), Δ————————Δ glutamic acid (mM per 100 mM glucose consumed).

FUNCTION OF ARTHROBACTER IN NATURE

The fact that bacteria of the Arthrobacter type occur wide- spread in soil, on plants (13), in activated sludge and in certain cheeses, clearly demonstrates the importance of this group of organisms in nature. Arthrobacters are able to grow slowly in the coccoid state under unfavorable conditions and rapidly in the rod form under favorable conditions. Presumably they are part of the autochthonous flora of soils and natural waters in the former state and of the zymogenous flora in the latter.

A further characteristic of Arthrobacter, probably of great importance in the degradation processes of plant residues in na- ture, is the capacity of certain strains to decompose compounds such as cellulose, lignin, and aromatic compounds such as phe- nols and certain herbicides. So far, it is unknown whether phe- nol-decomposing strains are present in soil, activated sludge, etc., or are selected as mutational forms upon the addition of

Fig. 26 (top)—Dilution series of a mixture of bacteriophages AR4L and AR4S on agar plates containing <u>Arthobacter</u> strain 4, from soil.
Fig. 27 (bottom)—Plaques of AR4L (left) and AR4S (right).

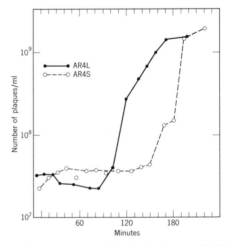

Fig. 28—Reproduction time of bacteriophages AR4L and AR4S.

the substrates. Audus (1, 2), and Gundersen and Jensen (14), in
studying the microbial break-down of herbicides in soil,
observed the development of a flora of herbicide-decomposing
Arthrobacter a considerable amount of time after the addition
of the substrate to the soil. Dr. Wieringa, in author's laboratory, after adding toluene to a peaty soil, found decomposition
of this compound by Arthrobacter strains after about three
weeks incubation. Van der Struik, studying phenol break-down
in activated sludge by gradually increasing the phenol concentration to 500 mg per liter, observed the development of a
phenol-metabolizing microflora, consisting mainly of Arthrobacter strains (cf. Tables 1 and 3). The latter organisms, as
well as the closely related Nocardia (25), may presumably be
used in the purification of phenol-containing waste waters.
    One of the reasons that arthrobacters are found so numerous-
ly in nature (Table 4) may be their resistance to desiccation. We
found that these bacteria can survive a stay in air-dried soil for
more than 10 months (Table 5). The persistence is, presumably, due
to their occurrence in the soil in the coccus stage. It is a well-known
fact that coccoid bacteria have a pronounced resistance to desiccation.

SUMMARY

    Summarizing the results of our investigations, it can be
stated that microorganisms of the Arthrobacter type belong to

Table 4. Number of microorganisms in different soils

Soil	pH	Number per gram of soil (10^5)			Number of bact. strains tested	Percentage		
		Fungi	Actino-myces	Bac-teria		Arthro-bacter	Bacilli	Remain-ing rods
Arable								
Sandy [a]	5.0	0.1	0.3	1.3	23	61.0	26.0	13.0
Sandy [a]	5.5	0	5.6	7.4	26	57.7	42.3	0
Sandy [a]	7.0	0	0.7	7.6	22	63.6	22.7	13.7
Clay [b]	7.9	3.6	11.0	70.0	130	75.0	14.0	11.0
Grassland								
Sandy [b]	5.2	2.5	44.0	61.0	65	43.0	14.0	43.0

[a] Fresh soil. [b] Dry soil.

the most important bacteria in nature. They are found in large
numbers not only in soils, on plants, and in activated sludge,
but also in certain cheeses.

Morphologically, the various Arthrobacter strains tested
were very similar, and they resembled organisms like Brevibacterium linens, Cellulomonas species, Mycobacterium phlei,
and certain plant-pathogenic Corynebacterium species.

Physiologically, however, there existed clear differences
between the different groups of Arthrobacter. Most of the
strains isolated from soil and from activated sludge were
Gram-negative or Gram-variable. They attacked a large variety of carbon compounds and utilized inorganic nitrogen, either
without any vitamin or in the presence of biotin and, sometimes, some additional vitamins.

Table 5. Effect of desiccation of the soil
on number of arthrobacters

Soil	Time of desic- cation (months)	Number of Bacteria (10^5) per gram dry soil	Bac- terial isolates tested	Percentages Arthro- bacters	Bacilli	Remain- ing rods
Sandy pH 7.0	0	33	18	50.0	38.9	11.1
	2	20	39	51.3	46.1	2.6
	10	5.6	19	31.6	68.4	0
	35	5.6	60	0	100.0	0
Sandy pH 7.0	0	40	19	36.8	57.9	5.3
	2	38	37	62.2	37.8	0
	35	10	55	0	100.0	0
Sandy + clover meal pH 7.0	0	120	16	56.3	37.5	6.2
	2	23	39	43.6	53.8	2.6
	10	28	50	58.0	42.0	0
	35	18	61	0	100.0	0
Sandy + clover meal pH 7.0	0	170	14	50.0	42.9	7.1
	2	58	39	35.9	64.1	0
	35	27	32	0	100.0	0

A number of Arthrobacter strains, isolated from acid peaty soil and from Nigerian soils, were Gram-positive. Their vitamin requirement was different from that of most other soil strains; furthermore, some of the peat strains required amino acids for growth. These strains resembled, more or less, the cheese strains which, for the greater part were also Gram-positive and often had more elaborate nitrogen and vitamin requirements. The strains from cheese had a less pronounced ability for utilizing a variety of carbon compounds than most strains from soil or activated sludge, except those from peaty soil.

Certain strains of Arthrobacter are able to attack compounds which normally are not attacked by microorganisms. Other strains may produce large amounts of certain compounds which have commercial value. Therefore these organisms are important not only in soil and water microbiology but also in industrial microbiology.

ACKNOWLEDGEMENT

The photographs and figures in this paper appeared in Mulder, E. and J. Antheunisse, 1963, "Morphologie, physiologie et écologie des Arthrobacter. Ann. Inst. Pasteur 105:46-74, a report of a lecture given at the Soil Microbiology Conference in Paris, February, 1963. These illustrations are reproduced with the kind permission of the editors.

LITERATURE CITED

1. Audus, L. J. 1949. The biological detoxication of 2:4-dichlorophenoxyacetic acid in soil. Plant and Soil 2:31-36.

2. Audus, L. J. 1951. The biological detoxication of hormone herbicides in soil. Plant and Soil 3: 170-192.

3. Blankenship, L. C. and R. N. Doetsch. 1961. Influence of a bacterial cell extract upon the morphogenesis of Arthrobacter ureafaciens. J. Bacteriol. 82: 882-888.

4. Chan, E. C. S., and I. L. Stevenson. 1962. On the biotin requirement of Arthrobacter globiformis. Canad. J. Microbiol. 8: 403-405.

5. Chao, K. C. and J. W. Foster. 1959. A glutamic acid-producing bacillus. J. Bacteriol. 77: 715-725.

6. Chaplin, C. E. 1957. Life cycles in Arthrobacter pascens and Arthrobacter terregens. Canad. J. Microbiol. 3: 103-106.

7. Chaplin, C. E. and A. G. Lochhead. 1956. Abnormal morphology of a bacterium resulting from vitamin B_{12} deficiency. Canad. J. Microbiol. 2: 340-342.

8. Clark, F. E. 1952. The generic classification of the soil corynebacteria. Intern. Bull. Bacteriol. Nomen. and Taxon. 2: 45-56.

9. Conn, H. J. 1928. A type of bacteria abundant in productive soils, but apparently lacking in certain soils of low productivity. N.Y. State Agr. Exp. Sta. Tech. Bull. 138, 24 p.

10. Conn, H. J., E. J. Bottcher, and C. Randall. 1945. The value of bacteriophage in classifying certain soil bacteria. J. Bacteriol. 49: 359-373.

11. Conn, H. J. and J. Dimmick. 1947. Soil bacteria similar in morphology to Mycobacterium and Corynebacterium. J. Bacteriol. 54: 291-303.

12. Gillespie, D. C. 1960. Isolation of bacteriophage for Arthrobacter globiformis. Canad. J. Microbiol. 6: 477-478.

13. Grainger, J. M., and R. M. Keddie. 1963. Nutritional studies on coryneform bacteria from soil and herbage. J. Gen. Microbiol. 31, viii-ix.

14. Gundersen, K., and H. L. Jensen. 1956. A soil bacterium decomposing organic nitro-compounds. Acta Agr. Scand. 6: 100-114.

15. Jensen, H. L. 1934. Studies on saprophytic mycobacteria and corynebacteria. Proc. Linn. Soc. New South Wales 59: 19-64.

16. Kinoshita, S. 1959. The production of amino acids by fermentation processes. Adv. Appl. Microbiol. 1: 201-214.

17. Kuhn, D. A., and M. P. Starr. 1960. Arthrobacter atrocyaneus, n. sp., and its blue pigment. Arch. Mikrobiol. 36: 175-181.

18. Lochhead, A. G. 1958. Two new species of Arthrobacter requiring respectively vitamin B₁₂ and the terregens factor. Arch. Mikrobiol. 31: 163-170.

19. Lochhead, A. G., and M. O. Burton. 1953. An essential bacterial growth factor produced by microbial synthesis. Canad J. Botan. 31: 7-22.

20. Lochhead, A. G., and M. O. Burton. 1955. Qualitative studies of soil nicroorganisms. XII Characteristics of vitamin B₁₂ requiring bacteria. Canad. J. Microbiol. 1: 319-330.

21. Morris, J. G. 1960. Studies on the metabolism of Arthrobacter globiformis. J. Gen. Microbiol. 22: 564-582.

22. Mulder, E. G., M. H. Deinema, W. L. van Veen, and L. P. T. M. Zevenhuizen. 1962. Polysaccharides, lipids and poly-β-hydroxybutyrate in microorganisms. Rec. Trav. Chim. Pays-Bas 81: 797-809.

23. Müller, J. 1957. Untersuchungen zur Morphologie und Physiologie der Corynebakterien. Arch. Mikrobiol. 27: 105-124.

24. Sacks, L. E. 1954. Observations on the morphogenesis of Arthrobacter citreus, spec. nov. J. Bacteriol. 67: 342-345.

25. Schertz, G., and R. Schweisfurth. 1963. Halbtechnische Versuche über die biologische Reinigung von Kokereiabwässern nach dem Nocardia-Verfahren. Gesundheits-Ingenieur 84: 145-149.

26. Shiio, J., S. J. Otsuka, and M. Takahashi. 1962. Effect of biotin on the bacterial formation of glutamic acid. J. Biochem. Tokyo 51: 56-62.

27. Starr, M. P., and D. A. Kuhn. 1962. On the origin of V forms in Arthrobacter atrocyaneus. Arch. Mikrobiol. 42: 289-298.

28. Stevenson, I. L. 1961. Growth studies on Arthrobacter globiformis. Canad. J. Microbiol. 7: 569-575.

29. Stevenson, I. L. 1962. Growth studies on Arthrobacter globiformis II. Changes in macromolecular levels during growth. Canad. J. Microbiol., 8: 655-661.

30. Sundman, V. 1958. Morphological comparison of some Arthrobacter species. Canad. J. Microbiol. 4: 221-224.

31. Taylor, C. B. 1938. Further studies of Bacterium globiforme and the incidence of this type of organism in Canadian soils. Soil Sci., 46: 307-320.

32. Topping, L. E. 1937. The predominant micro-organisms in soil. I. Description and classification of the organisms. Zentr. Bakt. Parasitenk. Abt. II. 97: 289-304.

33. Veldkamp, H. 1962. Glutamic acid producing Arthrobacter spec. Abstr. VIIIth Intern. Congr. Microbiol., C 21.1.

34. Veldkamp, H., G. van den Berg, and L. P. T. M. Zevenhuizen. 1963. Glutamic acid production by Arthrobacter globiformis. Antonie van Leeuwenhoek 29: 35-51.

DISCUSSION

Mr. Frankenfeld (Esso Research): Is it typical of Arthrobacter not to utilize fatty acids?

Dr. Mulder: Some of the Arthrobacter strains tested were found to be able to utilize acetate; higher fatty acids have not been tested.

Mr. Frankenfeld: Do you think they will not attack paraffins?

Dr. Mulder: Paraffins are frequently attacked by mycobacteria, organisms morphologically resembling arthrobacters. It is unknown whether or not arthrobacters with paraffin-decomposing capacities occur in soil or in activated sludge.

Dr. Wuhrmann (Swiss Federal Tech. Inst.): I can confirm
some of the observations of Dr. Mulder on the occurrence of
these organisms in activated sludge. We observed a rich formation—nearly an enrichment culture—of these arthrobacters,
in the form of a slight foam, under certain operating conditions;
namely, when a treatment plant was starting to nitrify heavily,
these arthrobacters appeared in the form of light flocs, and
each floc was carried up by a gas bubble, which was nitrogen.
The isolate did not denitrify.

I should like to know what ecological conditions may be
responsible for the heavy growth of these organisms under
these particular conditions, and whether you have isolated
strains which are active denitrifiers.

Dr. Mulder: I cannot tell what was happening under those
conditions. Denitrifying arthrobacters have not yet been found
in our collection of strains. Formation of nitrite from nitrate
is a rather common feature.

Dr. Louise Potter (Windham College): Are some of your
isolates chromogenic? And what color?

Dr. Mulder: The colonies of most Arthrobacter strains
are cream-colored and sometimes yellow. The strains from
activated sludge and from cheese are sometimes pink. The
pink strains from activated sludge often attack phenols.

Dr. John Sieburth (Univ. of Rhode Is.): Among bacteria
which we isolated from Narragansett Bay, Rhode Island, during
the last several years, there was a high percentage of Arthrobacter. It took us a long time to realize what they were. Now
that we know, in going over our collections from the ocean, we
find that a very high percentage of our cultures from, say, 500
miles at sea are composed of Arthrobacter and they were obtained, not only from surface waters, but at depths exceeding
1000 meters.

In answer to the question about fatty acids, using the usual
method of Tween 80 lysis, we did not detect lipolytic organisms.
However, they will utilize Tween 80 in the presence of amino
acids, but with ammonia or nitrate they will not. When amino
acids are added the organisms will break down fatty acids.

Besides lipolysis, we noticed the life cycle forms can be
caused, say, overnight by incubating cultures in a thermograd-
ient block, similar to those in use at Scripps by Dr. ZoBell.
We find the Gram-negative pleomorphic forms occurring at

about 9 C and lower; on the space between 20 and 26 C, we find the coccus forms; and around 32 to 34 C, we find the Gram-positive rods. We can, therefore, get all the morphological types by temperature control. When we change nutrients, we can also alter morphology.

I think these must be very important organisms, especially when we can grow them on parts per million of organic matter.

Dr. Mulder: This group of organisms indeed is very important in nature. Types different from those which I have discussed may be found. For instance, nitrogen-fixing arthrobacters have been isolated by Smyk and Ettlinger (1963). Katznelson and collaborators (1962) have found nitrifying arthrobacters.

The organisms which were able to decompose Tween 80 in our experiments were tested in the presence of yeast extract. Nothing can be said as to the ability of these strains to utilize fatty acids for growth.

Chairman Seeley (Cornell Univ.): Dr. Mulder, have you been able to alter the morphological sequence that you showed us? Can you make a rod change into a coccus and a coccus to a rod?

Dr. Mulder: Yes. Under poor nutritional conditions arthrobacters form cocci when they are aged 3 or 4 days. When these cocci are transferred to a rich medium, one gets the rod and branched forms which, upon ageing, give rise to large oval cells, cystites, (cf. Mulder and Antheunisse, 1963).

Dr. George Orgel (Colgate-Palmolive): Have you put the cocci into a nutritionally rich medium with avidin, or some other known chemical factor which would, let us say, compete with biotin?

Dr. Mulder: No.

Dr. Orgel: Would you venture a guess as to what might happen? Would you have rods, cocci, or dead cells?

Can one control morphogenesis through specific chemical means, as a further insight into the control mechanism responsible for morphogenesis? I mentioned avidin as a possibility in view of the biotin implication.

Dr. Mulder: The formation of cocci is not particularly connected with biotin. Poor nutritional conditions, including biotin deficiency in biotin-requiring strains or decrease of the pH, result in the formation of cocci. Poor conditions, apparently, are involved but, so far, we do not know what is basically responsible. It is not simply biotin deficiency.

Dr. John A. Winter (Academy of Natural Sciences, Phila.): What are your criteria for deciding whether cultures are arthrobacters? Many of what are called the degenerative nocardia or other mycobacteria are morphologically identical. The slides were startling because I could not tell the difference. Is it the formation of cystites only, or the accumulation of gelatinous materials which is decisive?

Dr. Mulder: The nocardias, in general, form mycelium-like cell masses as compared to Arthrobacter. In the colony form, the arthrobacters generally are smooth and not as dry as nocardias. Compared with the mycobacteria, we have found differences in the Gram reaction. Whether acid fastness and the breakdown of hydrocarbons are always typical characteristics for the mycobacteria is unknown. In the future, we have to test which of our 150 strains belongs more closely to the mycobacteria and which to the Arthrobacter globiformis type.

Dr. Martin Alexander (Cornell Univ.): Would you comment further on your statement that arthrobacter can use lignin?

Dr. Mulder: A study on the decomposition of lignin by arthrobacters has been made in the Department of Microbiology, University of Helsinki; we have not studied lignin decomposition.

LITERATURE CITED IN DISCUSSION

1. Katznelson, H. 1962. Research Report 1959-1962 Microbiology Research Institute, Central Experimental Farm, Ottawa.

2. Mulder, E. G., and J. Antheunisse. 1963. Morphologie, physiologie et écologie des Arthrobacter. Ann. Inst. Pasteur 105, 46-74.

3. Smyk, B., and L. Ettlinger. 1963. Récherches sur quelques éspèces d'Arthrobacter fixatrices d'azote isolées des roches karstiques alpines. Ann. Inst. Pasteur 105, 341-348.

14

ECOLOGY AND PHYSIOLOGY OF
THE PHOTOSYNTHETIC BACTERIA

E. S. Lindstrom
Department of Microbiology
The Pennsylvania State University

In writing this brief essay I felt that a general approach would be appropriate, though the imprecision of general-izations may offend some of the specialists in their own areas of competence. The photosynthetic bacteria have not yet be-come popular with the molecular biologists in their studies of cellular genetics and metabolic control. They have, however, provided many useful insights, in comparative studies, into both green plant and bacterial photosyntheses. Recently, these organisms have provided biological material attractive to the physicists and physical chemists who are studying the so-called primary photochemical act of photosynthesis. Their exciting results will be discussed here, but only briefly, as they are more of biochemical than of ecological interest.

In such an informal essay as I am attempting, the reference situation becomes a problem. Most of the information reported here is derived from published reports, but some comes from what I have heard, or been told at meetings, and some comes from unpublished (and unconfirmed) information from me or from graduate students working in my laboratory. However, recent reviews by Van Niel (1), Stanier (2), Gest and Kamen (3), and by Lascelles (4) and a book edited by Vernon and San Pietro (5) cover all the areas of current physiological interest.

I propose, first, to present what I know about the ecology of the photosynthetic bacteria, then to show how their physio-logy is related to their ecology, and then to give my impression of their place in aquatic microbiology.

What are these photosynthetic bacteria? They are a collection of microorganisms with widely varying metabolism, grouped by virtue of their possession of a photometabolism. The composition of the group ranges from strict anaerobes to organisms able to utilize oxygen. Their photometabolism may be keyed either to reduced carbon or to reduced sulfur, though many organisms can oxidize photochemically either reduced carbon or sulfur. They vary from strict photoautotrophs to facultative photoheterotrophs. All the common types of cell morphology can be found among the photosynthetic bacteria though the short, Gram-negative rod is, perhaps, most common.

The main taxonomic groups of the photosynthetic bacteria are listed in Table 1. The Rhodobacteriineae are presently classified in Bergey's manual in the Pseudomonadales. In aquatic environments, the purple non-sulfur bacteria perhaps predominate. The colors referred to represent the visually predominating photosynthetic pigment. The Athiorhodaceae usually require an organic electron donor for photosynthesis. The reason for this requirement will be discussed later. This electron donor is usually organic and, though these organisms have the non-discriminatory appetite typical of a Pseudomonas, at least one can use thiosulfate as an electron donor. The Athiorhodaceae differ in their tolerance for oxygen; some are quite sensitive to the presence of air, whereas others are able to function in the dark using an active, oxidative metabolism. All of these organisms have growth factor requirements for biotin, nicotinic acid, p-aminobenzoic acid, etc.

The Thiorhodaceae can use either reduced carbon or reduced sulfur compounds as the electron donors. The usual organic acids function well as reduced carbon, and sulfide or thiosulfate are used as sulfur electron donors. The sulfur purple bacteria are universally oxygen-sensitive and can grow in a strictly inorganic environment.

The Chlorobacteriaceae have an even more restricted metabolism. Though they can be tricked into using acetate, their usual electron donor is sulfide. The green photosynthetic bacteria are quite oxygen-sensitive and grow as strict photoautotrophs.

Why are such diverse groups of organisms classified together? They have several features in common that suggest that such a grouping is correct (6). As seen in Fig. 1, for example, these organisms have polar flagella. It is a picture of Rhodospirillum rubrum, one of the more popularly cultivated members of the tribe.

It is a long spiral, 1μ x 10μ, which is actively and persistently motile by virtue of the pseudomonas-like polar

Table 1. Rhodobacteriineae

Family	Usual electron donor	Respiratory metabolism	Growth factor requirement
Athiorhodaceae (Non-sulfur purple)	Carbon	Yes	Yes
Thiorhodaceae (Sulfur-purple)	Carbon and/or Sulfur	No	No
Chlorobacteriaceae (Green)	Sulfur	No	No

flagella. A second feature in common with the Pseudomonas is the possession of the dehydrative type of glucose-splitting, first found in Doudoroff's and Wood's laboratories (11).

Perhaps the most convincing evidence for such a grouping is the possession by all of these organisms of a photosynthetic metabolism. This photosynthetic metabolism is based on chlorophyll, carotenoids, cytochromes, and quinones and is similar to the photosynthesis of green plants; however, the three different bacteriochlorophylls are distinct from the chlorophylls a and b of green plants, and the carotenoids of bacteria are all aliphatic, in contrast to those of green plants. So, for reasons of both morphology and physiology, the photosynthetic bacteria are grouped with the Pseudomonas. They are grouped together because they have a similar photochemical metabolism that is distinct, but not greatly different, from plant photosynthesis, as we understand it.

Where are these photosynthetic bacteria found naturally? Obviously, to be included in this symposium they must be of aquatic origin. The photosynthetic bacteria are normally found in both fresh water and marine environments. Though these organisms have been isolated from soil (Dondero, personal communication), the soil is not a favorable region for their existence, as they need both light and anaerobic conditions, a situation common in water but seldom realized in the soil.

The photosynthetic bacteria are what I consider to be secondary anaerobes. My use of this term is illustrated in Fig. 2. The photosynthetics apparently thrive on the low molecular weight products of prior anaerobic decomposition of organic matter. They are able to utilize organic acids, alcohols, NH_4,

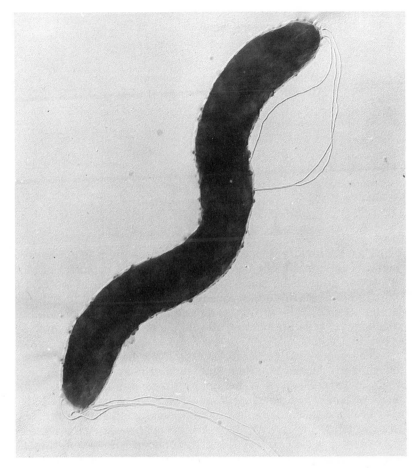

Fig. 1—Electron photomicrograph of Rhodospirillum rubrum; by permission of D.D. Hickman and A.W. Frenkel, The Journal of Biophysical and Biochemical Cytology, II, No. 2, 277-284, Fig. 2.

H S, that are usually depot products of heterotrophic metabolism. For a heterotrophic organism to use acetate or ammonium, it must be able to oxidize or dismute these molecules to get energy, something impossible for them under anaerobic conditions.

How can these photosynthetic organisms use anaerobically these reduced substances that can be used only by heterotrophic aerobes? The heterotroph requires oxygen for the metabolism of reduced substances, as oxygen provides a depot for the electron removal necessary in heterotrophic energy metabolism. However, the photosynthetic bacteria are able to use

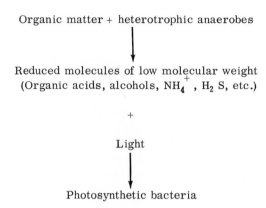

Fig. 2. Ecological relationships of photosynthetic bacteria.

these anaerobically, because light provides them with energy.
Light, thus, can also be considered to provide potential oxidizing power so that the photosynthetic bacteria can, in effect,
oxidatively assimilate these reduced molecules under anaerobic conditions. This ability, which no other group of organisms
possesses, gives the photosynthetic bacteria their own, private
ecological niche.

The ecological niche supporting these bacteria is widely
distributed. I have isolated photosynthetic bacteria from the
muds of Lake Mendota in Madison, Wisconsin, as well as from
muds of ponds and streams in central Pennsylvania. We have
also isolated these organisms from running stream water.
Most of the isolates have been Athiorhodaceae, organisms using organic, but not sulfur, electron donors. However, this
was the consequence of our enrichment techniques and may
not represent a true picture. Nevertheless, I suspect there is
more reduced carbon than reduced sulfur in these streams, so
our results may not be very incorrect.

To isolate photosynthetic bacteria, the ecological niche is
reproduced crudely in the laboratory (7). Mud or water is
added to a medium that will support active, anaerobic, heterotrophic growth. Yeast extract, glucose-nitrate, or almost any
bacteriological medium will do. The closed bottles are incubated under incandescent illumination at about 25 C. After 2
to 14 days, a positive enrichment will announce itself by be-
coming colored as the result of the secondary growth of the
photosynthetic bacteria. The usual colors range from brown
to red. The positive enrichment is then cycled through an organic acid-ammonium medium and incubated in the light to

favor the growth of the photosynthetics. After several cycles, the photosynthetics can be isolated in pure culture, using agar shake tubes. As these organisms are traditionally isolated by such enrichments, it is hard to give meaningful numbers for their occurrence in normal surface waters. However, in some of our local ponds, the majority of enrichments yield positive cultures of Athiorhodaceae, so they are not unusual members of the aquatic environment.

The ultimate fate of the nutrients assimilated by the photosynthetic bacteria is known to be almost solely new cullular material, though the physiology of these many conversions is ill-understood. In the light, from which they derive energy, the carbon, nitrogen, and, to a certain extent, the sulfur is assimilated with about 100 per cent efficiency. Only in the dark, where some photosynthetics carry on a heterotrophic metabolism, is any carbon lost as CO_2. But I doubt whether these organisms compete effectively in the dark. Thus, the photosynthetic bacteria make more photosynthetic bacteria in the light with amazing efficiency, assimilating the products of heterotrophic decomposition. In the light, they effectively reverse the effect of the majority of the microorganisms which specialize in decomposition. So the ultimate fate of the carbon, nitrogen, etc., of the photosynthetic bacteria depends on whatever protozoa ingest them or whatever microorganisms use the products of their lysis.

Since the physiology of any organism reflects its usual ecological niche, the photosynthetic bacteria will reflect their role as secondary anaerobes in their metabolism. However, an even more profound influence on their physiology is their possession of a mechanism for getting energy from light (8). All of the photosynthetic bacteria possess the chlorophyll, carotenoids, cytochromes, quinones, etc., associated with the chloroplasts of higher plants.

In the absorption spectrum of an extract of Rhodospirillum rubrum (Fig. 3), the major areas of light energy absorption for bacteriochlorophyll are 8800 A, 8000 A, 5900 A, and 3700 A. The carotenoids absorb energy in the 5000 A area, whereas the presence of cytochrome is shown by the peak at 5500 A, although other cytochromes are masked by the carotenoid peaks. These photosynthetic pigments are localized in the cell membranes of the bacteria. With the low light intensities found in muds, etc., the area for light absorption per cell is increased by the packing of the cell with apparently pinched-off membranes. These membrane vesicles are called chromatophores and are capable of energy transduction (9). With the higher

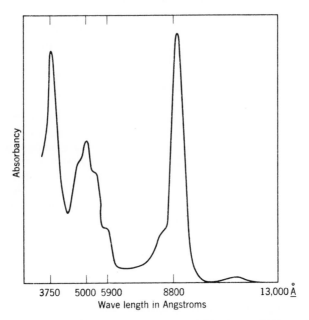

Fig. 3—Absorption spectrum of extract of Rhodospirillum rubrum.

light intensities used in laboratory culture of these microorganisms, these vesicles are located at the inside surface of
the plasma membrane.

The chromatophore can be considered as being analogous
to the chloroplast of green plants, as both are energy trans-
ducers; however, the chromatophore is a simpler structure
that contains none of the CO_2^- fixing enzymes or other mechanisms for carbohydrate synthesis. The bacteriochlorophyll
absorbs in the far red region in contrast to the green absorption of plant chlorophylls.

Inasmuch as photosynthetic bacteria have chlorophylls and
carotenoids, how similar is their photosynthesis to that of
green plants? The two processes are similar in outline and
outcome, but are different in detail. Some of the similarities
and differences are summarized in Fig. 4. The interaction of
light and chlorophyll or of light and bacteriochlorophyll can be
considered to cause a separation of electrical charges. Electrons are concentrated in one region, the reducing site, creat-
ing a different region of electron deficiency, the oxidizing site.
At the reducing site, the concentration of electrons may result

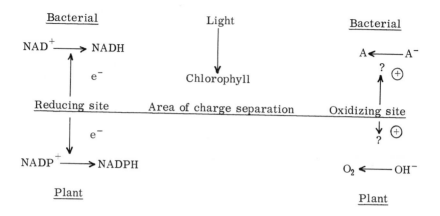

Fig. 4. Comparison of plant and bacterial photosyntheses.

NAD^+ and NADH - oxidized and reduced nicotine adenine
dinucleotide

$NADP^+$ and NADPH - oxidized and reduced nicotine adenine
dinucleotide phosphate

A^- - External electron donor required in bacterial photosynthesis

in the eventual enzymatic reduction of pyridine nucleotide,
NAD^+ (nicotine adenine dinucleotide), in the bacterial system
and NADP (nicotine adenine dinucleotide phosphate) in the
green plant. At the oxidizing site, the metabolic events are
less well understood. In the green plant, the oxidizing power
is apparently dissipated through oxygen evolution. In the bacteria, this potentially damaging oxidizing power is, presumably, detoxified through the oxidation of the obligatory external
electron donor, H_2A. Thus, in both types of photosyntheses,
light generates an electron flow. The electrons are used to
reduce pyridine nucleotides, or to react with the oxidizing site
through an electron transport system, resulting in the trapping of energy in ATP (adenosine triphosphate) via photosynthetic phosphorylation. The details of the electron transport
mechanism of photosynthetic phosphorylation have been found
to be quite similar to those of oxidative phosphorylation. The
residual oxidizing power is removed via oxygen evolution in
the plant, or via an oxidation of an electron donor in the bacteria.

What are the physiological gains from such an electron
flow? The interaction of light and bacteriochlorophyll initiates
the electron flow which also involves a number of electron
carriers (10), such as the cytochromes, reactions 1 and 2 (Fig.
5). However, from the standpoint of the cell, the important

1. Oxidation of bacteriochlorophyll: $BChl + light \rightarrow BChl^+ + e^-$

2. Oxidation of cytochrome: $Cyt^{++} + BChl^+ \rightarrow Cyt^{+++} + BChl$

3. Reduction of nucleotide: $NAD^+ + H^+ + 2e^- \rightarrow NADH$

4. Esterification of phosphate: $ADP + Pi + light \rightarrow ATP$

5. Reduction of sulfate: $SO_4^= + light \rightarrow SO_3^=$

Fig. 5. Photophysical and photochemical reactions
of photosynthetic bacteria*

BChl	Bacteriochlorophyll
Cyt	Cytochrome of the "C" type in spectrum
NAD^+	Oxidized nicotine adenine dinucleotide
NADH	Reduced nicotine adenine dinucleotide
ADP	Adenosine diphosphate
Pi	Inorganic (ortho) phosphate
ATP	Adenosine triphosphate

* From Frenkel (10).

gains are from the photoreduction of NAD^+ and from the photosynthetic esterification of phosphate, as shown in reactions 3
and 4. In effect, light generates NADH and ATP, which the cell
uses to drive its metabolism. This gives the cell almost an
excess of energy in the light and frees the carbohydrate metabolism to concentrate on synthetic reactions, not on the usual
energy-yielding reactions of the heterotroph. Light energy
also participates in other less pivotal, physiological reactions
such as the reduction of sulfate (reaction 5, Fig. 5).

It should be emphasized further, that the reaction of CO_2-
fixation, so closely related to photosynthesis in the chloroplast
of green plants, is only distantly related to bacterial photosynthesis. In these microorganisms, the NADH and ATP are ex-
ported out into the cytoplasm, where comparatively little CO_2-
fixation occurs if the cell is using an organic electron donor.

How do the other areas of carbohydrate metabolism of the
photosynthetic bacteria reflect the possession of the photometabolism by the cell and the fact that they are secondary anaerobes? Their identity as secondary anaerobes is reflected, in
the Athiorhodaceae, by their ability, typical of many pseudomonads, to use a wide variety of low molecular weight organic
acids, alcohols, etc. With the other two groups, low molecular
weight reduced sulfur compounds may be used in place of the
organic acids. The effect of the photometabolism is dually
shown: the carbohydrate ends solely as new cells and the

Table 2. Carbohydrate metabolism of photosynthetic bacteria

Group	EMP	WD	EDW	BC	C_3+C_1	TCA	KK
Athiorhodaceae	+	+	+	+	+	+	$\pm$
Thiorhodaceae	+	+	+	+	+	+	?
Chlorobacteriaceae	+ (?)		+ (?)	+ (?)	+	?	+	?

EMP	(Embden - Meyerhoff - Parnas) - Glucose splitting
WD	(Warburg - Dickens) - Glucose oxidation
EDW	(Entner - Doudoroff - Wood) - Glucose oxidation
BC	(Benson - Calvin) - Carbon dioxide fixation
C_3+C_1	Carbon dioxide fixation via usual heterotrophic pathway
TCA	(Krebs) Tricarboxylic acid cycle
KK	(Krebs - Kornberg) Glyoxylate by-pass

carbohydrate metabolism is keyed to synthesis, not to energy
release. The carbohydrate metabolism of the three groups of
photosynthetic bacteria is summarized in Table 2.

Two of the three groups have been shown to possess three
ways of metabolizing glucose (11, 12). The hexosediphosphate
sequence (Embden-Meyerhoff-Parnas), the hexose monophosphate (Warburg-Dickens), and the dehydrative attack found
usually in pseudomonads (Entner-Doudoroff-Wood) have been
shown in the Athiorhodaceae and Thiorhodaceae. However,
some strains of Rhodopseudomonas lack aldolase, the key enzyme in the EMP system. The presence of the EMP, HMP, and
EDW systems in the green sulfur bacteria is presumed. However, none of these organisms, apparently, uses glucose in its
natural habitat, probably because the heterotrophs utilize it
first. To get glucose utilization in laboratory culture, the
molar glucose concentration must be raised above that concentration used for good utilization of organic acids. Perhaps the
glucose metabolism of these organisms is keyed more to the
biosynthetic pathways than to catabolic energy-yielding reactions, so that the glucose permeation system is not active.

The photosynthetic bacteria are able to fix carbon dioxide
by both the Benson-Calvin (12) cycle ($C_5 + C_1 \longrightarrow 2C_3$) of
green plants and the $C_3 + C_1$ condensation more typical of heterotrophs. These fixations, mediated by soluble enzyme systems, are of varying importance. With the green or purple
sulfur bacteria, growing in a strictly inorganic medium, they
represent the main pathways for carbon assimilation for
growth. However, when the purple non-sulfurs or the purple
sulfurs grow at the expense of an organic electron donor, such

as malate, the majority of the cell carbon comes from the organic electron donor, such as malate. Under these conditions,
CO_2-fixation serves primarily to prevent the loss of any carbon which may come from a needed decarboxylation. When
growing in an organic environment, the $C_3 + C_1$ type of fixation
is usually quantitatively more significant in the photosynthetic
bacteria than the $C_5 + C_1$, which occurs, but to a much lesser
extent. Many of these organisms often exist in an area rich in
organic matter, where the fixation of carbon dioxide is not an
essential process. With photosynthetic bacteria, CO_2-fixation
is the main pathway of carbon assimilation only when both the
organism and the environment require fixation.

     In areas where organic matter decomposes, organic acids
and alcohols abound. For two groups of photosynthetic bacteria, these provide the external electron donors which permit
most rapid growth in laboratory culture. The occurrence of
the Krebs tricarboxylic acid cycle (TCA) has been demonstrated in several photosynthetic bacteria (13), and is inferred in
others by their ability to assimilate organic acids and alcohols
rapidly. There is some evidence that this TCA cycle may be
an anaerobic deviant involving citramalate in Chromatium and
Rhodospirillum. Further evidence for the occurrence of this
cycle is provided by the ability of all these organisms to grow
while fixing atmospheric N_2. Under these conditions, all the
amino acids must be synthesized, requiring the participation
of the TCA cycle. The glyoxylate by-pass has been reported
in Rhodopseudomonas, but may not be present in all strains of
Rhodospirillum. The last two columns of Table 2 summarize
the information that all three groups have the TCA cycle, but
show that the glyoxylate by-pass has been demonstrated in
only one genus.

     The abundance of photochemically produced energy prob-
ably makes these reaction sequences more important for generating useful synthetic carbon skeletons than for energy generation. These organisms often behave as though carbon for
synthesis, and not energy, is limiting for growth.

     Grown in the light, the photosynthetic bacteria are able to
assimilate carbohydrates completely. They are able to do this
as anaerobes because the energy for assimilation is provided
by light, and not from the catabolism of carbohydrates. The
purple non-sulfur bacteria that can grow in the dark utilize
carbohydrates by oxidizing or fermenting them, much as do
heterotrophs (14). Under these conditions the efficiency of
growth is much reduced, and acidic by-products may accumulate, but the photosynthetics can survive by such heterotrophic

mechanisms. However, they are probably at a competitive dis-
advantage in the dark, as it is difficult to isolate them except
under cultural conditions where they can use their photometabolism. Thus their "normal" carbohydrate metabolism, in contrast to that of other anaerobes, is keyed to synthesis, and not
to the extraction of both energy and useful fragments from the
carbonaceous substrate.

One of the usual products of the anaerobic decomposition
of organic matter is reduced sulfur. Members of the Thiorhodaceae and Chlorobacteriaceae are able to use these reduced
sulfur compounds as the external electron donors in their
photosyntheses. Surprisingly, the knowledge of the details of
this long-known photosynthetic sulfur oxidation is meager.
Elemental sulfur granules accumulate as transitory intermediates in some of these organisms, and polythionates are utilized
(15). The pathways of sulfur oxidation in these photosynthetic
organisms are apparently similar to the better known sulfur
oxidations of the chemosynthetic microorganisms, although
these photosynthetic bacteria derive energy from light and not
from these oxidations which, again, probably represent a method for detoxifying the photooxidant. More is known about the
less unique sulfate metabolism of the Athiorhodaceae (16). As
shown in Fig. 6, Rhodospirillum has been shown to activate sulfate, using the classical Robbins-Lipmann reaction (17). Phos-
phoadenosine phosphosulfate (PAPS) can be formed from ATP
in the dark, or from ATP synthesized in the light via photophos-
phorylation. Light has also been shown to reduce sulfate to a
volatile form of sulfur but the intermediates of this reaction
are unknown.

	Light	Dark
Activation	$ADP + Pi + SO_4^= \rightarrow PAPS$	$ATP + SO_4^= \rightarrow PAPS$
Reduction	$SO_4^= + e^- \rightarrow (SO_3^=)$	?

Fig. 6. Sulfate metabolism of rhodospirillum.

ADP	Adenosine diphosphate
Pi	Inorganic (ortho) phosphate
PAPS	Phosphoadenosine phosphosulfate
ATP	Adenosine triphosphate

There are several gases that are characteristic of anaerobic decomposition. The photosynthetic bacteria are able to
metabolize both CO_2 and H_2. As already pointed out, CO_2-
fixation is quantitatively more important in the Chlorobacteriaceae and Thiorhodaceae, because they are capable of a strict
inorganic existence. These must assimilate CO_2 at a rate sufficient to maintain growth. In contrast, the Athiorhodaceae,
though able to fix significant amounts of CO_2, usually acquire
most of their carbon via the photosynthetic assimilation of alcohols and acids. These organisms are also able to assimilate
H_2, presumably as a substitute for the organic electron donor.
Some are capable of growing in a CO_2 and H_2 environment,
provided adequate nitrogen and mineral sources are available.
Some photosynthetic bacteria are able to photoevolve H_2 (18).
There is good evidence that the throwing away of this potentially energy-rich hydrogen gas is a safety valve which the cell
uses to prevent the accumulation of too much energy within the
cell, when the cell is in the light and in an energy-rich medium.
The photosynthetic bacteria possess a versatile metabolism of
gases, all being able to use CO_2, H_2, and N_2 in the light, and
some can use O_2 in the dark.

Another usual product of anaerobic decomposition is ammonium. All photosynthetic bacteria can use ammonium as a
sole nitrogen source (Table 3). These organisms are able to
fix atmospheric nitrogen, using the energy they derive from
photosynthesis (19). Therefore, their nitrogen requirements
can be met easily by either the ammonium ion or the N_2 in
their usual environment. At least one group can assimilate
amino acids. In laboratory culture, the addition of amino
acids accelerates their relatively slow growth rate. Though
anaerobes, these organisms, when grown in the light, behave
nutritionally like aerobes since carbon, not energy, is growth-

Table 3. Nitrogen metabolism of photosynthetic bacteria

Group	Process		
	NH_4^+ Assimilation	N_2 Fixation	Amino acid Assimilation
Athiorhodaceae	+	+	+
Thiorhodaceae	+	+	−
Chlorobacteriaceae	+	+	−

limiting. None of the photosynthetic bacteria have the short generation time in pure culture, even in the presence of casein hydrolysate or yeast extract, that we associate with Pseudo-monas (20) in spite of nutritional studies to develop an optimal medium. Whether the slow growth rate is a reflection of our ignorance, or the consequence of an elaborate photosynthetic metabolism, is not known.

What use could be made of these photosynthetic bacteria in a domesticated aquatic environment? If their growth rate in nature is as low as in laboratory culture, and if their numbers are as low as the requirement for enrichment for isolation indicates, then they cannot carry out rapid conversions. The photosynthetic bacteria are able to assimilate a wide variety of low molecular weight carbon- and sulfur-containing molecules. The photosynthetic bacteria would be overgrown by the more aggressive heterotrophs in the usual aerobic aquatic environment. I do not know if they can metabolize any of the problem molecules from domestic or industrial wastes, even though they are related to the pseudomonads. If they do, they probably would be of little use in decreasing the biochemical oxygen demand because their photometabolism results in the assimilation, not in the oxidation of carbon or sulfur. If these photosynthetic bacteria were particularly attractive to some protozoan, or other grazing fauna, they might have a future in sanitary microbiology, but I suspect they will continue to be more interesting to those of us who wish to understand better the process of photosynthesis.

ACKNOWLEDGEMENT

I wish to acknowledge support, for our investigations into the photometabolism of Rhodospirillum, by the Pennsylvania Agricultural Experiment Station, the National Science Foundation, and the Air Force Office of Scientific Research.

LITERATURE CITED

1. Van Niel, C. B. 1962. The present status of the comparative study of photosynthesis. Ann. Rev. Plant. Physiol. 13: 1-26.

2. Stanier, R. Y. 1961. Photosynthetic mechanisms in bacteria and plants: development of a unitary concept. Bac-

teriol. Revs. 25: 1-17.

3. Gest, H. and M. D. Kamen. 1960. The photosynthetic bacteria. Handbuch der Pflanzenphysiologie 5: 568-612.

4. Lascelles, J. 1962. The chromatophores of photosynthetic bacteria. J. Gen. Microbiol. 29: 47-52.

5. Gest, H., A. San Pietro and L. P. Vernon, editors. 1963. Bacterial photosynthesis. Antioch Press, Yellow Springs, Ohio.

6. Stanier, R. Y. and C. B. Van Niel. 1962. The concept of a bacterium. Archiv. f. Mikrobiol. 42: 17-35.

7. Van Niel, C. B. 1944. The culture, general physiology, morphology, and classification of the non-sulfur purple and brown bacteria. Bacteriol. Revs. 8: 1-118.

8. Clayton, R. K. 1962. Symposium on autotrophy. III. Recent developments in photosynthesis. Bacteriol. Revs. 26: 151-164.

9. Cohen-Bazire, G. and R. Kunisawa. 1963. The fine structure of Rhodospirillum rubrum. J. Cell. Biol. 16: 401-409.

10. Frenkel, A. W. 1959. Light-induced reactions of bacterial chromatophores and their relation to photosynthesis. Ann. Rev. Plant. Physiol. 10: 53-70.

11. Szymona, M. and M. Doudoroff. 1960. Carbohydrate metabolism in Rhodopseudomonas spheroides. J. Gen. Microbiol. 22: 167-183.

12. Fuller, R. C., R. M. Smillie, E. C. Sisler, and H. K. Kornberg. 1961. Carbon metabolism in Chromatium. J. Biol. Chem. 236: 2140-2149.

13. Eisenberg, M. A. 1953. The tricarboxylic acid cycle in Rhodospirillum rubrum. J. Biol. Chem. 203: 815-836.

14. Kohlmiller, E. F. and H. Gest. 1951. A comparative study of the light and dark fermentations of organic acids by Rhodospirillum rubrum. J. Bacteriol. 61: 269-282.

15. Peck, H. D., Jr. 1962. Symposium on metabolism of inorganic compounds. V. Comparative metabolism of inorganic sulfur compounds in microorganisms. Bacteriol. Revs. 26: 67-94.

16. Peck, H. D., Jr. 1961. Enzymatic basis for assimilatory and dissimilatory sulfate reduction. J. Bacteriol. 82: 933-939.

17. Ibanez, M. L. and E. S. Lindstrom. 1962. Metabolism of sulfate by the chromatophore of Rhodospirillum. J. Bacteriol. 84: 451-455.

18. Gest, H., J. G. Ormerod and K. S. Ormerod. 1962. Photometabolism of Rhodospirillum rubrum: Light-dependent dissimilation of organic compounds to carbon dioxide and molecular hydrogen by an anaerobic citric acid cycle. Arch. Biochem. Biophys. 97: 21-33.

19. Lindstrom, E. S., J. W. Newton, and P. W. Wilson. 1952. The relationship between photosynthesis and nitrogen fixation. Proc. Nat. Acad. Sci. 38: 392-396.

20. Stanier, R. Y., M. Doudoroff, R. Kunisawa, and R. Contopoulou. 1959. The role of organic substrates in bacterial photosynthesis. Proc. Nat. Acad. Sci. 45: 1246-1260.

DISCUSSION

Dr. Richard Green (Washington State Univ.): The purple sulfur bacterium, Chromatium, is of interest in anaerobic lagoons. They grow in large numbers, turning the lagoons purple. They have been reported in several types of lagoons: those with petroleum wastes, those handling meat packing wastes, and also those with ordinary sewage. We have seen maximum growth of the Chromatium in 24 to 48 hours. Therefore, it may have some significance in those environments.

Dr. Lindstrom: At Pymatuning reservoir, in the northwestern part of Pennsylvania, significant amounts of nitrogen are fixed by the photosynthetic bacteria, according to evidence obtained by workers at the University of Pittsburgh.
There is a bay in Lake Mendota, in Madison, where a sulfur spring discharges. One can pick up Chromatium almost by the handful. However, I was surprised to be able to isolate them at all from streams. They are there in numbers detectable with enrichment cultures, but not with plates or similar inoculations.

Dr. Seeley (Cornell Univ.): The carotenoid pigments, in the past, were thought to be excess baggage in the photosyn-

thetics, but there is evidence that they also aid in trapping
light of different wavelengths. Would you comment on the extra advantage these might give to photosynthetic organisms?

Dr. Lindstrom: We happen to be working on the metabolism of carotenoid-deficient photosynthetic bacteria. These
mutants are fairly easy to use. Comparing the photometabolism of normal and mutant cells, it is apparent that carotenoids
can act as accessory pigments to a certain extent. We can get
photooxidative activity by using light, not only at 8000 A, which
is the main absorption frequency of bacteriochlorphyll, but also
with light at about 5000 A, the region of carotenoid absorption.
Thus these carotenoids are active as energy receptors. They
are also apparently involved in the metabolism of the photooxidant. The carotenoid-less cells of Rhodopseudomonas are
much more active in the photooxidation of reduced indophenol
than the ones with the normal carotenoid content, suggesting
that the carotenoids react with the photoxidant. But the present dogma is that the carotenoids function primarily as "trip-
let state quenchers" of the bacteriochlorophyll. We think that
we understand what the chlorophyll does, but the carotenoids,
in spite of a lot of good work, are really an ill-understood
group of pigments.

Dr. Antonio Romano (Univ. of Cincinnati): Do I understand
that the carotenoid-less mutants absorb principally around
6600 A?

Dr. Lindstrom: No. The carotenoid-containing organisms
have an absorption peak at about 5000 A. The chlorophyll
gives the 8000 A peak. The photosynthetic bacteria can use
green light, but not very efficiently. However, they can use
green light, and it is apparently the result of the carotenoids
acting as accessory pigments.

Dr. Romano: I do not quite understand. The 8800 A peak
is a chlorophyll peak?

Dr. Lindstrom: Right

Dr. Romano: And even the carotenoid-less mutants also
absorb at 8800 Angstroms?

Dr. Lindstrom: Right

Dr. Samuel Green (Wallerstein Co.): I think one will find that the chromatia exist in New Jersey in little rivulets and ponds off the Rahway River.

To concur with Dr. Green, Oswald has shown that some of the putrefaction of wastes has been significantly decreased by the purple sulfur bacteria in ponds and lagoons.

Dr. Lindstrom: They should act to increase the BOD rather than decrease it. Usually, in the light, they will reduce carbon rather than oxidize it, and if you are trying to clean up a stream I think you want the reverse process.

Dr. Orgel (Colgate Palmolive): I was particularly interested to hear about the CO_2-hydrogen utilizing organisms. Do these organisms have an active hydrogenating system?

Dr. Lindstrom: By all means.

Dr. Orgel: And does photosynthesis occur, in the strict sense, only as a light reaction, or will they fix CO_2 reductively in the dark?

Dr. Lindstrom: There will be a little CO_2-fixation in the dark, just as with any heterotroph, such as Escherichia coli.

Dr. Orgel: Is hydrogen oxidized under these conditions?

Dr. Lindstrom: The oxidation of hydrogen is light-dependent.

15

PROTISTS, PIGMENTS, AND PHOTOSYNTHESIS

Jerome A. Schiff
Department of Biology
Brandeis University

Photosynthesis is a subject which benefits greatly from a comparative approach. Although the present discussion is devoted mainly to the Protista, and what has been learned from them about photosynthesis, it would be impossible to convey any notion of the modern intellectual framework of photosynthesis without some references to other groups. We shall, therefore, try to document some of the characteristics of protists which have been valuable in the study of photosynthesis and also to place these attributes in the larger synthesis which has come about in the field.

Table 1 lists the groups of photosynthetic Protists together with some representatives which have been used in studies of photosynthesis. The intermixing of botanical and zoological names for the groups is not fortuitous and emphasizes the biological plasticity of the group as far as plant-like and animal-like characteristics are concerned. The definitions of "animal" and "plant" which seem so clear for metaphytes and metazoans break down at this level of evolution. Among the Protists, Chlorella and Scenedesmus lead the group as objects of photosynthetic experimentation, with Chlamydomonas, Euglena, and Porphyridium not far behind. These organisms are what Hutner has called "laboratory weeds"; they grow luxuriantly in uniorganismal culture on defined media under laboratory conditions. Other members of the group are available as seaweeds, and must be collected fresh for use in the laboratory. As more organisms become domesticated, we can expect the work on them to increase tremendously.

298

TABLE 1: Some genera of the Protista and Monera which
          have been popular in research on photosynthesis

Protista	
Chlorophyta (green algae)	Chlorella, Scenedesmus, Chlamy-domonas, Ulva, Spirogyra
Euglenophyta	Euglena Gracilis
Chrysophyta (Chrysomonads)	Ochromonas
Bacillariophyta (Diatoms)	Nitzschia, Navicula
Pheophyta (brown algae)	Coilodesme
Rhodophyta (red algae)	Porphyridium, Porphyra
Cryptophyta (Cryptomonads)	Hemiselmis, Cryptomonas, Cyanidium, Sennia
Xanthophyta (yellow algae)	Tribonema, Monodus
Charophyta (Stoneworts)	Nitella, Chara
Pyrrophyta (Dinoflagellates)	Gonyaulax

Monera	
Cyanophyta (blue-green algae)	Anacystis, Chroococcus, Anabaena, Oscillatoria, Nostoc
Schizomycophyta (bacteria)	Rhodospirillum, Chromatium, Rhodopseudomonas, Chlorobium

Table 1 also shows those members of the Monera which
have been popular in photosynthesis research. They differ
from the Protists in lacking obvious cellular organelles at
the level of resolution of the light microscope. In the
Protista, the site of photosynthesis is the chloroplast, an
organelle which exhibits a beautiful and remarkable diversity
among these organisms.

Fig. 1 shows an electron micrograph of a typical chloroplast from Euglena (1) containing lamellae, a pyrenoid, and
a limiting double membrane. Among the Monera, no chloroplasts are found, and the photosynthetic structures are either
simple invaginations of the cell membrane or isolated
lamellae which are not delimited from the surrounding
cytoplasm (2). In spite of this morphological difference between the photosynthetic structures of the Protista and Monera,
the Cyanophyta, or blue-green algae, are usually considered
along with the Protista in discussions of photosynthesis because

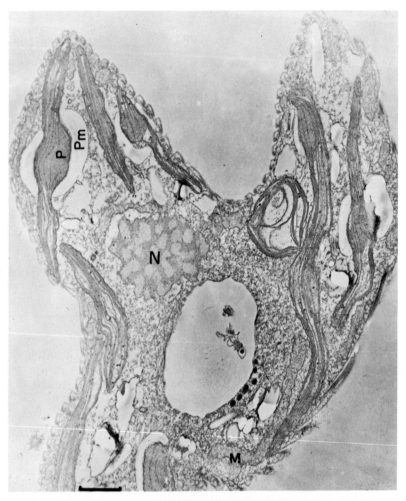

Fig. 1—Electron micrograph of a thin section of <u>Euglena gracilis</u> var. <u>bacillaris</u>, late in chloroplast development, showing chloroplasts containing pyrenoids (P) and paramylum plates (Pm). The nucleus (N) and mitochondria (M) of the cell are also shown. The scale marker indicates one micron.

they all exhibit photosynthetic oxygen evolution. The photosynthetic bacteria, however, constitute a separate physiological group because their photosynthesis does not involve
the formation of molecular oxygen. Indeed, the bacteria
stand out among photosynthetic organisms because of this
characteristic, since higher plants, the Protista, and the
Cyanophyta, all evolve oxygen during photosynthesis.

The usefulness of the protists in photosynthesis research
can be attributed to the extraordinary diversity of photosynthetic pigments to be found in this group. Table 2 shows
that the common denominator of all oxygen-evolving photo-
synthesizers is chlorophyll a (higher plants share this characteristic). In addition, there are three other chlorophylls,
a diversity of yellow and orange carotenoids (here lumped
for convenience under "other carotenoids"), brown carotenoids,
a nd the two phycobilins, phycocyanin and phycoerythrin. These
accessory pigments are distributed through the various groups
and form part of the basis for their classification. The search
for explanations for this diversity of pigments has opened an
extremely important modern area of photosynthesis, and
ultimately brings us to some ecological paradoxes which have
been known for some time.

If the green pigment, chlorophyll a, is indeed the universal
sensitizer of photosynthesis among oxygen-evolving plants,
evolutionary pressure in the past should have selected a
pigment optimally suited for absorbing the available light
energy. Figure 2 shows the spectral distribution of sunlight
as it reaches the surface of the earth. The major energy is
available in the blue-violet end of the spectrum and then declines to the red. There is considerable energy available,
however, in the green-yellow-orange regions of the spectrum.
Yet the absorption maxima of chlorophyll a occur in the blue-
violet and the red. Photosynthesis based solely on chlorophyll
a would be color-blind in the green region of the spectrum
where there is considerable energy available. This deficiency
of chlorophyll a as a photosynthetic light catcher is emphasized
even more strongly by the selective attenuation which occurs
when sunlight passes through seawater (Fig. 2). At a depth
of 5 meters, most of the energy remaining is in the green
part of the spectrum, with a great decline in the regions of
chlorophyll absorption. This effect increases with increasing
depth. Since over 90 per cent of the photosynthesis on earth
occurs in the oceans and some of this 90 per cent below the

TABLE 2: Distribution of photosynthetic pigments among the various divisions of the Protista and one group of the Monera (Cyanophyta)

Constituent	Charophyta Chlorophyta	Euglenophyta	Pyrrophyta	Xanthophyta	Chrysophyta	Bacillariophyta	Pheophyta	Cyanophyta	Rhodophyta	Cryptophyta
Chlorophyll a	+	+	+	+	+	+	+	+	+	+
Chlorophyll b	+	+	−	−	−	−	−	−	−	−
Chlorophyll c	−	−	?	−	+	+	+	−	−	+
Chlorophyll d	−	−	−	−	−	−	−	−	+	−
Brown carotenoids	−	−	+	−	+	+	+	−	−	−
Other carotenoids	+	+	+	+	+	+	+	+	+	+
Phycocyanin	−	−	−	−	−	−	−	+	+	+
Phycoerythrin	−	−	−	−	−	−	−	+	+	+

surface, the evolutionary selection of chlorophyll a would appear to be paradoxical. One could argue, however, that chlorophyll a was selected for its chemical ability to mediate photosynthesis by interacting with other enzymatic machinery of the cell and that the molecule which resulted represents a compromise between light-absorbing properties and chemical properties. As we shall see later, there is probably a good deal of truth in this idea.

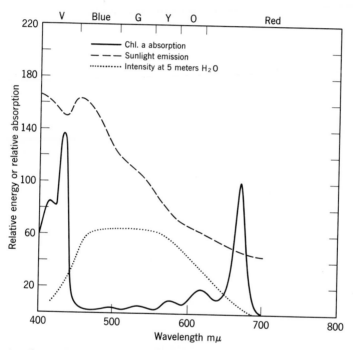

Fig. 2—Absorption spectrum of chlorophyll a, relative energy distribution of wavelengths in sunlight reaching the surface of the earth, and relative attenuation of various wavelengths by 5 meters of water. The two energy distributions indicate only relative values at various wavelengths and should not be compared, on an absolute scale, to each other (Compiled from E. Rabinowitsch, Research in Photosynthesis).

Have there been any evolutionary solutions to this dilemma? Referring again to Table 2, let us look at the other pigments which are found among the protists. We have three other chlorophylls, yellow, orange, and brown carotenoids, and phycocyanin, a blue pigment, and phycoerythrin, which is red. These have absorption properties which are different from chlorophyll a and lie at different wave lengths in the spectrum. If these pigments were capable of participating in photosynthesis, they might fill in the gaps in the chlorophyll absorption.

Figure 3 shows the absorption spectrum of the red alga, Porphyridium, as measured by Duysens (3). The various absorption peaks are attributed to the pigment which absorbs the most energy in each region of the spectrum. In this case, phycoerythrin and phycocyanin serve to fill in the gaps in the chlorophyll absorption in the green, yellow, and orange regions of the spectrum. But are these accessory pigments active in photosynthesis? The dotted line in the upper part of Fig. 3 shows that they are very efficient sensitizers of photosynthesis- - more efficient even than chlorophyll a '.

By optically dissecting the pigment system of Porphyridium and other algae, Duysens, Haxo and Blinks, and many others were able to formulate a scheme for the participation of the accessory pigments in photosynthesis. This dissection relied on the fact that most of these pigments are fluorescent, and when they absorb some light they can re-emit it at a longer wave length. It was soon found that light absorbed by carotenoids would cause phycoerythrin to emit its characteristic fluorescence. If the cells were given light absorbed only by phycoerythrin, the fluorescence of phycocyanin could be detected. Finally, absorption of light by any of the accessory pigments yielded fluorescence characteristic of chlorophyll a. From data of this sort, it was possible to formulate scheme 1, shown in Fig. 3, for Porphyridium. Energy was being transferred along a chain of accessory pigments in such a manner that it all ended up, eventually, in chlorophyll a, regardless of where it was absorbed initially. This placed chlorophyll a in the position of being the direct mediator of photosynthesis. In more general terms applicable to all photosynthetic systems, light energy absorbed by the accessory pigments present in each case could be transferred to chlorophyll a to mediate photosynthesis. Note that to avoid violating thermodynamic principles, energy must always be transferred to a pigment which absorbs at longer wave lengths from the pigment which initially absorbed the energy, because the energy per quantum decreases with increasing wave length.

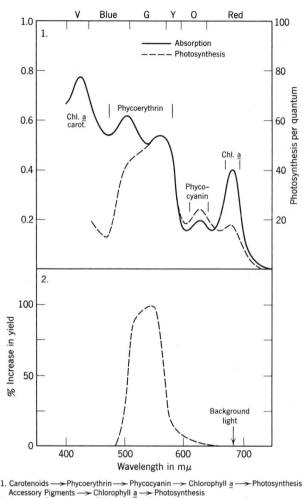

1. Carotenoids —→ Phycoerythrin —→ Phycocyanin —→ Chlorophyll a —→ Photosynthesis
   Accessory Pigments —→ Chlorophyll a —→ Photosynthesis
2. Accessory Pigments₁ —→ Chlorophyll₁ + Chlorophyll₂ ←— accessory pigments₂
                              ↓
                        Photosynthesis

Fig. 3—Upper frame: absorption spectrum and photosynthetic quantum
yield dependence on wavelength for Porphyridium.
Lower frame: action spectrum for enhancement of photosynthesis with
a background illumination in the region of the red decline in quantum
yield.
Bottom: two patterns of energy transfer in photosynthesis. (Graphs
after Haxo, (8).

Thus, the direction of energy transfer is always from blue
towards the red, rather than the reverse.

Having established that the accessory pigments which
fill in the gaps in chlorophyll a absorption do indeed participate in photosynthesis, we can now return to an explanation
of the paradox presented above. It is obvious that the direct
photochemical mediator of photosynthesis must have its
longest wave length absorption maximum at longer wave
lengths than any of the accessory pigments from which it
must receive light energy so as not to violate energy con-
servation principles. In the Protista, chlorophyll a satisfies
this condition, since its maximum in the red lies at longer
wave lengths than the absorption bands of carotenoids,
phycocyanin, and phycoerythrin. Thus we might suppose
that chlorophyll a was selected through evolution because
it could serve as the sink for the energy absorbed by other
pigments. It would also provide the irreducible link to
photosynthetic reactions and would thus be present in all of
the organisms, regardless of their accessory pigments. From
his studies of chlorophyll biosynthesis, Granick (4) has
suggested that the compounds which now serve as metabolic
precursors of chlorophyll might have served as the exclusive
photosynthetic pigment at each point in evolution of the pathway. If this were true, he points out, each successive
pigment in the pathway of chlorophyll would have been selected
because it was a more efficient sensitizer of photosynthesis
than its predecessors. These predecessors would successive-
ly be reduced to being only precursors of the new, more
efficient pigment. This process would have culminated in
the formation and selection of chlorophyll a. As Granick
points out, these precursors of chlorophyll (e.g., magnesium
protoporphyrin IX, magnesium vinyl pheoporphyrin a_5, etc.)
show an interesting progression of spectral shifts. The
longest wavelength of absorption shifts to longer and longer
wave lengths as one proceeds through the biosynthetic pathway towards chlorophyll, and this absorption maximum becomes more and more pronounced (i.e., it becomes a better
absorber at longer wave lengths). Incorporating this into
our scheme, we would visualize that in response to changing
spectral distributions of light available to photosynthetic
organisms during evolution, either due to geophysical change
or to the invasion of new habitats by organisms, accessory
pigments were evolved to trap efficiently the light which was

available. At the same time, this put a pressure on the
evolution of the pigments which served as the final chemical
mediator of photosynthesis by selecting those which had
absorption maxima at longer and longer wave lengths to serve
as a sink for the energy absorbed by the accessory pigments.
Thus, there would be a parallel evolutionary change in accessory pigments coordinated with the evolution of chlorophyll a.
Once the metabolic machinery became fairly complex, it
would be difficult to change the final mediator (resulting in
the near universal distribution of chlorophyll a), while the
accessory pigments could still be rather plastic in response
to the qualities of light available in the environment.

The pattern of accessory pigments which we find in contemporary organisms reflects these evolutionary pressures.
As many people have pointed out, in particular Stanier, organisms seem to group themselves according to their light-
absorbing abilities in ecological situations. Thus, in an
aquatic environment, we have the green, yellow, and brown
groups of organisms near the surface of the water. At great
depths where only green light is available (Fig. 2), the
colonizers are members of the red and blue-green algae
whose accessory pigments, phycocyanin and phycoerythrin,
permit them to photosynthesize with this limited region of
the spectrum which is not absorbed by chlorophyll a.

Scheme 1 in Fig. 3, while it adequately represents the
basic facts of energy transfer obtained from fluorescence
spectra, does not explain some later findings. Haxo and
Blinks (5) emphasized the quantitative discrepancy between
the absorption properties of the pigments and their abilities
to mediate photosynthesis. Their data, and that of Duysens
shown in Fig. 3, indicate that, for every quantum absorbed
by the pigments, those absorbed by phycocyanin and phycoerythrin appear to be far more effective in mediating photosynthesis than is light absorbed by chlorophyll. Scheme 1
would predict that all the pigments should be equally efficient
if energy transfer proceeded with 100 per cent efficiency.
If the efficiency is lower, the light absorbed by accessory
pigments should be less effective than chlorophyll a. This
discrepancy became even more disconcerting through the
work of Emerson (6) and Blinks (7) on enhancement phenomena,
the study of which has been the occupation of many laboratories
since. Referring to the upper figure in Fig. 3 once more, we
see that the quantum efficiency of photosynthesis falls off more

rapidly than chlorophyll absorption in the red region of the
spectrum. This has been demonstrated for many organisms.
Emerson found that the quantum efficiency in this region of
"red decline" could be raised by simultaneously supplying
light of short wave lengths. Some measurements of Haxo
for Porphyridium (8) are shown in the lower frame of Fig. 3.
If a "background" light is shone on the cells in the region of
the red decline and, simultaneously, another wave length of
light is presented, it is possible to measure how effective
this supplementary light is for increasing the yield as a
function of wave length. As may be seen, the effectiveness
of the supplementary light is maximal in the region of phycoerythrin absorption. Now, this is impossible if scheme 1
applies, since the accessory pigments can only increase the
amount of energy transferred to chlorophyll a, and should not
be able to raise the yield over that possible by fully exciting
chlorophyll a.

The finding of enhancement and the red decline, therefore,
necessitated a new hypothesis. An additional reason for
questioning this scheme arose from the nature of the red
decline itself. Light absorbed anywhere in an absorption band
of a pigment such as chlorophyll a should be equally effective
across the band. But, as noted above, the long wave length
side of the band is not as effective as the short wave length and
peak portions. This is a very strange way for a pigment to
behave and led to the suspicion that what appeared as a single
band belonging to one pigment might actually be due to a combination of pigments. French (9) was able to show by derivative
spectrophotometry that there were indeed several forms of
chlorophyll a in plants with distinctive absorption spectra which
summed to give the one curve already described. At least
two of these have been shown to be directly involved in photosynthesis. This led to the idea (shown in scheme 2, Fig. 3)
that these two chlorophylls together were necessary for photo -
synthesis to take place. If one assumed that the red decline
occurred because the form of chlorophyll a absorbing at longer
wave lengths was inactive by itself but could cooperate with
chlorophyll absorbing at slightly shorter wave lengths, an
explanation of enhancement became possible. The major
accessory pigments could transfer their energy to the shorter
wave length form of chlorophyll while the background light
excited the longer wave length form simultaneously. Since
Duysens found that both chlorophylls were associated with

accessory pigments (more for one than for the other), the
scheme shown in Fig. 3, scheme 2 became possible. Here
excitation of both forms of chlorophyll a is necessary to have
photosynthesis and also suggests why some accessory pigments
apparently can be more effective in photosynthesis than chlorophyll appears to be. It ultimately depends on how much light
is entering each of the two systems at a given wave length.

Scheme 2 suggests that both forms of chlorophyll should
have a place in the metabolic machinery of photosynthesis.
Let us turn now to a brief discussion of this mechanism.

The classical equation of photosynthesis in green plants
is shown in Fig. 4. It is well known that the oxygen evolved
in photosynthesis arises from water. Rubin, Kamen, and
Hassid (10) showed that photosynthesis on water labelled with
oxygen-18 yields labelled oxygen. Hill was able to demonstrate
that isolated chloroplasts would evolve oxygen when supplied
with only water and a suitable hydrogen acceptor such as
ferricyanide or quinone, according to the second equation in
Fig. 4. Photosynthesis in bacteria, however, does not yield
oxygen, and a source of reducing power (H_2A) must be supplied
to the cells from outside (equation 3 in Fig. 4).

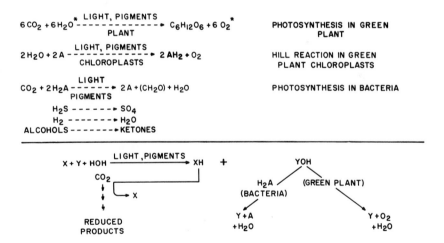

Fig. 4—Upper half: summary of photosynthetic reactions in green
plants, isolated chloroplasts, and certain bacteria.
Lower half: summary of Van Niel's hypothesis unifying green plant and
bacterial photosynthesis.

H_2A may be any of a variety of materials, depending upon the species. Hydrogen sulfide, hydrogen, alcohols, and other substances can serve in various cases and become oxidized during the photosynthetic process. We owe much of our knowledge of this area of photosynthesis to the brilliant work of Van Niel, who presented a hypothesis to unify bacterial and green plant photosynthesis. This is shown in the lower part of Fig. 4. The reactions common to green plants and bacteria were hypothesized to be the photochemical cleavage of water to yield a reducing moiety (XH) and a oxidizing one (YOH), and the reduction of carbon dioxide to more reduced carbon compounds using XH. Bacteria and green plants would then be different in the ways that they disposed of YOH. Green plants would convert this to oxygen and water, while the photosynthetic bacteria would use an external reductant (H_2A) to reduce YOH. While this hypothesis led to much fruitful work, it subsequently had to be modified when more became known about the pigment systems and the intermediary metabolism of the photosynthetic process. The Van Niel scheme suggests that the photochemical act in both cases is the photochemical dissociation of water, but we need a system which requires the participation of two different types of chlorophyll as described previously. Studies of the intermediary metabolism of photosynthesis have provided such a system.

To document completely the immense amount of work which has been done in this area would be impossible. The work of Arnon, Fraenkel, Nishimura and Chance, Duysens Witt, Kok, and many others could be cited. We must be content here with a brief summary in the form of the hypothetical scheme shown in Fig. 5 based largely on the suggestion of Hill and Bendall. The long-wave length form of chlorophyll becomes excited by absorption of a photon of light bringing about the dissociation of the chlorophyll into an electron and a positively charged chlorophyll. This electron has two alternatives. It can undergo recombination with its positively charged partner through a series of steps, which involves the liberation of the energy initially obtained from the photon with the energy being trapped in the form of ATP (dashed line in Fig. 5). The other alternative open to the electron is to reduce TPN to TPNH, thus leaving the photochemical cycle entirely. The ATP and TPNH thus formed constitute the "assimilatory power" for the reduction of

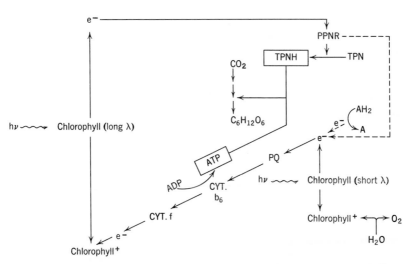

Fig. 5—Contemporary ideas of photosynthetic electron transport (from many sources). (PQ-plastoquinone; cyt. b_6-cytochrome b_6 ; cyt. f-cytochrome f; PPNR-photosynthetic pyridine nucleotide reductase).

carbon dioxide to carbohydrate, a series of dark reactions. Now, in the case where the electron leaves the cycle, how is the positively charged chlorophyll to receive an electron to keep the cycle running? It is here that the differences between photosynthetic bacteria and green plants are thought to reside. Green plants obtain these electrons by a second photochemical step involving the participation of the short-wave length absorbing form of chlorophyll. After photo-dissociation of this chlorophyll into an electron and a positively charged chlorophyll, the positively charged chlorophyll oxidizes water to obtain the electrons to restore its neutrality. The electron ejected by the photochemical reaction is used to neutralize the positively charged long-wave length chlorophyll left from the reduction of TPN to TPNH. It is thought that photosynthetic bacteria lack the short-wave length chlorophyll system or its equivalent and must, therefore, receive their extra electrons from an external source, H_2A (or AH_2). Thus, this hypothetical scheme would predict that all photosynthetic organisms have similar

systems for the production of ATP and TPNH (and thus for
the reduction of carbon dioxide) but differ in where they obtain
their extra electrons. In the case of green plants, these
come from a second photochemical reaction involving water,
while in the photosynthetic bacteria they arise from externally
added H_2S, H_2, etc. This would suggest that the reactions
mediated by the long-wave length form of chlorophyll arose
first in evolution as the common denominator of photosynthesis and, with the exhaustion of reduced compounds from
the environment, an additional light reaction to obtain reducing power from water was evolved. Of course, it is
important to realize that the photosynthetic bacteria employ
a somewhat different pigment (bacteriochlorophyll) from
green plants, but the metabolic picture seems remarkably
similar in both cases. One should also realize that the details
of these schemes are quite hypothetical, but the basic outlines are strongly suggested by the experimental data. Two
excellent reviews dealing with the pigments and reactions
of photosynthesis have recently been published (11, 12) and
will be of interest to those who wish to know the experimental
details.

The length of this manuscript precludes a discussion of
another aspect of photosynthesis to which studies with the
Protista have made large contributions. This aspect deals
with the development and heredity of the photosynthetic
structure itself, the chloroplast. This part of the subject
can be approached through the interesting and informative
reviews of Granick (13, 14).

This brief, general discussion of the protists, pigments,
and photosynthesis will, I hope, convey something of the
fascination which this varied group of organisms holds for
the investigator. These organisms will undoubtedly continue
to supply us with interesting questions for a long time to
come.

LITERATURE CITED

1.   Ben-Shaul, Y., J. A. Schiff, and H. T. Epstein. 1964.
Plant Physiol., 39:231-240.
2.   Fuller, R. C. and S. F. Conti. 1963. Studies on Micro-
algae and Photosynthetic Bacteria, 49-63.
3.   Duysens, L.N.M. 1952. Doctoral Thesis, University
of Utrecht, Holland.
4.   Granick, S. 1949. Harvey Lectures 1948-1949. Charles
C. Thomas (Springfield, Ill.).

5.   Haxo, F.T. and L.R. Blinks. 1950. J. Gen. Physiol. 33:
389-422.
6.   Emerson, R. and E. Rabinowitsch. 1960. Plant Physiol.
35:479-485.
7.   Blinks, L.R. 1960. Proc. Nat. Acad. Sci., 46:327-333.
8.   Haxo, F.T., in Comparative Biochemistry of Photoreactive
Systems (ed. M.B. Allen), Academic Press, N.Y. 1960.
pp. 339-360.
9.   French, C.S. Encyclopedia of Plant Physiol. 5 #1:
252-297 (1960).
10.   Ruben, S., M. Randall, M. Kamen, and J. L. Hyde.
1941. J. Am. Chem. Soc., 63; 877-879.
11.   Jagendorf, A. 1962. Survey of Biological Processes,
4:181-344.
12.   French, C. S. and J.H.C. Smith. 1963. Ann. Rev.
Plant Phys. 14:181-224.
13.   Granick, S., in The Cell (ed. Brachet and Mirsky)
Academic Press, N.Y. 1961. pp. 489-602.
14.   Granick, S., in Cytodifferentiation and Macromolecular
Synthesis (ed. M. Locke) Academic Press, N.Y., 1963.
pp. 144-170.

DISCUSSION

Mr. Zajic (Kerr-McGee Oil Ind.):   Is the pyrenoid a
light-activated structure in all algae?

Dr. Schiff: No. Euglena is one of the few algae which
have light-induced chloroplast development.   Most members
of the protista, particularly the green algae, make chlorophyll and chloroplasts in the dark; for these it is not a light-
induced process.   Euglena, however, is like higher plants
in that it requires light for chloroplast development.   There
are one or two others, but they are exceptions among the
algae, by and large.   So, the pyrenoid would be made in the
dark by the green algae.

Mr. Zajic: Dr. Lindstrom mentioned that the photosynthetic organisms can be rather wasteful at times and give
off free hydrogen.   I wonder where, in your scheme, one
could expect free hydrogen to be given off.

Dr. Schiff: I think it would be where TPNH (reduced
triphosphopyridine nucleotide) is produced.   If there is a
hydrogenase, the organisms should be able to produce hydrogen
from TPNH.

16

THE METHANE FERMENTATION

Perry L. McCarty
Department of Civil Engineering
Stanford University

Methane fermentation is widely used for the stabilization
of concentrated organic wastes or sludges at municipal waste
treatment plants. Here, optimum temperatures, concentrations of organic materials, and mixing are utilized to
achieve maximum rates of decomposition. However, the same
process, occurring naturally, is responsible for the destruction
of large quantities of organic matter which has settled to the
bottom of lakes, ponds, and streams, as well as in oxidation
ponds, anaerobic lagoons, and septic tanks. Here, under
layers of organic sediment, oxygen is excluded and the anaerobic environment required for methane fermentation becomes
established. Since the resulting temperatures are normally
less than optimum, the fermentation proceeds at reduced rates.
Even so, the quantities of organic matter destroyed by this
process can be considerable.

Although it is an important method of waste degradation,
relatively little is known of the microorganisms responsible
for methane fermentation and their requirements. This is
not because of a lack of interest in methane fermentation,
but rather because of the complexity of the over-all process
and the difficulty of isolating for study the microorganisms
responsible. The difficulty, in part, has been due to their
sensitivity to oxygen and to their slow rate of growth. For
this reason, most information on the methane fermentation
has been obtained from study of impure or partially purified
cultures.

Two Stage Process. Buswell (1) has shown that organic matter can be converted quantitatively to methane and carbon dioxide. This conversion, however, does not appear to be brought about by the methane-producing bacteria alone, but is carried on in two stages as shown in Fig. 1. In the first stage, a heterogeneous group of facultative and anaerobic bacteria termed "acid-formers" convert proteins, carbohydrates, and fats primarily into fatty acids by hydrolysis and fermentation. The methane-producing bacteria then utilize the organic acids, converting them into carbon dioxide and methane. Alcohols may be fermented also by methane-producing bacteria, but this is probably of significance only with carbohydrate fermentation. Although it appears possible that methane bacteria alone can carry on both stages of the fermentation, evidence is lacking to indicate that this actually occurs.

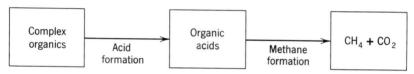

Fig. 1—Two stages of methane fermentation of complex organics.

The first stage conversion by the acid-forming bacteria is brought about with little or no change in BOD (biochemical oxygen demand) or COD (chemical oxygen demand) of the organic matter in suspension or solution. Here, simply, a change in form takes place, a portion being converted to end products such as organic acids and the other portion being converted to new bacterial cells. It is only in the second stage of methane formation that removal of oxidizable organics takes place, and this is directly proportional to the quantity of methane produced. Exceptions to this, under anaerobic conditions, are removals resulting from the occasional formation of hydrogen or reduction of inorganic hydrogen acceptors, such as sulfates, nitrates and nitrites. The oxygen equivalent of organic matter

removed by methane fermentation alone can be determined
as follows:

$$CH_4 + 2 O_2 \longrightarrow 2 CO_2 + 2 H_2O$$

Mol. Wt: 16   64

Thus, each 16 grams of methane produced and lost to the
atmosphere corresponds to the removal of 64 grams of oxygen
equivalent in the waste stream.

The first stage of acid formation is brought about by two
processes, hydrolysis and fermentation. Complex proteins
are first hydrolyzed with the aid of enzymes to polypeptides
and then to simple amino acids, complex carbohydrates such
as starch and cellulose are hydrolyzed to simple sugars, and
fats and oils are hydrolyzed to glycerol and fatty acids. The
amino acids, simple sugars, and glycerol formed by hydrolysis
are soluble and pass to the acid-forming bacteria by which they
are fermented. This fermentation consists of oxidation and
reduction of the organic matter. Here, in the absence of oxygen,
a portion of the organic molecule is oxidized, while another
portion of the same molecule, or in some cases a different
molecule, is reduced. It is from this oxidation-reduction of
organic matter that the acid-producing bacteria obtain their
energy for growth and reproduction. Under these conditions,
saturated fatty acids and carbon dioxide represent the reduced
and oxidized products, respectively, of this fermentation.
Ammonia is also produced, as an end product, from amino
acid fermentation.

Few studies have been conducted to determine the predominant acid-forming organisms associated with methane
fermentation. They no doubt range from facultative organisms,
which can anaerobically ferment simple carbohydrates, to
strict anaerobes capable of converting complex proteins and
carbohydrates to organic acids. The reactions of many of
these organisms are well known. It is also known that the end
products from fermentation of carbohydrates and proteins
vary markedly, depending upon the particular species involved. For example, with glucose fermentation, one organism may produce ethyl alcohol, another lactic acid, and still
a third may produce a variety of products such as acetic acid,
lactic acid, and ethyl alcohol. It can thus be expected that,
under natural conditions, shifting populations of acid-forming
organisms can result in the formation of different organic
acids at different times. Changing end products from acid

formation means changing types of food for the methane bacteria. This could temporarily affect methane fermentation and may be one reason for occasional upsets of the process.

The methane-producing bacteria comprise several different species of strictly anaerobic organisms. The major similar characteristic of these organisms is that they all produce methane from fermentation of simple organics under anaerobic conditions. However, each species has been found to have specific requirements and can ferment only a relatively restricted group of simple organic compounds. Only a few of these organisms have been isolated in pure culture, the rest being studied only in purified culture. In Table 1 is shown a classification of methane bacteria and the substrates they are capable of using, as indicated by Barker (2). The restricted number of substrates each species can ferment indicates that several species would be required for the complete methane fermentation of some substrates. Our laboratory studies have shown this to be the case. Studies on the anaerobic digestion of simple, as well as complex substrates, have indicated that organisms with similar characteristics to those reported by Barker (2) were usually present.

TABLE 1: Classification of methane bacteria (after Barker, 2)

A. Rod-shaped cells
    I. Non-sporulating: Methanobacterium
        1. Mbact. formicicum: formate, carbon monoxide, hydrogen
        2. Mbact. propionicum: propionate
        3. Mbact. söhngenii: acetate, butyrate

    II. Sporulating: Methanobacillus
        1. Mbac. omelianskii: primary and secondary alcohols, hydrogen

B. Spherical cells
    I. Cells not in sarcina arrangement: Methanococcus
        1. Mc. mazei: acetate, butyrate
        2. Mc. vannielii: formate, hydrogen

    II. Cells in sarcina arrangement: Methanosarcina
        1. Ms. barkerii: methanol, acetate, carbon monoxide, hydrogen
        2. Ms. methanica: acetate, butyrate (?)

Environmental Requirements of Methane Bacteria. The
methane bacteria are limited in the quantity of energy they
can obtain from substrate fermentation. This is because the
majority of substrate energy is lost in the methane gas which
has been produced. Because of the low energy yield, the rate
of growth is restricted. It has also been found that the rate
of substrate utilization per unit of organism is relatively low.
These two factors tend to restrict somewhat the over-all rate
of substrate utilization by methane bacteria. For this reason,
optimum environmental condtions must be maintained for
satisfactory rates of methane fermentation to occur. However,
some methane bacteria can survive under much less than
optimum conditions, as is evidenced by methane fermentation
in acid bogs and at relatively low temperatures.

Optimum methane fermentation has generally been found
to occur between the pH range of 6.7 to 7.4 (7)(8)(9). Values
of pH much below 6 or above 8 have been found to be very
restrictive and, in fact, somewhat toxic to the methane bacteria.

Two optimum temperatures for methane fermentation have
been noted (10). One of these is in the mesophilic range of
about 32 to 37 C, and the other in the thermophilic range of 50
to 55 C. Rates of fermentation at the thermophilic range have
been found to be significantly higher than at mesophilic temperatures. However, heating costs have normally limited waste
treatment to the lower temperature range.

Inorganic salts have also been found to have a significant
influence on methane bacteria (3). Optimum fermentation occurs
under a rather limited range of concentration of the inorganic
ions such as sodium, potassium, calcium, magnesium and
ammonium. However, methane fermentation can proceed in
the presence of high salt concentrations, but with reduced
efficiency. For example, Kugelman (4) obtained continuous
methane fermentation in the presence of about 1 M sodium
chloride.

The nutrient requirements for methane fermentation are
relatively small. Continuous fermentations for periods in
excess of one year have been obtained with the following
substrates as the sole source of organic carbon: glucose, starch,
cellulose, nutrient broth, leucine, oleic acid, palmitic acid,
octanoic acid, butyric acid, propionic acid, and acetic acid.
Other additions were the normal inorganic nutrients, nitrogen
and phosphorous, and other usually required trace inorganic
ions. In addition, Speece and McCarty (5) found

that from 20 to 50 mg per liter of iron, either in the ferric
or ferrous form, or simply iron filings, was necessary for
continuous fermentation. The reason for the requirement
for iron is not known, nor is it known whether some other
material may be just as satisfactory. The concentration is
much greater than should be needed to satisfy the trace requirements of the bacteria. There is also some evidence
(5)(6) that much greater rates of fermentation may be possible
in the presence of trace organic nutrients which would act as
stimulants.

In addition to the above requirements for methane fermentation, the complete absence of oxygen appears necessary (2).
In the methane fermentation of complex materials such as
sewage sludge, small quantities appear to have little detrimental
effect. This is, perhaps, due to the rapid removal of ex-
traneous oxygen by the facultative organisms present. However,
highly purified cultures of methane bacteria are extremely
sensitive to even small quantities of oxygen, and great care
must be taken in its exclusion.

Chemistry of Methane Formation. Since reduction of
oxidizable organic matter in the waste stream occurs from
methane formation, it is desirable to know how methane is
formed. It has been established, mostly through the work of
Buswell (11) and Barker (12)(13)(14) and their coworkers, that
methane results from two major sources, as follows:

(1) CO_2 Reduction: $\quad *CO_2 + 8H \longrightarrow *CH_4 + 2H_2O$

(2) Acetic Acid Fermentation:
$$*CH_3COOH \longrightarrow *CH_4 + CO_2$$

In the first case of carbon dioxide reduction, carbon dioxide acts as a hydrogen acceptor, just as oxygen does under
aerobic conditions, and is reduced to methane by hydrogen
enzymatically removed from the organic molecules. The other
major source of methane results from acetic acid fermentation.
Acetic acid is formed as a major intermediate from the fermentation of complex organics. Methane is formed from acetic
acid by a split of the acetic acid molecule, the methane resulting from the methyl carbon and its three hydrogens, while
the carbon dioxide results from the carboxyl carbon.

A third source of methane, reported by Stadtman and
Barker (15), results from the reduction of methanol. Later,
Pine and Vishniac (16) studied both the methanol and acetate
fermentation and presented good evidence to indicate that these

two substrates pass through a common intermediate while
being converted to methane. Although methane may be formed
directly from methanol, methanol is not a frequent intermediate
in the degradation of most natural compounds, and so is probably a relatively minor source of methane.

Since methane mainly results both from carbon dioxide
reduction and from acetic acid fermentation, the question
arises as to the importance of each mechanism in the over-
all fermentation of complex materials. The significance of
the two mechanisms can be illustrated for the complete
methane fermentation of ethyl alcohol as shown by Stadtman
and Barker (12)(17). The reactions involved are as follows:

(1) $2CH_3CH_2OH + 2H_2O \longrightarrow 2CH_3COOH + 8H$

(2) $8H + *CO_2 \longrightarrow *CH_4 + 2H_2O$

(3) $2CH_3COOH \longrightarrow 2CH_4 + 2CO_2$

Net: $2CH_3CH_2OH \longrightarrow *CH_4 + 2CH_4 + CO_2$

First, ethanol is oxidized to acetic acid by normal biochemical mechanisms of hydrogen removal and water addition,
as shown by the first equation. In equation 2, carbon dioxide
then acts as a hydrogen acceptor and is reduced to methane
gas. Finally, in step 3, the acetic acid produced from the
ethyl alcohol is converted into methane and carbon dioxide,
probably by a different bacterial species than that initially
converting the ethyl alcohol. Thus, in the over-all fermentation of two moles of ethyl alcohol, one mole of methane is
formed from carbon dioxide reduction and two moles are
formed directly from acetic acid. Here then, 67 per cent of
the methane results from acetic acid fermentation.

By the use of radioactive tracers Jeris and McCarty (18)
have investigated the methane fermentation of complex substrates to determine over-all biochemical mechanisms, as
well as the importance of carbon dioxide reduction and acetic
acid fermentation as sources of methane.

Fatty Acids. Fatty acids result largely from the hydrolysis
of fats and oils. Short chain fatty acids result also from the
fermentation of carbohydrates and proteins. By use of C^{14}
tracers, the fatty acids have been found to be fermented by
beta-oxidation or by a mechanism similar to this. This is
illustrated in Fig. 2 for caproic acid. Here, starting at the

carboxyl end of the molecule, the organism oxidizes the beta
carbon by the removal of hydrogen and addition of water, resulting in the conversion of the molecule into two-carbon,
acetic acid fragments. The organism then rids itself of the
removed hydrogen by reducing carbon dioxide to methane.
The even-numbered carbons of the original fatty acid, marked
with a star in the figure, end as the methyl carbon of the acetic
acid. Thus, when the acetic acid is fermented, these even-
numbered carbons end as methane gas. The odd carbon atoms,
on the other hand, end as carbon dioxide, some of which may
then act as a hydrogen acceptor and be reduced to methane.
Thus, in the over-all fermentation of caproic acid, as shown
in the figure, three moles of methane would result from the
even carbon atoms of the molecule and one mole of methane
would result from carbon dioxide reduction.

(1) Beta oxidation: $\overset{*}{C}H_3-CH_2 \vdots \overset{*}{C}H_2-CH_2 \vdots \overset{*}{C}H_2-COOH + 4H_2O \rightarrow 3\overset{*}{C}H_3COOH + 8H$

(2) CO_2 reduction: $CO_2 + 8H \rightarrow CH_4 + 2H_2O$

(3) Acetic acid ferm.: $3\ \overset{*}{C}H_3COOH \rightarrow 3CH_4 + 3CO_2$

Net: $\overset{*}{C}H_3-CH_2-\overset{*}{C}H_2-CH_2-\overset{*}{C}H_2-COOH + 2H_2O \rightarrow 3\overset{*}{C}H_4 + CH_4 + 2CO_2$

Fig. 2: Beta oxidation and methane fermentation
of fatty acids

In this particular example, then, 75 per cent of the methane
results from acetic acid. Jeris and McCarty (18) have shown
this mechanism to hold for the 8-carbon octanoic acid, and the
16-carbon palmitic acid. Thus, this mechanism appears valid,
regardless of chain length. Since no organisms other than the
methane formers are known to be able to ferment the fatty acids
in the absence of other organic substrates or hydrogen acceptors,
it appears the methane bacteria are solely responsible for fatty
acid fermentation. However, more species than one of methane
bacteria are probably involved in the over-all conversion.
    The above mechanism works satisfactorily with even-
numbered carbon fatty acids, but with odd-numbered carbon
acids the situation is somewhat different. In the latter case,
the bacteria split off two-carbon acetic acid groups by beta-
oxidation also until there remains at the end, the three-carbon
propionic acid. Propionate is then discharged to be fermented

by a different species of methane bacteria. This was shown
by Stadtman and Barker (14), using valeric acid. We, also,
have found equivalent amounts of propionic acid remaining
from the fermentation of odd-numbered carbon acids such as
valeric and heptanoic, by enriched cultures developed on even-
numbered carbon acids.

Stadtman and Barker (14) found propionic acid to be
fermented as follows:

(1) $4 CH_3CH_2COOH + 8H_2O \longrightarrow 4 CH_3COOH + 4 CO_2 + 24H$

(2) $3CO_2 + 24H \longrightarrow 3 CH_4 + 6 H_2O$

Net: $4 CH_3CH_2COOH + 2H_2O \longrightarrow 4 CH_3COOH + CO_2 + 3CH_4$

Their tracer experiments indicated the number 2 and 3
carbons of propionic acid ended up as the carboxyl and methyl
carbons, respectively, of acetic acid. Tracer experiments
by Buswell, Fina, Mueller, and Yahiro (19) were not quite
in agreement with this. However, their differing results
could have been due to biochemical side reactions, which are
quite possible under the mixed-culture conditions they used.

The methane fermentation of propionate is quite important,
as significant quantities of propionate have been found to result from fermentation of complex organics. Also, propionate
has been found to increase to significant concentrations under
adverse conditions (20)(21)(22), indicating its rate of fermentation may be one of the major limiting factors in methane
fermentation.

Although there is now a fair amount of information available on fatty acid fermentation, more data is needed for the
complex lipids. As has been pointed out, the long-chain
fatty acids are produced by hydrolysis of fats and oils.
Heukelekian and Mueller (23) found that this hydrolysis occurred
long before methane fermentation commenced, indicating that
this conversion could be brought about by acid-formers. They
also found that the unsaturated fatty acids, such as oleic acid,
were hydrogenated to saturated acids prior to methane fermentation, indicating the possibility that these acids could be used
as hydrogen acceptors. These investigators also found that
unsaponifiable lipids were not significantly removed in methane
fermentation. This is in agreement with the studies by
Lawrence (24), who found that the unsaponifiables, cholesterol
and lanolin, were not readily fermented.

Carbohydrates. The carbohydrates range from the simple
sugars through the complex carbohydrates such as starch and
cellulose. The complex carbohydrates, or polysaccharides,
must first be hydrolyzed to simple sugars, or monosaccharides,
which can then be fermented by a wide variety of facultative
and anaerobic organisms to organic acids and alcohols. Most
naturally occurring monosaccharides contain either five or
six carbon atoms.

Tracer studies (18) on the over-all methane fermentation
of the six-carbon glucose indicated two moles of acetic acid
were formed as intermediates in the fermentation of each
mole of glucose. This could be explained on the basis of
normal pathways of fermentation of hexoses, which are usually
split between the number 3 and 4 carbon atoms, as shown in
Fig. 3, one acetic acid being formed from each half.

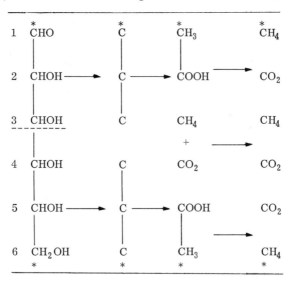

Fig. 3: Methane fermentation of glucose by
Embden-Meyerhof pathway

Hexoses are normally fermented by one of two main biochemical pathways, the Embden-Meyerhof pathway or the
hexose monophosphate pathway. By the Embden-Meyerhof
pathway, it would be predicted that the number 1 and 6 carbons
of glucose would end as the methyl carbons of the acetic acid
formed, and hence would finally be converted to methane in
the over-all methane fermentation as shown in Fig. 3. By

the hexose monophosphate pathway, on the other hand, the number 1 carbon would initially be converted to carbon dioxide. Tracer experiments (18) in which both the number 1 and 6 carbons were labeled, indicated both pathways were probably involved, with some preference for the Embden-Meyerhof pathway.

The over-all result of the methane fermentation of hexoses is that three moles of methane are formed, two of which come from the methane fermentation of acetic acid which is formed as an intermediate. The other mole results from carbon dioxide reduction. This is true for the complex carbohydrates, as well as the simple sugars.

It was desired to determine what other acids may be of importance in carbohydrate fermentation. Studies by McCarty, Jeris, and Murdock (20) indicated that propionic acid was rapidly utilized by mixed cultures developed on glucose, starch, and cellulose. Also, significant quantities of propionic acid were often found during the fermentation of these carbohydrates. The rate of utilization of propionate in these studies indicated the fermentation may proceed by the following pathway:

$$C_6H_{12}O_6 \longrightarrow CH_3CH_2COOH + CH_3COOH + HCOOH$$

Here, glucose would be fermented initially to one mole each of formic, acetic, and propionic acids. These acids would then be fermented by the methane formers. Although the formation of all these intermediates in exactly the quantity indicated has not been fully substantiated, it appears to be in good agreement with the results obtained. Whether the propionate is formed directly by the acid formers from glucose, or by the methane formers from the end products of the acid formers, is unknown. It was found that when lactic acid was added to an enriched mixed culture developed on glucose, the lactic acid was rapidly converted to propionic acid. Lactic acid is a common end-product of glucose fermentation by acid formers and may thus be intermediate in the production of propionate during carbohydrate fermentation. Buswell (1) also noted that propionate was formed from lactate in methane fermentation.

Although the five-carbon sugars were not studied, they would be expected to follow normal fermentation pathways with a split between the number 2 and 3 carbon atoms resulting in a two-carbon and a three-carbon fragment. These two fragments would then probably each pass through acetic acid as shown in the following scheme:

$$C_5H_{10}O_5 + H_2O \longrightarrow 2\ CH_3COOH + CO_2 + 4H$$

$$4H + \frac{1}{2}\ CO_2 \longrightarrow \frac{1}{2}\ CH_4 + H_2O$$

$$2CH_3COOH \longrightarrow 2\ CH_4 + 2CO_2$$

Net: $\quad C_5H_{10}O_5 \longrightarrow 2\frac{1}{2}\ CH_4 + 2\frac{1}{2}\ CO_2$

Thus, about one-half mole of methane would be expected from carbon dioxide reduction and two moles from acetate fermentation.

Proteins. In anaerobic fermentation, complex proteins are first hydrolyzed by bacterial enzymes into simple amino acids. The amino acids can then be fermented by various different pathways, depending upon the organisms involved. Also, the amino acids represent a variety of chemical structures, each of which may be fermented in a different way. Although many possibilities are present, the Stickland reaction appears to represent a general mechanism by which a majority of the amino acids may be deaminated and converted to organic acids. This reaction, as illustrated by Barker (12) for the amino acids, glycine and alanine, as shown in equations 1 to 3 , page 326.

By this mechanism, one amino acid is oxidized, decarboxylated, and converted to a saturated acid with one less carbon, while two other amino acids are reduced and converted to saturated acids with the same number of carbons. During this process, deamination occurs with the release of ammonia. Several amino acids can undergo this type of fermentation. Also, some individual amino acids undergo a reaction similar to this. Leucine is an example of this, as shown in the illustration on page 326 (equations 4 to 8). Thus, leucine appears to pass through isovaleric acid, which is probably fermented by the methane bacteria through the pathway shown, with the result that 80 per cent of the methane produced comes from acetic acid formed as an intermediate. This value was found in carbon tracer studies (18). Also, in the methane fermentation of leucine, a five-carbon volatile acid was observed by paper chromatography which probably was the isovaleric acid shown. The occasional persistance of this acid at relatively high concentrations in this fermentation indicated isovaleric was somewhat difficult to degrade by

(1) $CH_3CHNH_2COOH + 2H_2O \longrightarrow CH_3COOH + CO_2 + NH_3 + 4H$

(2) $2CH_2NH_2COOH + 4H \longrightarrow 2CH_3COOH + 2NH_3$

Net:

(3) $CH_3CHNH_2COOH + 2CH_2NH_2COOH + 2H_2 \longrightarrow 3CH_3COOH + 3NH_3 + CO_2$

(4) $(CH_3)_2CHCH_2CH(NH_2)COOH + 2H_2O \longrightarrow (CH_3)_2CHCH_2COOH + CO_2 + NH_3 + 4H$

(5) $(CH_3)_2CHCH_2COOH + 2H_2O + CO_2 \longrightarrow 3CH_3COOH + 2H$

(6) $3/4\ CO_2 + 6H \longrightarrow 3/4\ CH_4 + 3/2\ H_2O$

(7) $3CH_3COOH \longrightarrow 3CH_4 + 3CO_2$

Net:

(8) $(CH_3)_2CHCH_2CH(NH_2)COOH + 2\,1/2\ H_2O \longrightarrow 15/4\ CH_4 + 9/4\ CO_2 + NH_3$

methane fermentation. Such iso-acids may also be found from the fermentation of valine.

Jeris and McCarty (18) studied the fermentation of nutrient broth, which is a soluble proteinaceous substrate. Here 28 per cent of the methane was found to result from carbon dioxide reduction and 72 per cent from acetic acid fermentation. Since the nutrient broth is a mixture containing most amino acids, these results can be projected to proteins in general.

Volatile Acid Intermediates. The short-chain volatile organic acids are the major intermediates produced by the acid-forming bacteria from carbohydrates and proteins. As already indicated, acetic acid is the most prevalent intermediate and the source of a majority of methane formed in the methane fermentation of complex organics. A summary of the portion of methane formed from acetic acid for carbohydrates, proteins, and fats in shown in Fig. 4. For even-numbered carbon fatty acids, the percentage derived from acetic acid varies from 100 per cent with acetic acid itself, down to a lower limit of 66.7 per cent for infinitely long acids. For odd-numbered carbon acids, this percentage varies from 57 per cent for propionic acid up to a maximum of 66.7 per cent for longer acids. In the complete methane fermentation of carbohydrates, the quantity derived from acetic acid varies from a measured value of 67 per cent for hexoses up to a calculated value of 80 per cent for the pentoses. For proteins, the proportion of methane from acetic acid would differ for each particular amino acid, but for proteins in general, the value would be about 72 per cent. Thus, it appears, for the complete fermentation of mixed wastes, that the percentage of methane derived from acetic acid, formed as an intermediate, would be at least 70 per cent, the remainder of the methane formed resulting from carbon dioxide reduction.

The next most prevalent longer-chain, volatile acid formed as an intermediate in methane fermentation is propionic acid. This acid has been found to be produced in significant quantities both from proteins and from carbohydrates (20). Also, it is expected that propionic acid would be formed as an intermediate in the fermentation of the glycerol portion of fats and oils, as well as from aromatic ring-containing compounds. In the latter case, succinic acid is usually formed as an intermediate in the degradation of the aromatic ring and is a likely source for propionic acid.

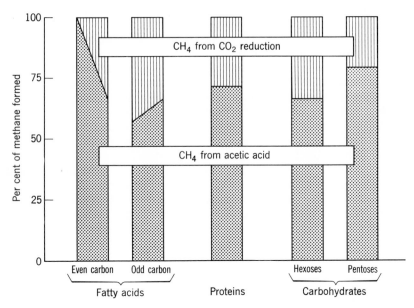

Fig. 4—Portion of methane formed during fermentation of various substrates from acetic acid fermentation and carbon dioxide reduction.

The actual quantities of propionic acid formed as an
intermediate in methane fermentation could not be measured
by tracer techniques as was acetic acid (18). However,
reasonable estimates were made by measuring the rate of
utilization of propionic acid by mixed cultures developed from
the continuous fermentation of various substrates, and
comparing these rates with the rate of acetic acid utilization
(20). These rates were measured manometrically. The
estimates of propionic acid formation are shown in Table 2.
The results indicate that both carbohydrates and proteins
are significant sources of propionic acid and any inhibition
of propionic acid fermentation would significantly affect methane
production. The sensitivity and importance of the bacteria
responsible for conversion of propionic acid to acetic acid has
already been mentioned.
    The longer-chain volatile acids, especially butyric, valeric,
and caproic, have frequently been observed to be present
during the methane fermentation of complex organics. Some

TABLE 2: Estimated per cent of total methane derived
from propionic acid fermentation

Substrate	Per cent methane from propionic acid
Fatty acids (even carbon)	0
Proteins	28
Carbohydrates (hexoses)	58

of these would , no doubt, be formed during the fermentation
of amino acids. Some may also occur during the beta- oxidation of longer-chain fatty acids. However, it has also
been found (20) that butyric, valeric, and caproic acids can
be synthesized by back-up reactions during the fermentation
of propionic acid, and caproic acid was found to be synthesized
during the fermentation of butyric acid. This synthesis
occurred with continuously fed cultures developed on propionic
and butyric acids, when either the rate of feed was suddenly
increased, or when concentrations of propionic or butyric
acids were maintained at values in excess of a few hundred
mg per l. Stadtman and Barker (14) also noted the occurrence
of synthesis, during the methane fermentation , of caproic
acid. Using labeled acetic acid as a tracer, they found that
both butyric and caproic acids were synthesized from acetic
acid at the same time as the caproic acid was being fermented.
However, they did not report the synthesis of acids higher
than caproic.

Such synthesis has not been found to occur when acetic
acid alone is the substrate. This may be because of the need
for synthesis of an enzyme-activated form of acetic or propionic
acid, which would be present only during the fermentation of
propionic or butyric acids to acetic acid. Such an active form
has been shown to be a requirement for Clostridium (2), which
can synthesis longer-chain acids in the fermentation of alcohols
and acids. Thus, although butyric, valeric, and caproic acids
are frequently found in methane fermentation, it does not
necessarily mean that they are intermediates in the breakdown
of complex organics. The evidence tends to indicate that they

are just as likely to result from the synthesis of the lower
volatile acids, especially when propionic acid is also present.
     One other volatile acid which as not yet been mentioned is
formic acid. This single-carbon acid may be formed both
from carbohydrates or by amino acid fermentation. Manometric studies (20), using mixed cultures developed from
methane fermentation of a wide variety of materials, ranging
from the short and long-chain fatty acids through several
carbohydrates and proteins, indicated that all cultures could
rapidly utilize formic acid. However, chemical tests seldom
indicated the presence of formic acid during the continuous
fermentation of these substrates. From the results, it could
be concluded either that (1) formic acid is an important intermediate in the methane fermentation of all substrates and
is readily fermented under most conditions, or (2) mixed
cultures adapted to most other substrates are simultaneously
adapted to formic acid.
     In summary, it appears acetic acid and propionic acid
are the major acid intermediates occurring in methane fermentation of complex organics. The longer-chain acids which
occur are of less importance as sources of methane gas, and
either result in small quantities as intermediates in substrate
degradation, or are synthesized during the fermentation of
other volatile acids. Formic acid may or may not be a significant intermediate but, in any event, it is readily fermented.
     Biological Growth and Kinetics. The free energy resulting
from the methane fermentation of organics is relatively low
compared to energy resulting from complete aerobic oxidation
to carbon dioxide and water. This is due to the energy, contained in the methane gas, which is not available to the microorganisms under anaerobic conditions. Because of this low
energy yield, the resulting bacterial growth from methane
fermentation is relatively small. This can be seen in Fig. 5,
which was prepared from studies reported by Speece and Mc-
Carty (5). Here is shown the percentage of substrate COD
which is converted into bacterial cells, the remainder being
converted to methane gas. The biological solids retention
time represents the average detention time in the methane
fermentation tank or digester of solids presumed to represent
bacterial cells. Thus, with increasing retention time, the
per cent of synthesis decreases, mainly because of the increased energy of maintenance for the organisms.

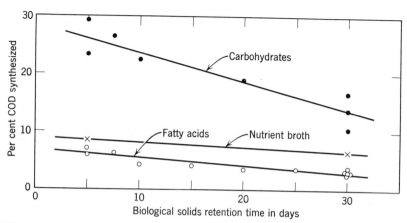

Fig. 5—Biological synthesis resulting from methane fermentation of various substrates. COD: Chemical Oxygen Demand; used here as a measure of organic substances capable of reacting with a standard potassium dichromate solution. It represents an approximate measure of cellular materials.

The curves show that greater synthesis results from carbohydrate fermentation than from protein or fatty acid fermentation. This difference is due to the significant energy which is available from conversion of carbohydrates into organic acids, and this difference thus represents the growth of acid forming organisms. Formerly (5), the synthesis from carbohydrates at low sludge retention times was reported to be even higher than shown in Fig. 5. These higher results were obtained by basing the growth on over-all lowering of COD. However, it was found that, at low sludge retention times for starch and glucose, the conversion to acids and resulting growth of the acid formers was complete, although methane fermentation of these acids and resulting over-all COD reduction was only about 60 per cent complete. By considering this difference, the more correct values shown in Fig. 5. resulted.

The fermentation of complex proteins, represented by nutrient broth, gives relatively low bacterial yields, on the same order as that obtained for the volatile acids. This indicates relatively little energy is available from deamination and fermentation of amino acids into fatty acids, and, hence,

the acid-forming population here must be relatively small.
For proteins and fatty acids it can be seen that less than 10
per cent of the substrate is synthesized into cells, compared
to the 50 per cent, or more, synthesis which may result under
aerobic conditions.

The small growth of methane formers represented, in
Fig. 5, by synthesis of COD from fatty acids is important
because it indicates that a relatively large quantity of substrate
must be fermented in order to double the population. The
generation time, or time required to double the bacterial
population, is of interest because it is related to the minimum
sludge retention time at which an anaerobic digester can be
operated. If the sludge retention time is decreased below
this generation time, the bacteria will be wasted from the
system faster than they can reproduce themselves, resulting
in the eventual failure of the process.

The bacterial generation time is related, not only to the
percentage of substrate synthesized, but also to the rate of
substrate utilization. For example, Speece and McCarty(5)
formulated the relationship of growth and acetic acid fermentation as follows:

$$dM_V/dt \; = \; 0.054 \, dF_r/dt \; - \; 0.038 \, M_V$$

where
dM_V/dt is bacterial volatile (on ignition) solids growth
in g per day,

dF_r/dt is acetic acid utilization in g COD per day,

$M/_V$ is grams volatile (on ignition) bacterial solids
in system.

This equation states that the growth of bacterial solids
is related, not only to the quantity of acetic acid utilized, but
also to the number of organisms already in the system. The
greater the quantity of organisms, the greater is the amount
of substrate which must be utilized for maintenance of these
organisms and, hence, the smaller is the energy available
for new growth.

The rate of substrate utilization is related both to the mass
of microorganisms and the concentration of substrate. How -
ever, at some high substrate concentration, the rate reaches
a maximum which is dependent only upon the concentration of
microorganisms, and so for this case:

$$dF_r/dt = k_r M_v$$

Substituting this into the preceding equation gives the maximum rate of growth, as follows:

$$dM_v/dt = (0.054 \, k_r - 0.038) \, M_v$$

or, $\quad dM_v/M_v = (0.054 \, k_r - 0.038) \, dt$

Integrating:

$$\ln \frac{M_v(2)}{M_v(1)} = (0.054 \, k_r - 0.038) \, T$$

The generation time is the time, T (days), required to double the biological mass, $M_v(2) = 2 \, M_v(1)$, so that:

$$\text{Generation time} = \frac{0.693}{0.054 \, k_r - 0.038}$$

This equation is shown plotted in Fig. 6.

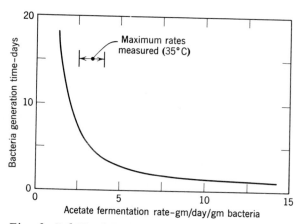

Fig. 6—Relation between acetate fermentation rate and bacterial generation time.

To obtain some idea of the generation time for the acetic acid-fermenting bacteria, the rate of substrate utilization was measured in several different laboratory digesters receiving acetic acid as a sole organic source. These digesters

were continuously fed and the acetic acid concentration was
maintained above 1, 000 mg per 1 to obtain maximum rates of
utilization. The inorganic nutrients were essentially those
reported previously (5). The normal high values for the rate
of utilization varied from 3 to 4 grams per day of acetic acid
per gram of bacteria (volatile solids, i. e., volatile on ignition),
which corresponds to a minimum generation time of 4 to 6
days. This generation time appears quite long compared to
that of aerobic organisms, some of which have generation
times measured in minutes. However, the value obtained
corresponds favorably to minimum sludge retention times
obtained for high rate digestion (25)(26)(27). It indicates also
why such long times are required for starting digesters, or
for gas production in studies on enumeration of these organisms
as reported by Heukelekian and Heineman (28).

Since the generation time of the methane bacteria is limited,
both by the small energy yield from substrate fermentation
and rate of substrate utilization, it is desirable to determine
whether these two factors may be increased to obtain maximum
efficiency. Since the maximum energy the bacteria can obtain
from fermentation is limited by thermodynamic considerations,
there is probably little chance of increasing the growth yield
significantly. Therefore, the rate of substrate utilization
appears to be more worthy of consideration.

Heukelekian and Heineman (28) found, while enumerating
the methane forming bacteria, that the addition of yeast extract
about halved the time required for gas formation. McCarty
and Vath (6) also found that the volumetric rates of fermentation
could be increased materially by adding dried powder obtained
from municipal digester supernatant liquor. By this procedure
they were able to obtain the fermentation of 21.9 and 13.3 g
per 1 per day for acetic and butyric acids, respectively. Unfortunately, the addition of this powder made it difficult to
evaluate the numbers of bacteria present, so that the rate
per organism could not be obtained. Speece and McCarty (5)
found the addition of thiamine, proline, glycine, cobalt, and
iron also to be beneficial.

Although the addition of certain inorganic and organic compounds has been found to increase the rate of acetic acid
fermentation, it appears that significantly higher rates will
require the addition or presence of a wide variety of materials.
Certainly this should prove a fruitful area for further research.
More information is required on kinetics of acetic and propionic

acid utilization, not only to determine maximum rates of
utilization, but also rates at lower substrate, limiting concentrations. Information on rates of hydrolysis and acid
fermentation is also desirable to determine when these may
be limiting. This information will not only give a more
rational basis for design of anaerobic treatment systems,
but will allow evaluation of the ability of such a system to
respond to increased loads.

SUMMARY

Methane fermentation is responsible for removal of large
quantities of organic matter from waste streams, both under
controlled and natural conditions. This process has proven
very beneficial in the past, in spite of our lack of knowledge
of the complex microbiology and biochemistry involved. However, recent advances have given greater insight to the process
and have indicated the advantages which might be obtained if
methane fermentation could be exploited to its maximum
potential. Exceptionally high volumetric rates of fermentation
have been shown to be possible, with the accompanying production of relatively small quantities of bacterial cells for
ultimate disposal. In streams or ponds, removal of organic
matter can proceed by methane fermentation in the bottom
muds without depletion of the oxygen resources of the water
above. Realization of the potentials of methane fermentation
has recently stimulated considerable research in this area
and it can be expected that much progress will be made towards
a full understanding of this process in the next few years.

ACKNOWLEDGEMENT

This investigation was supported in part by research grants
WP-173, WP-482, and WP-483 from the Division of Water
Supply and Pollution Control, Public Health Service. The
author wishes to express his appreciation to his former
students, J. S. Jeris, I. J. Kugelman, A. W. Lawrence, W.
Murdock, C. A. Vath, and R. E. Speece, whose data he
freely used.

LITERATURE CITED

1.   Buswell, A. M. 1936. et al, Anaerobic fermentations
Illinois State Water Survey, Bulletin 32.
2.   Barker, H. A. 1956. Bacterial fermentations. John Wiley,

New York
3.   McCarty, P. L. and R. R. McKinney. 1961. Salt
toxicity in anaerobic digestion. J. Water Poll. Contr. Fed.
33:399-415.
4.   Kugelman, I. J. 1962. Progress report on effect of inorganic ions on methane fermentation. Massachusetts Institute of Technology.
5.   Speece, R. E., and P. L. McCarty. 1962. Nutrient
requirements and biological solids accumulation in anaerobic
digestion. Proc. Int. Conf. on Water Pollution Res. London,
September 1962.
6.   McCarty, P. L., and C. A. Vath. 1962. Volatile acid
digestion at high loading rates. Int. J. Air Water Poll. 6:65-
73.
7.   Fair, G. M., and C. L. Carlson. 1927. Sludge digestion-
reaction and control. J. Boston Soc. Civil Eng. 14:82-112.
8.   Keefer, C. E., and H. Kratz. 1929. Digesting sewage
sludge at its optimum pH and temperature. Eng. News-Record
102:103-105.
9.   Barker, H. A. 1956. Biological formation of methane. Ind.
Eng. Chem. 48:1438-1442.
10. Fair, G. M., and E. W. Moore. 1934. Time and rate of
sludge digestion and their variation with temperature. Sew.
Works J. 6:3-13.
11. Buswell, A. M., and F. W. Sollo. 1948. The mechanism
of the methane fermentation. J. Amer. Chem. Soc. 70:1778-
1780.
12. Stadtman, T. C., and H. A. Barker. 1949. Studies on
the methane fermentation. VII. Tracer experiments on the
mechanism of methane formation. Arch. Biochem. 21:256-
264.
13. Pine, M. J., and H. A. Barker. 1956. Studies on the
methane fermentation. XII. The pathway of hydrogen in the
acetate fermentation. J. Bacteriol. 71:644-648.
14. Stadtman, T. C., and H. A. Barker. 1951. Studies on
the methane fermentation. VIII. Tracer experiments on fatty
acids oxidation by methane bacteria. J. Bacteriol. 61:67-80.
15. Stadtman, T. C., and H. A. Barker. 1951. Studies on
the methane fermentation. IX. The origin of methane in
acetate and methanol fermentation by Methanosarcina. J.
Bacteriol. 61:81-86.
16. Pine, M. J., and W. Vishniac. 1957. The methane fermentations of acetate and methanol. J. Bacteriol. 73:736-742.

17. Barker, H. A. 1941. Studies on the methane fermentation. V. Biochemical activities of Methanobacterium Omelianskii. J. Biol. Chem. 137:153-167.

18. Jeris, J. S., and P. L. McCarty. 1962. The biochemistry of methane fermentation using C14 tracers. 17th Purdue Industrial Waste Conference, May, pp. 181-197.

19. Buswell, A. M., L. Fina., H. F. Muller, and A. Yahiro 1951. Use of C14 in mechanism studies of methane fermentation. II. Propionic acid. J. Amer. Chem. Soc. 73:1809-1811.

20. McCarty, P. L., J. S. Jeris, and W. Murdock. 1962. The significance of individual volatile acids in anaerobic treatment. 17th Purdue Industrial Waste Conference, May, pp. 421-439.

21. Pohland, F. G., and D. E. Bloodgood. 1963. Laboratory studies of mesophilic and thermophilic anaerobic sludge digestion. J. Water Poll. Control Fed. 35:11-42.

22. Mueller, L. E., E. Hindin., J. V. Lunsford., and G. H. Dunstan. 1959. Some characteristics of anaerobic sludge digestion. Sew. Ind. Wastes 31:669-677.

23. Heukelekian, H., and P. Mueller. 1958. Transformation of some lipids in anaerobic sludge digestion. Sew. Ind. Wastes 30:1108-1120.

24. Lawrence, A. W. 1960. Anaerobic decomposition of lipid material M. S. Thesis, Massachusetts Institute of Technology.

25. Sawyer, C. N., and H. K. Roy. 1955. A laboratory evaluation of high rate digestion. Sew. Ind. Wastes 27:1356-1363.

26. Morgan, P. F. 1954. Studies of accelerated digestion of sewage sludge. Sew. and Ind. Wastes 26:462-476.

27. Torpey, W. N. 1958. Loading to failure of a pilot high rate digester. Sew. and Ind. Wastes 27:121-133.

28. Heukelekian, H., and B. Heineman. 1939. Studies on methane producing bacteria. I. Development of a method for enumeration. Sew. Works J. 11:426-435.

DISCUSSION

Dr. ZoBell (Scripps Inst. Oceanogr.): I understood Dr. McCarty to point out that the optimum conditions for methane fermentation were mostly under pH 8, mostly low salinity, mostly high temperature. It will be of interest that, in the world's largest septic tank, which has been in operation for

a long while, the pH is mostly above pH 8, the salinity averages 3.5 per cent about 95 per cent, of the marine environment
is always colder than 5 C -- conditions under which we have
a very effective methane fermentation. This leads me to
believe that there must be a different type of flora in the sea
than in septic tanks in the world above sea level. My serious
question had to do, primarily, with your comment that the
carbon could be accounted for almost exclusively by the production of methane or bacterial biomass. This must be true
only of pure or highly purified cultures, because I would
expect some quantity of carbon dioxide, some hydrogen. I
wonder if you have ever had occasion to explore the possibility
of there being hydrocarbons higher than methane as has been
reported, in certain types of septic fermentation; that is,
ethane and propane.

Dr. McCarty: Methane fermentation does proceed under
lower than optimum temperatures and at low pH's as well
as high pH's. It seems to occur under these conditions, however, at less than maximum rates. Optimum conditions are
not needed, especially in a natural environment. In the ocean
there are years in which to carry out this fermentation; however, we are interested in doing it in days in digesters.

We found, from our high salinity studies, that there was
methane fermentation, but at comparatively low rates, -- low
in terms of rate per gram of organism -- but when there is
an infinite amount of time the rates do not make much difference. Significant quantities of methane are produced under
less than optimum natural conditions.

Regarding the question about conversion of carbon, I was
not referring to organic carbon but to organic COD, which is
a measure of oxidizable organic material. As Dr. ZoBell
suggests, a good portion of the carbon is lost as carbon dioxide.
However, the decrease in COD is not at all related to organic
carbon or to carbon dioxide production. It is related to
methane production because under anaerobic conditions, the
only way oxidizable organics can be removed is to have a
reduced compound leaving the environment, and the only one
in this case is methane.

As for the synthesis of higher hydrocarbons, there have
been reports of such but I think there is still some doubt about
it. In our studies with methane fermentation in complex media,
as well as in simple media, we obtained very good quantitative
results for the conversion to methane and biological cells.

Perhaps some of the higher hydrocarbons could be formed, but, if so, they are not formed in very significant quantity.

Dr. Heukelekian (Rutgers Univ.): Dr. ZoBell, has much been done on methane fermentation in ocean bottom oozes?

Dr. ZoBell: Relatively little, but, nevertheless, there have been a few reports which indicate that there is an extensive methane fermentation on the sea floor.

If I may reply further to Dr. McCarty, in the ocean there are not eons for the methane fermentation to take place. It must take place rather quickly because the sea is in a state of dynamic equilibrium, where organic production, acre per acre, is, perhaps, from five to ten times higher than on the land, and in view of the fact that organic matter is not accumulating it is, a priori, evident that the decomposition is taking place at the same rate as production. Furthermore the production of organic matter is, perhaps, going on at a faster rate than in the world above sea level; therefore, I claim that methane fermentation must be taking place at a very substantial rate, probably faster than in the world above sea level.

The evidence is to be found in the sea, where we rarely find more than five mg per 1 of organic matter accumulating, despite the vast volumes of water concerned, but the production is from five to ten times higher than in the world above sea level. In view of the fact that the organic matter is not accumulating in the mud, building up as fossil fuel, it seems to me to be evidence that decomposition is taking place at a fast rate.

Dr. McCarty: I think we are talking about different things. You are talking about volumetric rate and I am talking about rate per organism. From our findings, the rate per organism is low, although there can be exceptionally high volumetric rates if sufficient numbers of bacteria are involved.

For example, Oswald, at the University of California, has been working on oxidation ponds, or stabilization ponds, as some people now call them. He found a reduction of BOD in the stabilization pond -- at normal temperatures, however; not the low temperature you are talking about -- of 1000 pounds per acre per day resulting from methane fermentation under some optimum conditions. Under average conditions the decrease was about 50 pounds per acre per day, which is still a significant reduction of organic material. The rate per organism there was probably low, but there were probably a lot of methane organisms present. That is the difference.

Dr. Alexander (Cornell Univ.): What is the ultimate electron acceptor for beta-oxidation of long-chain fatty acids under anaerobic conditions?

Dr. McCarty: The carbon dioxide acts as an electron accepter.

Dr. Alexander: The terminal electron accepter is commonly CO_2, as you point out, but with long-chain fatty acids, which are, in effect, hydrocarbons, there is not much oxidized material to serve as electron accepters at the time of origin. What is the electron acceptor prior to getting methane from CO_2?

Dr. McCarty: There is thirty per cent, carbon dioxide, to start with in the environment, in these fermentations. In fact, our buffer is bicarbonate.

Dr. Alexander: Will fermentation proceed in the absence of CO_2?

Dr. McCarty: I think not. This situation is a little aside from the practical problem because we do not have such a condition naturally. I think Barker has indicated that carbon dioxide is necessary to start the fermentation. Once present, it is naturally further produced. There are some cases, with pure cultures and pure substrates, where there is a net decrease in carbon dioxide. In this case, one must supply carbon dioxide. But in the methane fermentation where acetate is fermented, there is an excess of carbon dioxide.

Dr. Heukelekian: With complex organic materials, such as those in sewage sludge, the acid formation stage produces CO_2, as well as the methane fermentation stage. There is CO_2 present in the water and also bicarbonate, so there is no deficiency of carbon dioxide.

Dr. Alan Molof (New York Univ.): In your discussion of the necessary environmental conditions you mentioned anaerobic environment. Have you had the opportunity to follow quantitatively, through oxidation-reduction potentials, the anaerobic environment?

Dr. McCarty: We have made some ORP measurements during acetate fermentation and we found that, if we continued fermentation in the absence of sulfates, the ORP, as we measured it, apparently increased to a positive value. Although there was no oxygen present, the ORP seemed to increase.

I believe you feel that we made our measurements incorrectly, and it may be true. Initially, the ORP started at a negative value of about three to four hundred, based on calomel for reference, and then increased after several weeks of digester operation.

Dr. Molof: O-R potentials become important in the feeding of these systems. Does one slow the maximum fermentation rate by changing the potential with the addition of new material? I had opportunity to study an artificial system with a base of culture media and I found it acted differently in respect to potential response than did the natural system.

Dr. McCarty: I can add that we have added sulfides. The addition of sulfide alone lowered the ORP, but we are not sure whether it helped.

If one adds too much sulfide a toxic condition results; but we were adding less than an inhibitory concentration.

Dr. Kallio (State Univ. Iowa): Do I understand correctly that, from the fermentation of glucose labelled in the number 1 and number 6 positions, you isolated two moles of acetic acid labelled on the number 2 carbon, or did you infer their formation from the counts from the resulting methane?

Dr. McCarty: This was inferred from the resulting methane.

Dr. Frederick Pohland (Georgia Tech.): From a practical standpoint of controlling the environment, I wonder if we might consider whether we might separate physically the acid fermentation and the methane fermentation stages in an artificial system and thus, possibly control the process a little differently. If we could, in fact, do that, then I would like to know whether you think the ammonia is produced in the acid stage or whether it is produced in the methane fermentation stage?

Dr. McCarty: Ammonia can certainly be released in the acid stage. There are anaerobic organisms that are not methane producers, but they can convert amino acids to fatty acids and release ammonia. In an effectively separated system ammonia would be released in the first stage of acid formation

because there are organisms that can do this. We presently
do not have sufficient knowledge to state definitely that methane
organisms cannot use amino acids; none have been found, so
far, which can do so.   However, I am not sure we can make
the general statement that there are none.

Dr. Pohland: I was thinking in terms of the environmental
requirements for the methane organisms and, perhaps, the
organisms responsible for deamination of the protein fractions.
We know that the methane organisms are much more sensitive
to adverse environmental conditons, and if we could separate
the acid stage from the methane stage we would probably have
very rapid production of acid which might preclude the methane
organisms if they were, in fact, more sensitive to adverse
environmental conditions.

Dr. McCarty: I think there would be some advantages
in separation, mainly because the volatile acids formed in
the first stage are soluble. With a soluble substrate one can
operate the methane fermentation much more efficiently by
the recycling of the methane organisms, much like the activated sludge process, something which we cannot do now with
sewage sludge. The problem of acid conditions may still
remain. Even though ammonia is released in the first stage
of production, there is still a question, because of carbohydrates and so forth, whether there would be enough ammonia
released to buffer the system. And, although we commonly
talk of the methane organisms as being sensitive to environmental changes, I think one will find that the acid formers
are also quite sensitive, not perhaps as much as the methane
bacteria, but they are sensitive to accumulation of certain
materials, too, and that may become limiting.

Dr. Orgel (Colgate-Palmolive, Inc.): Do you visualize
cleavage of acetate at a relatively high oxidation level and
then reduction to methane? For example, would you consider
to be possible the cleavage of acetate to two one-carbon units
-- one being formate, the other one CO_2 and followed by reduction of CO_2 by hydrogen? Is there evidence for such a
conversion?

Dr. McCarty: The evidence is this: Barker and his co-
workers, using carbon-labelled acetic acid, have shown that
the methyl portion goes to methane; the carboxyl to carbon
dioxide. Using also acetate with labelled hydrogens on the

methyl carbon, they found that the three hydrogens were quantitatively converted also to methane, indicating that the methyl carbon was not first converted to carbon dioxide and subsequently reduced.

Dr. Orgel: I refer now to a reaction observed some time ago with bacteria, in which we found that doubly-labelled acetate -- that is, C^{14} - labelled acetate -- arose from $C^{14}O_2$ and molecular hydrogen in the presence of oxygen. It appeared that we were dealing with direct reduction of carbon dioxide by activated hydrogen, the formation of a C_1 compound, with subsequent condensation of two C_1 units. This result was obtained at very brief intervals of exposure of growing organisms to these conditions.

Dr. McCarty: Our studies with acetate were with mixed cultures, not pure cultures. We know little of the enzymes involved in this transfer. However, carbon dioxide reduction can be determined by adding labelled carbon dioxide to the medium. With acetate fermentation, if one adds labelled carbon dioxide to the medium there is no conversion to methane, but there is with almost all other substrates.

17

TRANSFORMATIONS IN INFILTRATION PONDS AND IN THE SOIL LAYERS IMMEDIATELY UNDERNEATH

J. K. Baars
The Water, Soil, and Air Division
Research Institute for Public Health
Engineering T.N.O.
The Hague, The Netherlands

Engineering T. N. O.

The change in quality of water stored in ponds for the purpose of infiltrating it into the subsoil for transformation into ground water is of the utmost importance to those who are forced by growing populations to increase their ground water reservoirs.

In the western part of the Netherlands the necessity for artificial infiltration has arisen because the original quantity of ground water was no longer sufficient for the water supply of the towns in or near the dune area, such as Amsterdam, Haarlem, Leyden, and The Hague.

It is for this reason that, for about ten years past, the Institute for Public Health Engineering T. N. O. has been carrying out investigations on the purifying capacity of the soil and the biology of infiltration ponds.

Although we might try to analyse which organisms and which chemical components are present in the supernatant liquid, it is very difficult to give a detailed picture of what happens in the mud layer, as this layer is to be considered as a non-homogeneous medium in which the conditions may vary from spot to spot.

In the top layers of the sand bottom, the situation is slightly better; but the greater the depth at which samples are taken, the more general a picture is obtained, although even at these greater depths, the body of sand may contain clay lenses which can change the general pattern completely.

The raw water used for these infiltrations is taken either from a branch of the Rhine, from the Amsterdam-Rhine shipping canal, or even from a canal that receives a mixture of dune water which drains off into the polders with canal water.

In the first two cases, the water is pre-treated by rapid sand filtration and incidentally chlorinated. However, many microorganisms orginally present in the Rhine water may be traced into the infiltration ponds, as there is no residual chlorine. In the Leyden system, the water is pumped into the infiltration ponds without any pretreatment.

As we shall consider several infiltration ponds, the chemical analysis of the water can only be given in general. Seasonal variations in its chemical composition are noticed; there are even more pronounced variations in biological forms.

TABLE 1: Composition of pond water and filtrate

Analyses	Pond water	Filtrate
Color (Pt-scale)	70	30-40
$KMnO_4$ consumption (mg/1)	60	20
Chlorides "	125-300	125-300
Nitrites "	trace	absent
Nitrates "	2-21	trace-14
Ammonia "	2-15	trace
Sulfates "	220	120
Bicarbonates "	150-320	140-310
Carbon dioxide "	9.0	16
Phosphate "	0.10-1.2	trace-0.1
Organic ammonia "	0.07	trace
Iron, ferric "	1.0	absent
Iron, ferrous "	absent	0.4-1.0
Manganese, divalent "	trace-0.30	0.20-0.90
Dissolved oxygen "	5 to super-saturation	absent
Hardness ($CaCO_3$) "	400-500	300-400
Suspended matter "	5.0	absent
Total bacterial content per ml:		
on nutrient agar after 48 hr at 37 C	400-5000	10
" " " " " " " 20 C	2000-25000	
" gelatin " " " " " 20 C	1000-12000	
E. coli count per ml, as M.P.N.	100-200	absent in 100 ml

Figure 1 shows how the nitrate concentrations in Rhine water vary with temperature during the seasons. The same effect, although less pronounced, is found in the ponds, and

one is tempted to explain these variations as being due to
assimilation by plants, the activity of which is known to be
more intense during summer than in winter. Nitrates can be
traced only in minute concentrations (less than 0.05 mg per
l). The ammonia content also varies with season; in winter
it is usually high, in summer low. The hardness varies
somewhat during the year, but has an average value of 400 to
100 mg $CaCO_3$. The pH may vary with sunshine, the variation
being due to CO_2 assimilation. In the same way, the O_2
content may fluctuate considerably.

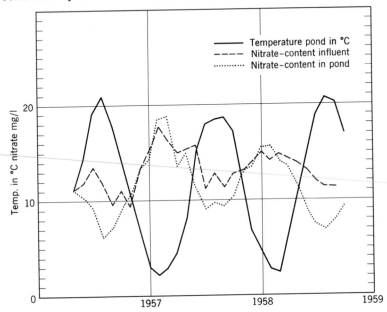

Fig. 1—Temperature and nitrate contents of infiltration water from
April, 1957 to November, 1959.
_____ Temperature pond in °C
— — — — — —Nitrate-content influent
— — — — — — — Nitrate-content in pond

Besides testing for the presence of Escherichia coli, the
character of the bacterial flora in general was investigated.
Counts on nutrient agar with pond water at 37 C gave numbers
varying from 400 to 5000 per ml. In places where there are
many birds, even higher figures may be found. On the other
hand, there are many places where a significant self-purification

takes place under the influence of sunshine, temperature, and oxygen produced by algae (Fig. 2). No positive results have been found in the search for bacteriophages (see also Pretorius, 1).

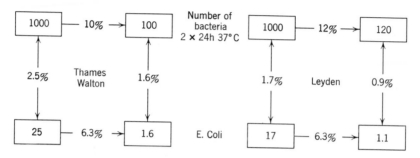

Fig. 2—Self-purification in storage reservoirs.

Species of Pseudomonas and Mycobacterium were present. Of the total bacterial number, about 1 to 2 per cent were spore-forming bacteria, such as Bacillus subtilis, Bacillus mycoides and Bacillus mesentericus.

The algal growth in these ponds is quite normal, depending, more or less, on weather conditions (2). The water is mostly clear to a depth of 80 to 100 cm. In spring, the growth of Diatomea is noticeable, mostly in the deeper layers, in quiet corners, and on the beaches. Incidentally, growth of Clado-phora is seen. In the benthos, Flagellata were noticed especially in springtime; ciliates also were present.

Higher plants like Ranunculus circinatus and Potamogeton pusillus may develop in ponds with permanent water supply; in the intermittent system, where infiltration is stopped during four summer months, they have no chance to grow.

During summer, the vegetable matter accumulates at the bottom in the permanent ponds, forming a bottom mud which will be considered further on. The general impression is that these ponds belong to the beta-mesosaprobic zone according to the classification of Kolkwitz (3). The ponds of the inter-mittent system will be considered separately.

When we analyse what is found at the other end of our biological course, and take samples of the water that has filtered through bottom mud and a body of sand, the result is as follows:

The chloride content has practically not changed. The fate of the nitrates, however, is quite different. In a special situation in which the sand has a grain size of about 0.1 to 0.15 mm, a distance of 40 m with a difference in level of 0.4 m is traversed in about 90 days. In other situations the detention time in the soil may be as long as 900 days, depending on the distance of the drainage wells from the ponds, the difference in water levels, etc. The grain size is mostly the same over the whole dune area. It often happened that no residual nitrates were found in the filtered water. Only in cases where the pond water contained more than 10 mg per l nitrate was there a chance of residual nitrate.

Nitrite could not be traced, nor ammonium, nor proteid ammonia. The hardness was 400 to 500 mg per l $CaCO_3$, the pH 7.6. Temperature was more uniform in the filtered water than in pond water. Free oxygen was often absent. Iron was present in a reduced form up to 0.6 mg per . The permanganate number for organic matter (expressed in mg $KMnO_4$ per l) was, at times, reduced from 60 to 20.

No algae or similar organisms were found in the filtrate. The bacterial content decreased to less than 10 per ml and E. coli was absent.

Before proceeding to the analysis of the transformations that take place in the water on its way downward, two remarks must be made:

The systems of infiltration vary; towns such as Amsterdam and The Hague use permanent infiltation with different rates, one operating at 10 cm per day, the other at 40 cm per day. The town of Leyden uses an intermittent method of operation, in which infiltration is stopped in spring-time and restarted in fall; here the rate of infiltration is also 10 cm per day, but in the summer period the bottom mud is completely dried and mineralized. In this way, it has been possible to maintain the same downward speed at the restarting time of infiltration for over twenty years. Other consequences of this technique will be considered separately.

The second point is that, when one wishes to investigate biological processes and their effect with time, it is necessary to have a yardstick for measuring the period over which the changes are noticed. Fortunately, the chloride content of Rhine water varies from week to week and, as it is not subject to biological transformations, a certain body of water may

be traced through the ponds and even after entering the subsoil. In analysing this same volume of water the changes in
nitrate content with time may be studied. In Fig. 3, the
peaks in the main pond water have the same corresponding
positions as those in the filtered secondary pond water, and
although heavy rainfall or evaporation under very dry weather
conditions may influence the extreme peaks, they are still
identifiable. In the investigations comprised in the present
report, the detention time in the soil was about 90 days.

For safety's sake, we checked the speed of migration of
the chloride and the nitrate under normal conditions in the
soil and it was found that there was no difference in velocity,
which is not the case with ions or molecules of much larger
diameter such as fluorescein, glucose, or iodides, nor with
ammonium salts, which are mostly absorbed to the sand grains.

When we now come to the biological transformations, we
wish to analyse them according to the general scheme of
hydrogen transfer as formulated by Kluyver.

Principles of bacterial metabolism

$$AH + B \longrightarrow A + BH$$

Dehydrogenation with oxygen: oxidation

Dehydrogenation with NO_3^- : denitrification

Dehydrogenation with SO_4^{2-}: sulfate reduction

$$A. BH \longrightarrow AH. B \longrightarrow AH + B$$

Internal dehydrogenation: methane fermentation

$$AH + BH \longrightarrow AB + H_2$$

Co-dehydrogenation: H_2-producing fermentations

The biological transformations take place under very
moderate climatological conditions, as the soil always equalizes
temperature differences. For nearly two years, temperatures
were measured in the ponds and after 40 m of soil passage.
The extreme temperature range from 1 C to 25 C was reduced
to differences from 6 C to 15 C (Fig. 4). Thus, denitrification
in winter was not influenced by low temperature.

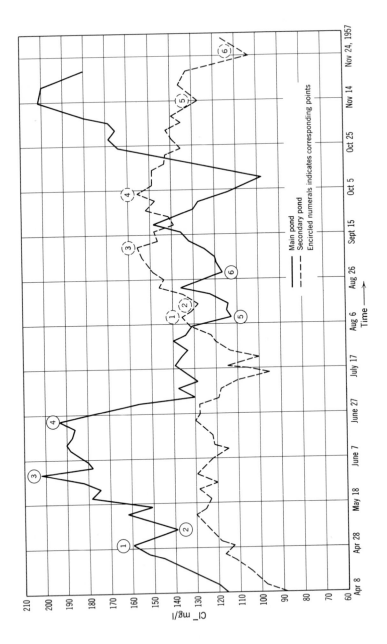

Fig. 3—Variations in chloride content of main pond and secondary pond at 35m.

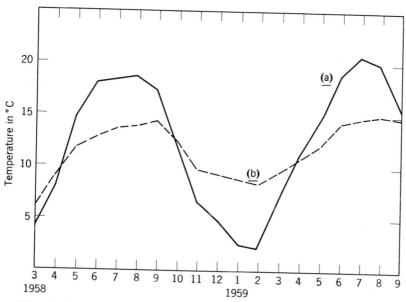

Fig. 4—Temperature of water in pond (a) and after 40m filtration through soil (b) March, 1958 to Sept., 1959.

The permanent infiltration systems. For the dehydrogenation of organic matter, a hydrogen acceptor will always be needed. In the aerobic or facultative aerobic processes, the H-acceptor may be free oxygen or nitrate oxygen. If any anaerobic transformation such as sulphate reduction should occur, it would necessarily result in the decrease of sulphate oxygen after depletion of the nitrate. However, in the situations considered, there was usually a residual nitrate content and, although signs of H_2S production resulting in a faint bluish color of the dune sand were incidentally observed, there was no sulphate reduction of any importance.

To find a good yardstick for the content of oxidisable organic matter is not easy. For potable water and fairly pure surface water, the acid permanganate method is generally used. There is, of course, no guarantee whatsoever of any identity between the H-atoms which may be used in bacterial mineralisation and those accessible for oxidation by $KMnO_4$ under acid conditions at 100 C. The same holds good for the COD (chemical oxygen demand) value, where even much stronger H_2SO_4 and potassium dichromate are used. The BOD (biochemical oxygen

demand) test is not suitable when we want to analyze water
containing very few bacteria and very small amounts of
organic matter. Therefore, notwithstanding all the objections,
the KMnO4 test was ultimately used.

To obtain an insight into the transformations in the benthos
we should consider the decrease of oxidant and the decrease of
organic matter (the oxidant is considered to be the sum of free
oxygen and nitrate oxygen, as these latter function as hydrogen
acceptors in transformation effected by aerobic and facultative
aerobic bacteria). Therefore, two situations were investigated,
viz:

(1) the travel of water through a body of sand only, and
(2) the travel of water from a pond through the benthos,
followed by filtration through sand.

For this purpose a number of wells were constructed at
5 m and 30 m distance from a pond, in the direction of the
ground water flow.

The water of these wells was analysed, taking into consideration the lapse of time required for the water to travel
from the wells at 5 m to those at 30 m.

The following results were obtained:

(1) Water passing through a body of sand only:

Well at 5 m	Well at 30 m	Oxidant consumption
Free O_2 7.5 mg/l	4.0 mg/l	15.6 - 9.6 = 6.0 ppm (a)
NO_3-O_2 8.1 mg/l	5.6 mg/l	

Decrease KMnO4, as ppm O_2 in water   4.25 ppm (b)

Ratio (a) : (b) about 1.5:1.

(2) Water passing through benthos and a body of sand:

Water in pond	After infiltration	Oxidant consumption
Free O_2 11.9 mg/l	1.6 mg/l	20.2 - 3.5 = 16.7 mg/l (a)
NO_3-O_2 8.3 mg/l	1.9 mg/l	

Decrease KMnO4, as mg/l O_2 in water   2.8 mg/l (b)

Ratio (a) : (b) about 6:1.

Thus, not only dissolved organic matter, as determined by
the KMnO4 method, is mineralized, but much more oxidant is
used, and it is evident that this may take place in the benthos.

There is a noticeable increase in free CO_2 content of the water, but it is difficult to draw a quantitative conclusion. We prefer to point to the fact only.

For the mineralisation of organic matter, the presence of algae is often considered to be an advantage. It is true that, by CO_2 assimilation, pure O_2 is produced, and as this O_2 is set free under atmospheric pressure, it might be possible, theoretically, that about 5 times oversaturation occurs. However, the greater part of the oxygen which is dissolved in excess of the saturation value escapes into the air.

When we write the equation as

$$x\ H_2CO_3 \longrightarrow (H_2CO)_x + x\ O_2,$$

we have to realize that the orgin of organic matter is linked to the O_2 production, and when this organic matter sinks to the bottom it may consume about the same quantity of oxygen as liberated originally, to be reoxidized into H_2CO_3. Only when humic substances are formed may the consumption of O_2 be less.

In the case of methane fermentation there may even be a real gain in mineralisation, for CH_4 and CO_2 can be produced without any active participation of an extra hydrogen acceptor. However, no evidence was found that, under normal conditions, methane fermentation took place in the bottom mud or in the sand layers immediately underneath.

One might conclude from the high oxidant consumption that the reduction of organic matter is intense. However, it often happens that organic substances, which are present in very small concentration but which are detectable by their effect on the taste of the water, are not completely eliminated by the infiltration technique. When, in 1955 to 1957, three large waterworks started production of artifical ground water with Rhine water, taste-correcting measures had to be taken, such as addition of activated carbon, break-point chlorination, and ClO_2 treatment of the water pumped from the wells. It is known that the Rhine water contains organic components which give severe trouble in direct chlorination, but there was a real chance that storage in ponds and very slow sand filtration, with a detention time in the soil of at least a few months, might eliminate the taste. This, however, could not be realized.

There is an indication that the difficulty may be caused by homologues of phenol. We know that phenol itself may be of vegetable origin as a deterioration product of leaves. Human beings also produce phenols as a dissimilation product, and still another source is industrial waste. Although the phenol proper is easily oxidized by bacteria, this reaction is strongly influenced by low temperatures. In winter, the phenol content of the Rhine water may amount to 1 mg per l; whereas in summer time, the figures are about 0.010 mg per liter.

When the nitrogen content of pond water and filtrate is analyzed, the following figures are obtained (Table 2):

TABLE 2: N content of pond water and in filtrate

Analyses		Pond water	Filtrate
NO_2 - N	(mg/l)	0.04	0.02
NO_3 - N	"	1.95	0.12
NH_4 - N	"	0.19	0.14
proteid - N	"	0.22	0.30
Total	"	2.40	0.58

The main cause of the decrease in N content is in the nitrate consumption and there must have been a noticeable denitrification. We know from the experiments of Verhoeven (4) that, under exceptional conditions, the process of nitrate reduction may lead to an even more reduced state of nitrogen (NH_3), but it is not probable that these conditions occur in the soil. That the proteid N content has increased slightly, may be due to the dissolving of seashells which are present in dune sand.

From the analyses in Table 1, we see that the iron content usually increases. Originally present in the ferric form, it is often reduced to the ferrous form, and although the ground water as collected from the wells is quite clear, it has to be deferrisated by aeration and filtration. One has to be very careful in drawing conclusions from the mere facts as observed. At one place, ferric deposits were found in the transport systems of artificially produced ground water. As the iron salts in this water were supposed to be in a reduced state, and the water had just been filtered through fine dune sand, it should have been impossible that a ferric deposit was formed. The water in question, however, turned out to be a mixture of deep ground water and rainwater (containing oxygen), the latter forming a top layer on the actual ground water near the well. When they were mixed by pumping a precipitate resulted.

When we now come to the biological analysis of what happens in the benthos and the underlying soil layers, we first might consider the living organic matter. It was not possible to study the antagonistic action of microorganisms, although there might have been antibiotic action and activity of protozoa against bacteria. Anyhow, there is a certain amount of oxidant available for mineralisation. The extra oxidant consumption, as previously shown, is an indication that when there is a constant supply of new oxidant, dead biological materials may be mineralized aerobically.

If, however, this supply is terminated, anaerobic transformations may dominate. During one winter, when the ponds were covered with an ice layer with snow on top, infiltration was stopped and all the water was drained. Under the ice there was only a mud layer, in which very pronounced sulphate reduction resulting in H_2S production was found. At a depth of only a few inches below the bottom of the pond, no more algae, diatoms, etc. could be found.

A different picture is obtained when the bacterial flora is studied (5). For the investigation of a dam (Fig. 5) surrounding an infiltration pond and having drains at a distance of about 28 m, we took samples from the ground water zone as wet sand. This is done by using a brass tube of 5 cm diameter and sometimes 2 to 3 m length, which is driven into the soil by mechanical force. When it is filled with sand from the desired depth, the top is sealed with a rubber stopper. When the tube is pulled up again, the vacuum which is created at the top of the tube prevents the sand from leaving the tube. By gently knocking on the tube after the stopper has been removed, a sample from the desired depth can be selected. The wet sand is brought into a wide-mouthed vial. By gently knocking the bottle, the sand grains can be more closely compacted, so that a supernatant liquid is obtained which is, in fact, the water that filled the capillaries between the sand grains.

This enables us to trace a decrease in bacterial numbers in the water on its way through the body of sand. It is interesting that, at 1 m from the shore, the water still contains about the same bacterial number as in the pond itself, so there is no evidence of decrease in the number of bacteria caused by protozoa.

When, however, 1 gram of sand is gently shaken with 20 ml of sterile water, it is possible to determine the bacterial

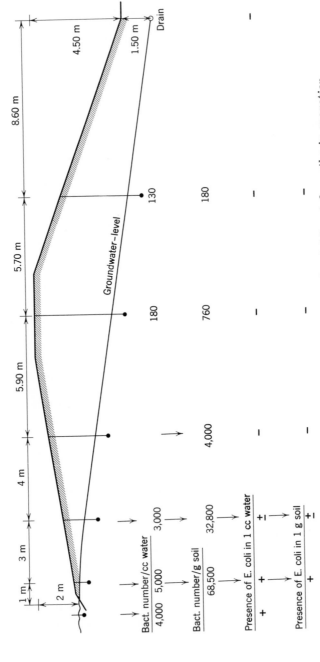

Fig. 5—Infiltration through a body of sand (grain size 0.15mm) 6 months in operation.

number per gram of sand, and in that case, a totally different picture is obtained. The bacteria are present in this 1 gram of sand and only gradually does their number decrease with distance. We have to state here that the dune sand concerned is very fine-grained (0. 10 to 0. 15 mm). A coarser material will give a different effect, because the filtering effect, as such, per unit of length may be less, although it is known that very small particles may be filtered off in capillaries which have a much larger diameter.

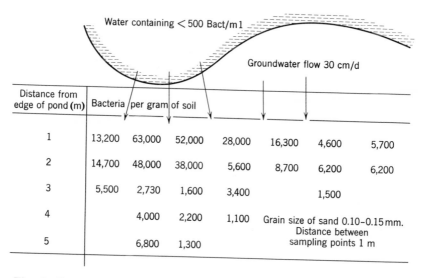

Fig. 6—Purification of surface water during infiltration horizontal pattern. Decrease in bacterial content/g soil from phreatic zone with distance from shore of infiltration pond.

The general impression obtained from the analysis is that the bacteria are strongly adsorbed to the sand grains in concentrations which result in an intense struggle for life; those bacteria which can stand unfavorable conditions have the best chance of survival. It is not astonishing when we see the percentage of spore-forming bacteria increase from 1 to 2 per cent to 20 to 30 per cent. One cannot say that this increase is due only to the dying-off of the nonspore-forming bacteria,

because the spore formers also decrease in number, but they
are able to keep alive longer on the poor food supply.

We could compare the situation in these upper sand layers
with what happens in biological treatment of sewage with
activated sludge. There we have a bacterial floc, a supply of
organic food (BOD), and a supply of oxygen. If only we supply
enough BOD and O_2, the bacteria will do the mineralisation.
If the oxygen supply is insufficient for the amount of BOD,
there will be an excess of BOD left in an anaerobic situation
and this is what may also happen in the soil underneath the
ponds.

If the quantity of organic substances present in the water
is too great (serious pollution), all the free oxygen and nitrate
oxygen will be used (6) and strict anaerobic transformations
resulting, inter alia, in H_2S production, again will take place.
The mineralisation of the organic components comes to a
standstill, and once they have penetrated the ground water they
may stay there for a very long time without any further change.

It is also possible that, although the oxidant supply is
sufficient, the bacterial flora fails. When special organic
compounds which might be mineralized only when a special
flora is available (7) are introduced incidentally into the
system of ponds and soil layers, it is possible that mineralisation will not take place for some time. A case is known in
which accidental pollution with hydrocarbons from an airplane
crash near the ponds resulted in the ground water having a
very objectionable taste.

Finally, there is the possibility of pollution of surface waters
with substances that have no possibility of bacterial mineralisation at all, such as hexachlorocyclohexane, used in the
control of cockroaches (see also Sayre and Stringfield, 8, on
the weed-killer case near Los Angeles). They will also pass
unchanged. We know what trouble pollution with organic fuel
has caused, and still causes, once it has reached the ground
water stream.

When there is no man-made dike and the water simply
infiltrates into the surrounding dunes, a picture similar to
that shown in Fig. 5 is obtained (see Fig. 6). Although the
bacterial numbers may vary in an absolute sense, the general
impression is confirmed that the number of bacteria adsorbed
on the sand grains decreases rapidly with increasing distance
from the pond.

A certain ripening in the sand layers is noticeable, as seen

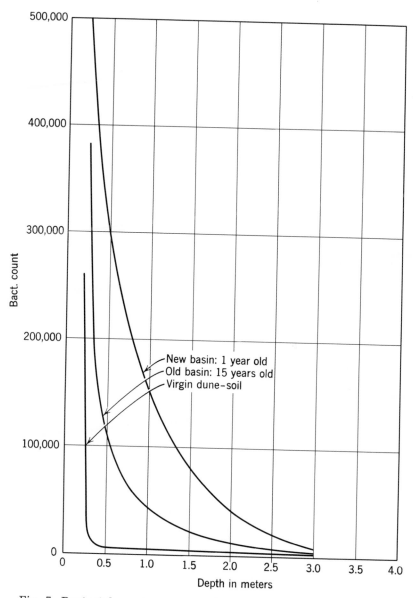

Fig. 7—Bacterial count per gram of soil at increasing depth under bottom infiltration basin.

from Fig. 7. Here samples were taken in two different situations, from the bottom of the ponds downwards and in virgin dune soil (9): (a) in an old basin (15 years in operation), (b) in a new basin (1 year in operation), and (c) in virgin dune soil (for comparison).

In the dune soil, the bacterial number at 0.5 m depth was very low. In the old basin there also was a very pronounced decrease over the first 0.5 m, but the new basin had not yet attained its full purification capacity.

It will be obvious that if the water contains even a small amount of silt, there is a severe risk of clogging the soil, and elaborate measures have to be taken to clean the permanent infiltration systems. It has been noticed, however, that if the speed of infiltration is very low this risk is less. A theory is advocated that the CO_2 production resulting from the mineralisation of organic matter is a favorable factor in maintaining the permeability; however, there is no definite proof of this.

Thus, the general impression of permanent infiltration of slightly polluted water in a pond is that the organic matter is largely mineralized in an aerobic medium and bacteria are filtered off in the fine-grained sand over a relatively short distance. The concentration of oxygen and nitrates in the water, however, limits the purifying capacity of the pond and the soil.

The intermittent infiltration. A different picture is obtained in the intermittent system as applied, for instance, for the town of Leyden. Infiltration is started in fall and finished late in spring. The water level is then lowered and the bottoms of the ponds become dry. The benthos may then be oxidized by free oxygen from the air and, as the water level descends more and more, the capillaries in the top layers will be filled with air. Not only no oxygen or nitrates from the water are needed for the mineralisation of the benthos, but the free oxygen penetrating into the top layers may be an important aid to mineralisation, as shown in the following calculation.

When, during the summer, the water level is lowered 2.5 m, a volume of 1 x 1 x 25 l of sand is drained. As the actual pore volume of the sand is about 0.3, a total volume of 7.5 l of air is drawn in through the surface of 1 dm^2. This volume contains about 2000 mg O_2 (1 liter contains 300 mg O_2).

It is possible that just after the ground water level has been lowered, the organic matter and the bacteria adsorbed to the sand are already mineralized. Redox-potential determination gave values of + 0.480 to + 0.380 mV over a depth of 1 m (pH 7.0 to 7.3).

To prove this, a series of samples was taken of this "dry" soil and compared with similar samples from a wet soil. The results are given in Fig. 8, where the organic matter, expressed in KMnO4 figures, is plotted for both situations. A similar picture could be given for the bacterial content under these circumstances. Further supply of free oxygen, which is governed by the deficit in oxygen in the lower layers, will take place.

Hence, when filtration is recommended in fall with a speed of 10 cm per day, there might be an extra quantity of 10 mg O_2 per 1 water available during 180 days. This indrawn air will be trapped by the water, as the resistance of the air-filled

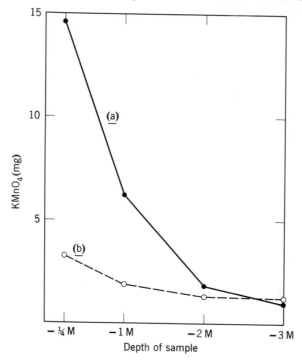

Fig. 8—Content of organic matter during infiltration (a) and at the end of a day (b) in mg KMnO$_4$/g soil.

capillaries is much greater than at the sides of the ponds.
So transportation in a direct vertical direction is slow and
there is a good possibility of ultimate mineralisation.

It is quite astonishing that this intermittent system enables
one to start infiltration afresh, each year with the same
permeability of the sand. The Leyden waterworks have been
operating since 1940 without any artificial cleaning of the
ponds. The main reason for this must be considered to be
the consequent use of the purifying factors that are available
in nature, based on the correct application of the theory of
hydrogen donors and hydrogen acceptors in the fight against
increasing pollution and the maintainance of sound and whole-
some ground water.

SUMMARY

An approach is given to the chemical and biological transformations, which take place in the benthos and the underlying
soil layers.

The decrease in organic matter, as well as in bacterial
numbers is analyzed, considering, at the same time, the
possibilities for mineralisation.

A comparison is made between the method of permanent
infiltration and the intermittent system. It turns out that the
latter has some distinct advantages over the former, which
is explained in detail, based on the theory of hydrogen transfer
as the basis of bacterial metabolism.

LITERATURE CITED

1.   Pretorius, W. A. 1962. Some observations on the role
of coliphages in the number of E. coli in oxidation ponds. J
Hyg., Camb. 60:279-281.
2.   le Cosquino de Bussy, I. J. 1961. Limnologische Untersuchungen an Infiltrationsteichen zur Trinkwassergewinnung in
Dünengebieten. Verh. Int., Verein Limnol. 14:1049-1053.
3.   Kolkwitz, R. 1950. Ökologie der Saprobien, Schriftenreihe
des Vereins für Wasser-, Boden- und Luft-hygiene No. 4
Piscator Verlag, Stuttgart, 64 pg.
4.   Kluyver, A. and W. Verhoeven. 1954. Studies on true
dissimilatory nitrate reduction. II. The mechanism of
denitrification. Antonie van Leeuwenhoek 20:241-262.
5.   Baars, J. K. 1957. Travel of pollution and purification
en route in sandy soils. Bull. World Health Org. 16:727-747.
6.   State Water Pollution Control Board of California, (USA)

1954. Report on the Investigation of travel of pollution.
7.   Baars, J. K. and H. J. Boorsma. 1957. Pollution of
ground water. Proceedings General Assembly Int. Union
Geodesy and Geophysics, Toronto. Tome II p. 279-289.
8.   Sayre, A. N. and V. I. Stringfield. 1948. Artificial
recharge of ground water reservoirs. J. Amer. Water Works
Assn. 40:1153-1158.
9.   Baars, J. K. and I. J. le Cosquino de Bussy. 1960.
Infiltration von Fluszwasser in Dünengebieten, Schw. Zeitschr.
Hydrol. 22:380-395.

DISCUSSION

Mr. Benjamin C. Nesin (City of New York): What was the
turbidity of the water being infiltrated?

Dr. Baars: The water had passed rapid sand filters, so
the turbidity was very low. If there is much suspended matter
in it, difficulties will certainly result. One of the systems
has river water which still contains suspended matter, and
they have to clean up their infiltration canals with bulldozers,
which is quite an elaborate undertaking.

Mr. Morris Smith (Toms River Chemical Corp.): I did
not recall from your original map whether the water, after
being recovered from ground water sources and being used
in the municipalities, was then returned to the Rhine or
whether it was disposed of to the sea. Is there any danger
of a chloride or sulfate build-up as a result of continual
recirculation?

Dr. Baars: No. After use, the Rhine water turns into
sewage and is dispersed in another way. They do not bring
back any purified sewage into the dunes.

Dr. Alexander (Cornell University): How serious a
problem, in terms of water infiltration to the dunes, is the
clogging of the infiltration ponds as a result of bacterial
growth on the mud-soil interface layer?

Dr. Baars: So far as we know, there has been no accumulation even with continuous infiltration of clear water, but
accumulation is very strongly influenced by the speed of infiltration. These ponds are run at the speed of only five
inches per day, which is possible by regulating the difference
of head between the pumping wells and the ponds; but if one
infiltrates too quickly, at a speed of, let us say, five meters,

or something like 20 feet per day, it is possible that the
bacteria can penetrate much further and that algae also are
found at the depth of 20 feet. It is the very slow speed that
is important. It is quite a problem to explain how these
bacteria are retained in the sand. As we know, very small
particles can be filtered off in capillaries which are much
larger in diameter, so I'm inclined to suppose absorption
may be possible at this very low speed. When water is rushed
through these capillaries, the bacteria have no possibility of
being absorbed and they penetrate much further.

Chairman Heukelekian (Rutgers University): Is the infiltration rate after the drying of the pond the same as before?
Is there no decrease in the filtration rate over the years?

Dr. Baars: No. This discontinuous system has been
operating since 1940 and each fall the ponds start again with
the same permeability as before.

Dr. John E. McCroan (Georgia Health Dept.): Has anyone
isolated pathogens from Rhine water and are there pathogens
in these ponds?

Dr. Baars: We could not find pathogens. Mostly we rely
on the safety barrier provided by Escherichia coli. However,
I think there would not be many pathogens in the Rhine either.
In purified effluents, of course, we know that there are a lot
of pathogens still left in the water. But the detention time in
the Rhine and the ponds, for which I quoted here an example
of two weeks but which sometimes is much longer, will also
have a quite noticeable effect on the decrease in concentration
of any pathogens, as E. coli also is decreased to a great
degree.

Chairman Heukelekian: But you have another barrier,
that is, chlorination of the water before consumption. Is not
that so?

Dr. Baars: Yes, we have a barrier in the possibility of
chlorination.

Dr. McCroan: Do you have a mosquito problem in these
fresh water ponds and dunes? And if so, do you do anything
about controlling them?

Dr. Baars: No. there is no problem. This is a restricted
area, forbidden for the public, so although there may be some

flies or other insects, they do not give any trouble. There are many ducks in the ponds and also sea gulls and those are quite a problem -- but that is another question.

Mr. Purkerson (Taft Sanitary Engineering Center): Are there problems of taste and odors as a result of algal blooms in the ponds?

Dr. Baars: No, fortunately not.

Mr. Purkerson: Would you outline briefly your methods for enumeration and identification of Escherichia coli, please?

Dr. Baars: We do it with a full IMViC test.

Dr. Pohland (Georgia Tech.): What effect has this method of recharge of the ground water had on salt water intrusion?

Dr. Baars: After fresh water infiltration was begun, much more fresh water than was needed for the water supply was infiltrated, so they have pushed back the fresh water zone again downward, not only to be safe for their water supply catchment area but also to be safe against brackish water intrusion into the hollows. The inland polders in Holland have to be flushed with fresh water, which is the reason why we are so interested in having Rhine water from the east which has a low chloride content.

Chairman Heukelekian: Have you made any observations on detergent removal by the infiltration process in the pond itself?

Dr. Baars: Yes, the detergent content of the Rhine is about 0.3 mg per l, but we could not detect any alkyl benzene sulfonate in the water pumped from the wells, so I suppose that it may have been very well oxidized.

Chairman Heukelekian: I think these results are extremely interesting from the standpoint of certain areas in this country, such as southern California, where there is a water shortage problem and salt water intrusion problem, and in Asia, as well. You are familiar with the work they are going to do in Israel, reclaiming the sewage by infiltrating through sand?

Dr. Baars: Yes, and I can say that, if there is any system that would apply, it would be an intermittent system from which they would obtain the maximum profit.

18

SOME ASPECTS OF THE BACTERIOLOGY
OF THE RUMEN

Marvin P. Bryant
Animal Husbandry Research Division
ARS, Agricultural Research Center
Beltsville, Maryland

All herbivorous animals have an expanded part of the
alimentary tract where bulky fibrous foods, which form a
large part of their diet, can be delayed in passage through
the tract to undergo the extensive microbial fermentation
necessary for utilization.

In ruminants the expanded part of the tract is represented
by the rumen. Figure 1 shows a schematic representation
of the ruminant stomach. The ingested food first enters the
reticulo-rumen. It then passes on through the omasum to
the abomasum (true stomach) where digestion more or less
equivalent to that in non-ruminants is initiated. As an
estimate of the size of the reticulo-rumen, it represents
about 85 per cent of the total stomach capacity in the adult
cow (Sisson and Grossman, 1938) and may contain 250 lb of
digesta, about 20 per cent of the total body weight, in a hay-
fed cow (Campling, Freer, and Balch, 1961).

The importance of rumen microbial digestion of food is
indicated by the estimate that 70 to 85 per cent of the total
digestible dry matter of the usual type of diet is digested in
the rumen (Gray, 1947) and all of the digestion appears to
be due to microbial enzymes rather than to enzymes secreted
by the animal.

The Rumen Environment. The rumen is different from
many other natural microbial habitats in its relative constancy.
There is a relatively constant influx of food and water, and
passage of undigested food residues and microbial cells on to
the lower tract. The dry matter percentage of the contents

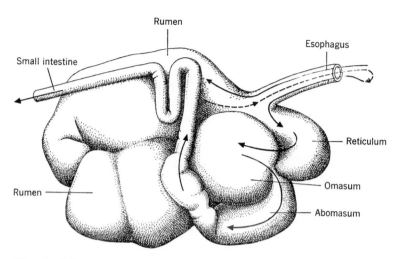

Fig. 1—Schematic representation of the stomach of ruminants (after Scientific American, 1958, 198, 34.)

tends to be rather constant regardless of the water intake (Balch et al., 1953) and the osmotic pressure is maintained close to that of blood (Parthasarathy and Phillipson, 1953). The temperature is usually about 38 to 42 C. The pH, usually between 6 and 7 , is held relatively constant by the influx of large amounts of saliva containing a large amount of sodium bicarbonate as the main buffer (McDougall, 1948), by the absorption of volatile fatty acids and NH_3 produced in the fermentation into the blood stream, and by the tendency toward an equilibrium in ions between the ingesta and the blood stream (Masson and Phillipson, 1951).

The ingesta are highly anaerobic with an oxidation-reduction potential usually of about -400 mv when measured with bright platinum and calomel electrodes (Broberg, 1957). The gaseous phase in the dorsal rumen usually contains 50 to 70 per cent of CO_2 and the remainder is chiefly CH_4 with small amounts of other gases (see Barnett and Reid, 1961). Although some oxygen gains entrance with the feed, it is rapidly utilized by the microbial population.

The ingesta is constantly mixed by a complex series of contractions (Balch, 1961), and rumination, involving remastication of the food, provides an increased surface area from microbial attack (Bell, 1961).

Urea continually enters the rumen via the saliva of which it is a constituent, and across the rumen wall from the blood stream (Houpt, 1959; Decker et al., 1960). Ammonia is rapidly produced from the urea so that, over short periods, growth of rumen microbes is not completely dependent on the animal's dietary nitrogen. Schmidt-Nielsen and Osak (1958) showed that urea is returned to the blood stream by the kidney of ruminants during periods of low nitrogen intake.

Some Functions of Rumen Microorganisms. Perhaps the most important function of the microorganisms is the fermentation of carbohydrates such as cellulose, pentosans, and pectin, which are not available without microbial attack, for use by the animal. These and other materials such as starch, sugars, and organic acids, which could be directly utilized by the animal, are fermented with the production of CO_2, CH_4, and volatile fatty acids. The volatile fatty acids are absorbed and serve as the most important energy source of ruminants (Blaxter, 1961), whereas the energy of the methane is lost. Although the proportions of the various products vary somewhat, depending on the feeding regime, an approximation of the theoretical fermentation balance for carbohydrate would be as shown in Table 1. These data were calculated for steers weighing an average of 433 kg and consuming feed at an energy level of 1.5 times the basal metabolism (see Brody, 1945). The assumptions made in the calculations have been discussed by Wolin (1960). In this case the energy available to the animal from volatile fatty acids (8787 kc) represents about 76 per cent of the net energy available to the animal. This value would be increased somewhat by including the energy available from the microbial cells produced. A small part of the volatile acids is present as valeric acid.

A large proportion of the protein in the diet is hydrolyzed to amino acids and peptides by the rumen microbes, and these intermediates are either rapidly incorporated into microbial protein or rapidly catabolized to volatile fatty acids, CO_2, and ammonia so that, under usual conditions, free amino acids and peptides are present in very small amounts in rumen fluid (Annison and Lewis, 1959). Carbohydrate, volatile fatty acid, and CO_2-carbon, and NH_3, in addition to amino acids, are utilized for synthesis of microbial protein (see Bryant and Robinson, 1963, for further references). Often from 50 to 90 per cent of the protein nitrogen of a diet is converted to rumen microbial protein before being utilized by the animal

(McDonald and Hall, 1957; Weller et al., 1958). Also, because of microbial synthesis of protein using inorganic nitrogen and sulfur, the ruminant can be maintained, and limited production obtained, on diets practically devoid of amino acids or protein (Loosli et al., 1949). Nitrate and other nitrogen compounds which are rapidly converted to ammonia can also serve as sources of nitrogen. The efficient use of dietary nitrogen by ruminants depends, to a considerable extent, on the rate at which it is converted to microbial protein as compared to the rate at which it is converted to ammonia. If the diet contains a large amount of nitrogen in relation to energy materials for microbial growth, then a considerable amount of nitrogen is absorbed from the rumen in the form of NH_3, converted to urea, and excreted (see Annison and Lewis, 1959).

Rumen microorganisms have also a great effect on dietary lipids (Garton, 1961). Glycerides and phospholipids are hydrolyzed and the glycerol is fermented mainly to propionic acid (Johns, 1953; Garton et al., 1961). Unsaturated fatty acids are hydrogenated (Reiser, 1951) and the bacteria synthesize large quantities of odd-numbered carbon and branched fatty acids, characteristic of ruminant body and milk fat, utilizing the corresponding volatile fatty acids such as n-valerate and isovalerate (Keeney et al., 1962; Allison et al., 1962b; Wegner and Foster, 1963).

TABLE 1: A theoretical rumen fermentation balance

Materials	Moles [a]	kcal
Substrate fermented as $C_6 H_{12} O_6$	17.31	11,650
Fermentation products		
Acetic (30.3 molar %)	17.45	3,647
Propionic (10.6 molar %)	6.11	2,242
Butyric (9.6 molar %)	5.53	2,898
Methane (17.3 molar %)	9.96	2,100
Carbon dioxide (32.2 molar %)	18.55	0

[a] Calculated using the methods of Hungate (1960) and the values of Carroll and Hungate (1954) for products and values of Forbes for methane (see Brody, 1945). Gross energy of the ration = 26,700 kc, digested energy = 18,900 kc, net energy = 11,520 kc, basal metabolism 7,680 kc, average weight of steers = 433 kg.

The ruminant does not require an exogenous supply of
B-vitamins or vitamin K, because of the synthesis of these
by rumen microorganisms (see Porter, 1961).

It is apparent that the rumen fermentation is intimately
connected with the well-being and productive capacity of the
animal. For example, acute indigestion caused by feeding
large amounts of grain is associated with a drastic change
in the flora, with an increase in lactic acid bacteria, lowering
of the pH, and accumulation of lactic acid (Hungate et al.,
1952). Bloat is caused by the inability of the animal to
eructate the fermentation gases produced in the rumen, usually
because of the entrapment of the gas in a stable foam caused
by as yet unknown interactions between dietary constituents
and microorganisms (See Gutierrez et al., 1961; Mangan
et al., 1959; Fina et al., 1961). Nitrate poisoning is due
to the ruminal formation of nitrite in quantities sufficient to
poison the animal. Depression of the percentage of fat in
milk is usually associated with a decreased proportion of
acetate to propionate in the rumen (see Van Soest, 1963).

It is apparent that for a more complete understanding of
ruminant metabolism, we need a much more complete ecological analysis of the rumen microbial population (Hungate,
1960). In addition to quantitative information on the entire
complex of reactions occurring, we need to identify and
determine the metabolic characteristics of the individual
groups of microorganisms concerned.

Although it is difficult to generalize on the contribution
of bacteria and ciliate protozoa, the chief microorganisms
concerned in the rumen fermentation, Gutierrez (1955)
estimated that the protozoa may contribute 20 per cent of
the fermentation acids and they might contribute about the
same proportion of the protein available to the animal (Hungate,
1955). Because Dr. Gutierrez will discuss the protozoa, I
will discuss further only the rumen bacteria.

The Culture of Rumen Bacteria. During the first half of
the century, a large number of workers attempted the pure
culture of bacteria functional in the rumen, with major
emphasis on the cellulolytic bacteria (see Sijpesteijn, 1948).
However, it was not until 1946 that unqualified success was
obtained by Hungate (1947), who obtained pure cultures of
bacteria which were morphologically similar to cellulolytic
bacteria observed in direct microscopic studies and present
in the rumen in large numbers. The success of the method

of Hungate was due to the use of culture media similar in composition to the rumen environment. The media contained minerals, including ammonia and bicarbonate, so that, with the CO_2 gaseous phase, a pH of about 6.7 was obtained. Sterile rumen fluid was added as a source of growth factors, finely dispersed cellulose was added as energy source, and the oxidation-reduction potential was kept low by adding small amounts of cysteine or sodium sulfide. By addition of agar and preparation of roll tubes after inoculation with serial dilutions of rumen contents, counts of colonies showing zones of cellulose digestion could be made and colonies could be picked to obtain pure cultures. Hungate indicated that many more colonies of noncellulolytic than of cellulolytic bacteria developed, and showed that very high colony counts could be obtained when noncellulosic substrates were used.

At the present time, two general types of culture media are in use: media more or less selective for enumeration and isolation of specific groups of bacteria, and relatively non-selective media for total viable counts and isolation of a wide variety of species. Although many different nonselective media have been used, those most successful in terms of the variety of species cultured and colony counts obtained appear to be rumen fluid agar media similar to that of Hungate (1947, 1950), but with small amounts of glucose, cellobiose, and sometimes, maltose or starch added as energy sources (see Bryant, 1959; Hobson, 1961). Bryant and Robinson (1961) recently described an improved non-selective medium for viable counts and for culture of almost all of the bacteria that have been isolated in large numbers from rumen contents. Organisms which fail to grow in this medium include Methanobacterium ruminantium (Smith and Hungate, 1958) which requires an extremely low oxidation-reduction potential and H_2 or formate as energy sources, and other bacteria such as the lipolytic, glycerol-fermenting vibrio of Hobson and Mann (1961) and the lactate-fermenting Veillonella alcalescens which do not utilize glucose, cellobiose, or starch as energy sources. Ruminococci utilizing cellobiose but not glucose or maltose and Bacteroides amylophilus, utilizing maltose but not glucose or cellobiose, are quite numerous in the rumen, and it is possible that bacteria utilizing other energy sources but not those listed above will be found.

Direct microscopic counts of rumen contents reveal that numbers of bacteria present in the rumen vary, depending

on many variables, such as the type of sample, the time of
sampling in relation to feeding time, the number of times a
day the animal is fed, the diet fed, and unknown differences
between animals (see Warner, 1962, for further references),
but usually the contents contain between 10 and 100 billion
bacteria per g. Although adequate comparisons of microscopic
and colony counts have not been made, it seems probable that
colony counts in improved media such as that of Bryant and
Robinson (1961a) account for about 10 to 30 per cent of the
microscopic count, and results suggest that many of the
cells not cultured represent species that are regularly grown
(Bryant, 1961). Also, the colony counts show trends similar
to direct microscopic counts in the variables indicated above
(Bryant and Robinson, 1961a); Maki and Foster, 1957; Kistner
and Gouws, 1962; Bryant et al., 1962; Brüggemann et al.,
1962).

Although it seems probable that rumen fluid should be
used in culture media for primary isolation of bacteria of
unknown nutritional requirements, different samples of
rumen fluid vary somewhat, even if obtained under a standard
set of conditions, and the fluid is not readily available to some
workers. Recent, unpublished data of Bryant, Thorley, and
Sharpe indicate no significant difference in colony counts obtained from rumen contents from a cow fed dried grass when
the rumen fluid agar medium of Bryant and Robinson (1961 a)
was compared with a medium otherwise the same but with the
rumen fluid replaced by a mixture of volatile fatty acids
similar to those in rumen contents, hemin, 0.2 per cent
trypticase and 0.05 per cent of yeast extract (Oxoid, see
Bryant, 1963).

For the most part, only rather crude culture media are
presently available for the selective or differential enumeration
and isolation of species or physiological groups of rumen
bacteria. Most of the media are selective only as to the main
energy source, and the media usually support considerable
growth of other bacteria. Also, where rumen fluid has not
been added, the absence of volatile fatty acids and heme
(see below) would not allow growth of some very numerous
bacteria within certain physiological groups. Media selective
only as to the main energy source include those for methanogenic
bacteria (Smith and Hungate, 1958), galactomannan-fermenting
bacteria (Williams and Doetsch, 1960), xylan-fermenting
bacteria (Butterworth et al., 1960; Hobson and Purdom, 1961),

hemicellulose-fermenting bacteria (Walker, 1961), saponin-fermenting bacteria (Gutierrez et al., 1959a), lactate-fermenting bacteria (Gutierrez et al., 1959b ; Eadie et al., 1959; Johns, 1951), and glycerol-fermenting bacteria (Hobson and Mann, 1961). Media which are somewhat selective as to energy source and in which the bacteria can be enumerated on the basis of hydrolytic zones include those for cellulolytic bacteria (e.g. see Hungate, 1950; King and Smith 1955; and Kistner, 1960); proteolytic bacteria (Blackburn and Hobson, 1962; Giesecke, 1962; Fulghum and Moore, 1963), amylolytic bacteria (Hamlin and Hungate, 1956; Provost and Doetsch, 1960) and lipolytic bacteria (Hobson and Mann, 1961). A medium somewhat more selective than usual for isolation of butyrivibrio was obtained by replacing the CO_2-bicarbonate of the medium with an N_2 gaseous phase (Lee and Moore, 1959; Brown and Moore, 1960), as many of the predominant rumen bacteria, but not butyrivibrio, require a large amount of CO_2 for growth (e.g. see Anderson and Ordal, 1961; White et al., 1962; Bryant, 1959). The present knowledge available on cultural and physiological characteristics and nutritional requirements should be exploited in a search for better selective and differential culture media.

Kinds of Rumen Bacteria. The rumen contains a wide variety of bacteria, many of which are present in large numbers. For example, Moir and Masson (1952) catalogued 33 different types on the basis of microscopic observations alone. In a review of bacteria cultured from the rumen (Bryant, 1959), 29 genera and 63 species were mentioned, of which 16 genera and 28 species were almost certainly of functional significance, and additional species have since been described. Most of the predominant species are nonsporeforming anaerobes and have been isolated only from the rumen (Bryant, 1959). However, the exacting anaerobic culture procedures used for isolation of rumen bacteria have not been applied to many other anaerobic microbial habitats, and present information suggests that many similar species will be found in other habitats such as the gastro-intestinal tract of nonruminants, sediments of natural waters and sewage sludge, e.g., strains of the genus Butyrivibrio have been isolated from human, rabbit, and horse feces (Brown and Moore, 1960); Ruminococcus flavefaciens was isolated from the rabbit cecum (Hall, 1952) and similar cellulolytic bacteria, from the guinea pig cecum (Bryant and Lev, 1963); anaerobic spirochetes similar to those of the rumen have been isolated from pond mud (Veldkamp, 1960) and from the guinea pig cecum (Bryant and Lev, 1963); an organism apparently identical with M. ruminantium was isolated from sewage sludge (Smith, 1961); and Selenomonas species cultured from the human mouth and rumen seem to be almost identical (Macdonald et al., 1959; Bryant, 1959), and similar organisms are seen in the intestinal contents of other mammals (Lessel and Breed, 1954) and in river water (Leifson, 1960).

Table 2 shows some characteristics of some of the bacterial groups which present evidence suggests are very important components of the rumen fermentation. They are placed in the table in the approximate order to their versatility in utilizing different energy sources. It is evident that some species are quite specific as to energy sources used for growth, for example Methanobacterium ruminantium utilizes only H_2 or formate, and Bacteroides amylophilus, only starch, glycogen, dextrins, and maltose. Others appear to be intermediate in their specificity for energy sources, but of particular interest is the great versatility of some groups such as Butyrivibrio fibrisolvens and Bacteroides ruminicola. In addition to the substrates listed, strains of these groups ferment saponin (Gutierrez et al., 1959a), grass levan and many other sugars, glycosides, and polysaccharides.

In most cases, a number of bacterial species, each found in large numbers, are known to attack each of the quantitatively important constituents of ruminant diets. At least four species are significantly involved in cellulose digestion and other cellulolytic bacteria have been described. Six species have been shown to ferment lactate, and materials such as xylan, starch, and pectin are each fermented by many species. Strains within a large number of predominant species are known to be proteolytic (Blackburn and Hobson, 1962; Giesecke, 1962; Fulghum and Moore, 1963), but very few species appear to be able to utilize protein hydrolysates as the source of energy. Peptostreptococcus elsdenii will grow with protein hydrolysate as the energy source and produce ammonia and volatile acids, but Bacteroides ruminicola and Selenomonas ruminantium, which present evidence suggests are usually more important in amino acid or peptide catabolism, seem to require carbohydrate for growth (Bladen et al., 1961a, b).

It can be seen from information in Table 2 (supported by data on other species not shown) that, with the exception of

TABLE 2: Some compounds attacked and products produced by some representative anaerobic rumen bacteria

Species [a]	Energy sources [b]							Fermentation products [d]
	Cellulose	Xylan	Starch	Other carbohydrates [c]	Lactate	Glycerol	Amino acids	
(1) Methanobacterium ruminantium	0	0	0	0 (hydrogen, formate)	0	0	0	CH_4
(2) Unnamed vibrio Hobson and Mann (1961)	0	0	0 (lipolytic)	+	0	+	?	P
(3) Bacteroides amylophilus	0	0	+	+	0	0	0	S,A,F,L
(4) Bacteroides succinogenes	+	0	±	+	0	0	0	S,A,F
(5) Ruminococcus albus and flavefaciens	±	±	0	+	0	0	0	S,A,F,E,L,H_2,CO_2
(6) Peptostreptococcus elsdenii	0	0	0	+	+	±	+	B,V,P,A,C,H_2,CO_2
(7) Lachnospira multiparus	0	0	0	++	0	0	0	L,A,F,E,H_2,CO_2
(8) Succinivibrio dextrinosolvens	0	0	0	++	0	0	0	S,A,F,L
(9) Eubacterium ruminantium	0	±	0	++	0	0	0	B,F,A,L,CO_2
(10) Borrelia sp.	0	0	0	++	0	0	0	S,A,F,L,E
(11) Anaerobic lactobacilli	0	0	±	+++	0	0	0	L,A
(12) Selenomonas ruminantium	0	0	±	+++	±	±	?	L,P,A,CO_2
(13) Bacteroides ruminicola	0	±	±	+++	0	0	?	S,A,F
(14) Butyrivibrio fibrisolvens	±	±	±	+++	0	0	0	B,L,F,A,H_2,CO_2

[a] See Bryant (1959) for references.
[b] O = not attacked, ± = many strains attack, ∓ = few strains attack.
[c] + = few attacked, +++ = many attacked.
[d] A = acetate, B = butyrate, C = caproate, E = ethanol, F = formate, L = lactate, P = propionate, S = succinate, V = valerate.

methane production, for which only one species is known
(Smith and Hungate, 1958), numerous species produce one
or more of the major end-products of the fermentation including acetic, propionic, and butyric acids and CO_2. However, most of the carbohydrate-fermenting bacteria also
produce large amounts of fermentation products that do not
normally accumulate during rumen fermentation. Succinic,
lactic, and formic acids, H_2, and ethanol are each produced
by a number of different species. The fact that mixed rumen
bacteria contain a very active succinic decarboxylase (Johns,
1951) plus the fact that many species, numerous in the rumen
and fermenting many different carbohydrates, produce
succinic acid as the major fermentation product led to the
conclusion that much of the rumen propionate was produced
from carbohydrate via succinate production by some species
and via decarboxylation by others. This conclusion is supported by recent studies of pool size and turnover rate of
succinate in rumen contents by Blackburn (see Hungate, 1963).
Also, studies on propionate formation from position-labeled
glucose in rumen fluid suggest that most is produced via
succinate (Baldwin et al., 1962a). The organisms responsible
for succinic decarboxylation are not definitely known.
Veillonella alcalescens (V. gazogenes, Micrococcus lacti-
lyticus) actively decarboxylates succinic acid (Johns, 1951)
but is often present in only very small numbers in the rumen.
S. ruminantium produces propionate from either glucose or
lactate via succinate but does not actively decarboxylate
exogenous succinate (Paynter and Elsden, 1960). The same
is true of propionibacteria, and the latter, though sometimes
present in large numbers (Gutierrez, 1953), often are not
found in significant numbers.

Lactic acid is produced by many species, but except for
organisms such as Streptococcus bovis and lactobacilli,
which often are not among the predominant species, the
amount produced is usually small as compared to other
products. Lactate in the diet, or produced in the rumen,
is converted to volatile fatty acids by other species.
Peptostreptococcus elsdenii produces acetic, propionic,
butyric, and valeric acids and CO_2 and H_2 in the lactate
fermentation (Elsden et al., 1956), and produces propionate
via the acrylate pathway (Ladd and Walker, 1959). Some
strains of S. ruminantium, propionibacteria, and V. alcalescens
produce propionate, acetate, CO_2, and in the latter case,

H_2, in the lactate fermentation and produce propionate via the succinate pathway; however, the latter two groups are often not numerous in the rumen. Lactate fermenting Bacteroides sp. and Ramibacterium sp. have been isolated (Bryant, 1959; Clarke, 1963), but their fermentation of lactate has not been studied in detail. The turnover of lactate in rumen contents is usually very small, accounting for less than 1 per cent the food fermented in a hay-fed cow; but when the diet is largely grain, as much as one-sixth of the substrate could be fermented via lactate (Jayasuriya and Hungate, 1959). Acetate is the main volatile acid produced from lactate in rumen contents but, with diets containing relatively large amounts of lactic acid or grain, production of propionic acid increases (Baldwin et al., 1962b; Jayasuriya and Hungate, 1959). Baldwin et al., (1962b) showed that 70 to 90 per cent of the propionate produced from lactate is produced via the acrylate rather than via the succinate pathway, suggesting that an organism such as Peptostreptococcus elsdenii is mainly involved. The amount produced via acrylate increased when the diet contained a large amount of lactic acid or starch.

The formate produced by many species is rapidly converted to CO_2 and H_2 by other species (Doetsch et al., 1953; Carroll and Hungate, 1955).

Though many species produce hydrogen, it is usually present only in traces in the rumen gas and is rapidly taken up by rumen contents. The capacity for utilization exceeds that for production and much of the hydrogen is utilized in methane production (Carroll and Hungate, 1955). Smith (1959) demonstrated that washed suspensions of M. ruminantium containing numbers similar to those found in the rumen can produce methane from H_2 at a rate which might account for all of the methane produced in the rumen. H_2 is also used in sulfate reduction(Lewis, 1954), nitrate reduction (Lewis, 1951) and, probably, in hydrogenation of unsaturated fatty acids.

Although a number of predominant rumen species in pure culture produce some ethanol in carbohydrate fermentation, present evidence suggests that these species do not produce it in the rumen because ethanol has almost never been detected in rumen contents and it is metabolized by rumen contents at an extremely slow rate. Hungate (1963) suggests that ethanol may be produced because of the low pH during the later stage of fermentation by pure cultures

or because of accumulation of hydrogen. Most of the
bacteria that form large amounts of ethanol in pure culture
also produce hydrogen. In the mixed culture of the rumen,
organisms such as the methanogenic bacteria keep the
concentration of hydrogen so low that equilibrium in the
direction of ethanol might be insufficient to permit formation
of appreciable quantities. It also seems possible that many
of the species producing lactic acid in pure culture might
produce less in the rumen for similar reasons.

There is some conversion of acetate and propionate to
butyrate and valerate in rumen contents (Gray et al., 1952).
P. elsdenii (Elsden et al., 1956) is concerned in these reactions, and Butyrivibrio fibrisolvens often showed a large
net uptake of acetate during glucose fermentation, suggesting
that it produces butyrate from acetate. An interesting
difference between the sewage sludge and rumen fermentations
is that in sludge, acetate, propionate and butyrate are converted to methane while in the rumen this does not occur to
any significant extent. The reason for this difference is as
yet unexplained (Hungate, 1963).

Some Nutritional Requirements. In the early studies of
Hungate (1947, 1950) it was indicated that many of the
cellulolytic bacteria required growth factors present in
rumen fluid that were not present in many of the dietary
constituents of ruminant rations, or crude protein hydrolysates, or in extracts commonly used to culture bacteria.
Bryant and Doetsch (1955) showed the "rumen fluid" factor
required by B. succinogenes to consist of a two-component
requirement for volatile fatty acids. One component consists of a branched-chain volatile acid such as isobutyrate
or 2-methylbutyrate and the other consists of any one of the
straight-chain acids containing five to eight carbons or
longer-chained acids such as palmitic or pentadecanoic
(Wegner and Foster, 1963). Bentley et al. (1955) found
that similar combinations of volatile fatty acids were
stimulatory to cellulose digestion and protein synthesis by
the mixed rumen bacteria when grown in culture media devoid
of amino acids. Allison et al. (1958) then showed that
strains of Ruminococcus albus and R. flavefaciens required
volatile fatty acids, but only the branched-chain acids,
isobutyrate, 2-methylbutyrate, and isovalerate were involved.
Many species of noncellulolytic bacteria, numerous in the
rumen, are now known to require one or more of these acids.

These include Borrelia sp., Eubacterium ruminantium, and some strains of butyrivibrio and S. ruminantium, and one unnamed species (Wegner and Foster, 1960; Bryant and Robinson, 1962). In addition, some strains of other species are stimulated by the acids, and the acids may be required for growth when casein hydrolysate is not included in the medium (Bryant and Robinson, 1962). It is of particular interest that an aerobic, non-ruminal organism was recently shown to have this requirement (Larson et al., 1963).

In studies on the function of the volatile acids, it has been shown that the intact carbon skeletons of the branched-chain acids are used for synthesis of the corresponding amino acids (Allison et al., 1962a; Allison and Bryant, 1963), i.e., isovalerate, 2-methylbutyrate and isobutyrate are utilized for synthesis of leucine, isoleucine, and valine. This synthesis differs from that shown in other microorganisms and occurs in R. flavefaciens in the presence of exogenous amino acids. The branched-chain volatile acids and straight-chain acids are also utilized in synthesis of the corresponding 13 to 17 carbon branched-chain or straight-chain acids and aldehydes of the bacterial lipid and are mainly in the phospholipid (Allison et al., 1962b; Keeney et al., 1962; Wegner and Foster, 1963). Studies to date suggest that some of the rumen bacteria require these acids because of their limited ability to utilize exogenous amino acids and to synthesize the isopropyl moiety found in the branched-chain amino acids and fatty acids or the short-chain precursors of straight-chain fatty acids. Rumen contents usually contain little free amino acid but almost always contain relatively large amounts of the volatile fatty acids and ammonia, which are produced from the corresponding amino acids (See Annison and Lewis, 1959; Bladen et al., 1961a). n-Valerate is also produced from carbohydrate or lactate (Elsden et al., 1956).

Bacteroides ruminicola subsp. ruminicola, another organism which had a "rumen fluid" requirement, was shown to require one of certain tetrapyrroles for growth (Bryant and Robinson, 1962; Caldwell et al., 1962). These included compounds such as heme, protoporphyrin IX, hemato-, meso-, and deuteroporphyrin, and uro- and coproporhyrinogen. Many other compounds including intermediates in tetrapyrrole synthesis, iron chelating agents, bile pigments and chlorophyll were inactive. The tetrapyrrole appears to be required mainly for synthesis of a cytochrome of the b type, which is involved in an electron

transport system for the reduction of fumarate to succinate
by DPNH (White et al., 1962). B. ruminicola carries out
a CO_2- dependent fermentation, similar to Cytophaga
succinicans (Anderson and Ordal, 1961), with succinic acid
being the major fermentation product. B. ruminicola subsp.
brevis does not require tetrapyrrole but synthesizes hemo-
protein identical with that of the other subspecies grown in
the presence of hemin.

The nitrogen requirements of many rumen bacteria are
quite unusual compared to those of heterotrophic bacteria
so far studied. Most species can be grown with NH_3 as the
main source of nitrogen, and strains which require amino
acids often require only one or two amino acids (Gibbons
and Doetsch, 1959; Phillipson et al., 1962; Pittman and
Bryant, 1963) and often belong to species many strains of
which do not require amino acids (Bryant and Robinson, 1962).
A few strains require nucleic acid degradation products
(Wasserman et al., 1953; Ayers, 1958) but most strains of
most species do not (Bryant and Robinson, 1962). Although
a number of species will utilize either NH_3 or casein hydrolysate nitrogen for growth, many of the species require NH_3
in amounts approximating the amount of cellular nitrogen
produced even when grown in media containing large amounts
of amino acid and peptide nitrogen (Phillipson et al., 1962;
Bryant and Robinson, 1961b; Bryant and Robinson, 1963).
and are very inefficient in incorporation of amino acid-C^{14}
(Allison et al., 1962a; Bryant and Robinson, 1963). The
results of these studies on pure cultures add weight to the
suggestion of Warner (1955), based on $N^{15}H_3$ and lysine-C^{14}
incorporation by the mixed microbial population, that the
rumen contains some microbial species which utilize NH_3
for growth in preference to organic nitrogen. The results
also suggest that the rumen micro-environments that have
selected these bacteria contain little amino acid which is
available for microbial growth, and that a considerable
amount of dietary protein in ruminant rations is degraded
further than the amino acid state, e.g., to NH_3, CO_2, and
volatile fatty acids, before being utilized in microbial protein synthesis (see Bryant and Robinson, 1963, for further
references).

Some other rumen bacteria which are very inefficient in
utilization of exogenous, free amino acids do not require NH_3
if enzymatic hydrolysate of casein is included in the medium

(Bryant, and Robinson, 1962). Studies on one of these species, B. ruminicola, indicate that the nitrogen of undegraded casein of peptides of enzymatically hydrolyzed casein or the peptides, oxytocin and vasopressin, very effectively replaces NH_3 as the nitrogen source but mixtures of free amino acids and many single nitrogen compounds including dipeptides do not (Pittman and Bryant, 1963).

Studies on the reasons for the very inefficient incorporation of amino acids, on the lack of metabolic control of amino acid biosynthesis by exogenous amino acids, or on the mechanisms of NH_3 incorporation in these bacteria have not yet been initiated.

Very little work has been done on the mineral requirements for growth of rumen bacteria; however, it is of considerable interest that Na^+ is essential for growth of B. succinogenes and that the concentrations of Na^+ and K^+ necessary for optimum growth are similar to those required by certain marine bacteria (Bryant et al., 1959). Whether other rumen bacteria require Na^+ is not known.

Some information is available on other aspects of the nutrition of rumen bacteria such as B-vitamin, CO_2, acetate, sulfur, and mineral requirements (see Bryant and Robinson, 1962, and Bryant, 1961, for further references) but require further study. Although most strains of most predominant species grown on a nonselective rumen fluid medium can be grown in defined media, a considerable number of strains require as yet unidentified growth factors.

Conclusion. Information on the microbial metabolism in the rumen, including information on the individual microorganisms concerned, is essential for a more complete understanding of ruminant nutrition and physiology. Although new bacterial species will undoubtedly be isolated in the future, many species present in sufficient numbers to be functional in the rumen and carrying out many of the reactions known to be of importance have been described. Studies on the individual species have aided materially in the accumulation of knowledge on rumen reactions; and, as many of these bacteria differ in certain nutritional and metabolic characteristics from most bacteria so far studied that have been isolated from other natural habitats, they are of interest from the viewpoints of comparative biochemistry and nutrition. Most of the species are nonsporeforming anaerobes and often have been isolated only by workers using very strictly anaerobic techniques and media similar to those of Hungate and co-

workers. Present evidence indicates that some of these
bacteria function in anaerobic habitats other than the rumen,
and future work will undoubtedly show that similar bacteria
are of greater significance in nature than is now generally
realized.

LITERATURE CITED

Allison, M. J. and M. P. Bryant. 1963. Biosynthesis of
    branched-chain amino acids from branched-chain fatty
    acids by rumen bacteria. Arch. Biochem. 101:269-277.
Allison, M.J., M.P. Bryant, and R. N. Doetsch. 1958. A
    volatile fatty acid growth factor for cellulolytic cocci of
    the bovine rumen. Science 128:474-475.
Allison, M. J., M. P. Bryant, and R. N. Doetsch. 1962a.
    Studies on the metabolic function of branched-chain
    volatile fatty acids, growth factors for ruminocci. I.
    Incorporation of isovalerate into leucine. J. Bacteriol.
    83:523-532.
Allison, M. J., M. P. Bryant, I. Katz, and M. Keeney.
    1962b. Studies on the metabolic function of branched-
    chain volatile fatty acids. II. Biosynthesis of higher
    branched-chain fatty acids and aldehydes. J. Bacteriol.
    83:1084-1093.
Anderson, R. L. and E. J. Ordal. 1961. CO_2-dependent
    fermentation of glucose by Cytophaga succinicans. J.
    Bacteriol. 81:139-146.
Annison, E. F. and D. Lewis. 1959. Metabolism in the
    Rumen. John Wiley and Sons, New York, N. Y.
Ayers, W. A. 1958. Nutrition and physiology of Ruminococcus
    flavefaciens. J. Bacteriol. 76:504-509.
Balch, C. C. 1961. Movement of digesta through the digestive
    tract. pp. 23-32. In D. Lewis (ed.), Digestive Physiology
    and Nutrition of the Ruminant. Butterworths, London.
Balch, C. C., D. A. Balch, V. W. Johnson, and J. Turner.
    1953. Factors affecting the utilization of food by dairy
    cows. 7. The effect of limited water intake on the
    digestibility and rate of passage of hay. Brit. J. Nutrit.
    7:212-224.
Baldwin, R. L., R. S. Emery, and W. A. Wood. 1962a.
    Propionate formation in rumen fluid with position-labeled
    glucose and lactate. Abstracts VIII Intern. Congress
    Microbiol. p. 41.

Baldwin, R. L., W. A. Wood, and R. S. Emery. 1962b.
Conversion of lactate-C^{14} to propionate by the rumen
microflora. J. Bacteriol. 83:907-913.

Barnett, A. J. G. and R. L. Reid. 1961. Reactions in the
Rumen. Edward Arnold Ltd., London, England.

Bell, F. R. 1961. Some observations on the physiology of
rumination. pp. 59-67. In D. Lewis (ed.), Digestive
Physiology and Nutrition of the Ruminant. Butterworths,
London.

Bentley, O. G., R. R. Johnson, T. V. Hershberger, J. H.
Cline, and A. L. Moxon. 1955. Cellulolytic-factor
activity of certain short chain fatty acids for rumen
microorganisms in vitro. J. Nutrit. 57:389-400.

Blackburn, T. H., and P. N. Hobson. 1962. Further studies
on the isolation of proteolytic bacteria from the sheep
rumen. J. Gen. Microbiol. 29:69-81.

Bladen, H. A., M. P. Bryant, and R. N. Doetsch, 1961a.
The production of isovaleric acid from leucine by
Bacteroides ruminicola. J. Dairy Sci. 44:173-174.

Bladen, H. A., M. P. Bryant, and R. N. Doetsch. 1961b.
A study of bacterial species from the rumen which produce
ammonia from a protein hydrolysate. Appl. Microbiol.
9:175-180.

Blaxter, K. L. 1961. Energy utilization in the ruminant.
pp. 183-197. In D. Lewis (ed.), Digestive Physiology and
Nutrition of the Ruminant, Butterworths, London.

Broberg. G. 1957. Measurements of the redox potential in
rumen contents. I. In vitro measurements on healthy
animals. Nord. Vet. Med. 9:918-930.

Brody, S. 1945. Bioenergetics and Growth. Reinhold Publish-
ing Corp., New York, N.Y.

Brown, D. W. and W. E. C. Moore, 1960. Distribution of
Butyrivibrio fibrisolvens in nature. J. Dairy Sci. 43:
1570-1574.

Brüggemann, J. , D. Giesecke, and K. Drepper. 1962. Die
Beeinflussung von Zusammensetzung und Leistung der
Pansenflora durch verabreichung unterscheidlicher
Stickstoffquellen. Ztschr. Tierphysiol. Tierernährung
Futtermittelk. 17:162-188.

Bryant, M. P. 1959. Bacterial species of the rumen.
Bacteriol. Revs. 23:125-153.

Bryant, M. P. 1961. The nitrogen metabolism of pure
cultures of ruminal bacteria. U.S.D.A., ARS 44-92, 15
pages.

Bryant, M. P. 1963. Symposium on microbial digestion in
    ruminants: Identification of groups of anaerobic bacteria
    active in the ruminal fermentation. J. Animal Sci. 22:
    801-813.
Bryant, M. P. and R. N. Doetsch. 1955. Factors necessary
    for the growth of Bacteroides succinogenes in the volatile
    acid fraction of rumen fluid. J. Dairy Sci. 38:340-350.
Bryant, M. P. and M. Lev. 1963. Unpublished data.
Bryant, M. P. and I. M. Robinson. 1961a. An improved
    non-selective culture medium for ruminal bacteria and
    its use in determining diurnal variation in numbers of
    bacteria in the rumen. J. Dairy Sci. 44:1446-1456.
Bryant, M. P. and I. M. Robinson. 1961b. Some nutritional
    requirements of the genus Ruminococcus. Appl. Microbiol.
    9:91-95.
Bryant, M. P. and I. M. Robinson. 1962. Some nutritional
    characteristics of predominant culturable ruminal bacteria.
    J. Bacteriol. 84:605-614.
Bryant, M. P. and I. M. Robinson. 1963. Apparent in-
    corporation of ammonia and amino acid carbon during
    growth of selected species of ruminal bacteria. J. Dairy
    Sci. 46:150-154.
Bryant, M. P., I. M. Robinson, and H. Chu. 1959. Observations
    on the nutrition of Bacteroides succinogenes -- a ruminal
    cellulolytic bacterium. J. Dairy Sci. 42:1831-1847.
Bryant, M. P., I. M. Robinson, and D. Waldo. 1962.
    Unpublished data.
Butterworth, J. P., S. E. Bell, and M. G. Garvock. 1960.
    Isolation and properties of the xylan-fermenting bacterium
    11. Biochem. J. 74:180-182.
Caldwell, D. R., D. C. White, and M. P. Bryant. 1962.
    Specificity of the heme requirement for growth of
    Bacteroides ruminicola -- a ruminal saccharolytic bacterium.
    J. Dairy Sci. 45:690.
Campling, R. C., M. Freer, and C. C. Balch. 1961. Factors
    affecting the voluntary intake of food by cows. 2. The
    relationship between the voluntary intake of roughages,
    the amount of digesta in the reticulo-rumen and the rate of
    disappearance of digesta from the alimentary tract. Brit.
    J. Nutrit. 15:531-540.
Carroll, E. J. and R. E. Hungate. 1954. The magnitude of
    the microbial fermentation in the bovine rumen. Appl.
    Microbiol. 2:205-214.

Carroll, E. J. and R. E. Hungate. 1955. Formate dissimilation and methane production in bovine rumen contents. Arch. Biochem. 56:525-536.

Clarke, R. T. 1963. Personal communication.

Decker, P., H. Hill, K. Gärtner, and H. Hörnicke. 1960. Über die Wiederverwertung des Körperharnstoffes in Pansen des Wiederhäuers nach Versuchen mit ^{14}C-Harnstoff an der Ziege. Deutsche Tierärztliche Wocheschr. 67:539-542.

Doetsch, R. N., R. Q. Robinson, R. E. Brown, and J. C. Shaw. 1953. Catabolic reactions of mixed suspensions of bovine rumen bacteria. J. Dairy Sci. 36:825-831.

Eadie, J. M., P. N. Hobson, and S. O. Mann. 1959. A relationship between some bacteria, protozoa and diet in early weaned calves. Nature (London) 183:624-625.

Elsden, S.R., B. E. Volcani, F. M. C. Gilchrist, and D. Lewis. 1956. Properties of a fatty acid forming organism isolated from the rumen of sheep. J. Bacteriol. 72:681-689.

Fina, L. R., E. E. Bartley, and B. Mishra. 1961. Role of mucinolytic bacteria in feedlot bloat. J. Dairy Sci. 44:1202.

Fulghum, R. S. and W. E. C. Moore. 1963. Isolation, enumeration, and characteristics of proteolytic ruminal bacteria. J. Bacteriol. 85:808-815.

Garton, G. A. 1961. Influence of the rumen on the digestion and metabolism of lipids. pp. 140-151. In D. Lewis (ed.), Digestive Physiology and Nutrition of the Ruminant, Butterworths, London.

Garton, G. A., A. K. Lough, and E. Vioque. 1961. Glyceride hydrolysis and glycerol fermentation by sheep rumen contents. J. Gen. Microbiol. 25:215-225.

Gibbons, R. J. and R. N. Doetsch. 1959. Physiological study of an obligately anaerobic ureolytic bacterium. J. Bacteriol. 77:417-428.

Giesecke, D. 1962. Proteolytische Bakterienstämme aus dem Rinderpansen. Zentr. Bakteriol. Parasitenk. 186:170-178.

Gray, F. V. 1947. The extent of cellulose digestion at successive levels of the alimentary tract. J. Exp. Biol. 24:15-19.

Gray, F. V., A. F. Pilgrim, H. J. Rodda, and R. A. Weller. 1952. Fermentation in the rumen of the sheep. IV. The nature and origin of the volatile fatty acids in the rumen of the sheep. J. Exptl. Biol. 29:57-65.

Gutierrez, J. 1953. Numbers and characteristics of lactate utilizing organisms in the rumen of cattle. J. Bacteriol. 66:123-128.

Gutierrez, J. 1955. Experiments on the culture and physiology of holotrichs from the bovine rumen. Biochem J. 60:516-522.

Gutierrez, J., R. E. Davis, and I. L. Lindahl. 1959a. Characteristics of saponin-utilizing bacteria from the rumen of cattle. Appl. Microbiol. 7:304-308.

Gutierrez, J., R. E. Davis, I. L. Lindahl and E. J. Warwick. 1959b. Bacterial changes in the rumen during the onset of feed-lot bloat of cattle. Appl. Microbiol. 7:16-22.

Gutierrez, J., R. E. Davis, and I. L. Lindahl. 1961. Some chemical and physical properties of a slime from the rumen of cattle. Appl. Microbiol. 9:209-212.

Hall, Elizabeth R. 1952. Investigations on the microbiology of cellulose utilization in domestic rabbits. J. Gen. Microbiol. 7:350-357.

Hamlin, L. J. and R. E. Hungate. 1956. Culture and physiology of a starch-digesting bacterium (Bacteroides amylophilus n. sp.) from the bovine rumen. J. Bacteriol. 72:548-554.

Hobson, P. N. 1961. Techniques of counting rumen organisms. pp. 107-118. In D. Lewis (ed.), Digestive Physiology and Nutrition of the Ruminant, Butterworths, London.

Hobson, P. N. and S. O. Mann. 1961. The isolation of glycerol-fermenting and lipolytic bacteria from the rumen of the sheep. J. Gen. Microbiol. 25:227-240.

Hobson, P. N. and M. R. Purdom. 1961. Two types of xylan fermenting bacteria from the sheep rumen. J. Appl. Bacteriol. 24:188-193.

Houpt, T. R. 1959. Utilization of blood urea in ruminants. Am. J. Physiol. 197.115-120.

Hungate, R. E. 1947. Studies on cellulose fermentation. III. The culture and isolation of cellulose-decomposing bacteria from the rumen of cattle. J. Bacteriol. 53:631-645.

Hungate, R. E. 1950. The anaerobic mesophilic cellulolytic bacteria. Bacteriol. Rev. 14:1-49.

Hungate, R. E. 1955. The ciliates of the rumen. pp. 159-179. In S. H. Hutner and A. Lwoff (ed.), Biochemistry and Physiology of Protozoa, Vol. II, Academic Press, New York, N. Y.

Hungate, R. E. 1960. Selected topics in microbial ecology. Microbial ecology of the rumen. Bacteriol. Revs 24: 353-364.

Hungate, R. E. 1963. Symbiotic associations: the rumen bacteria. pp. 266-297. In P. S. Nutman and B. Mosse (ed.), Symbiotic Associations, Cambridge U. Press, Cambridge, England.

Hungate, R. E., R. W. Dougherty, M. P. Bryant, and R. M. Cello. 1952. Microbiological and physiological changes associated with acute indigestion in sheep. Cornell Vet. 42: 423-449.

Jayasuriya, G. C. N. and R. E. Hungate. 1959. Lactate conversion in the bovine rumen. Arch. Biochem. 82: 274-287.

Johns, A. T. 1951. Isolation of a bacterium producing propionic acid from the rumen of the sheep. J. Gen. Microbiol. 5: 317-325.

Johns, A. T. 1953. Fermentation of glycerol in the rumen of sheep. N. Z. J. Sci. Tech. 35: 262-269.

Keeney, M., I. Katz and M. J. Allison. 1962. On the probable origin of some milk fat acids in rumen microbial lipids. J. Am. Oil Chem. Soc. 39: 198-201.

King, K. W. and P. H. Smith. 1955. Comparisons of two media proposed for the isolation of bacteria from the rumen. J. Bacteriol. 70: 726-729.

Kistner, A. 1960. An improved method for viable counts of bacteria of the ovine rumen which ferment carbohydrates. J. Gen. Microbiol. 23: 565-576.

Kistner, A. and L. Couws. 1962. Bacteria of the ovine rumen. II. The functional groups fermenting carbohydrates and lactate on a diet of lucerne (Medicago sativa) hay. J. Agric. Sci. 59: 85-91.

Ladd, J. M. and D. J. Walker. 1959. The fermentation of lactate and acrylate by cell-free extracts of the rumen microorganism LC. Biochem.J. 71: 364-373.

Larson, A. D., L. V. Hattier, and C. S. McCleskey. 1963. The volatile fatty acid requirement of a strain of Listeria monocytogenes. Bacteriol. Proc. p. 98.

Lee, H. C. and W. E. C. Moore. 1959. Isolation and fermentation characteristics of strains of Butyrivibrio from ruminal ingesta. J. Bacteriol. 77: 741-747.

Leifson, E. 1960. Atlas of Bacterial Flagellation, Academic Press. New York, N. Y.

Lessel, E. R. Jr., and R. S. Breed. 1954. Selenomonas
    Boskamp, 1922 - A genus that includes species showing
    an unusual type of flagellation. Bacteriol. Revs. 18:165-
    169.
Lewis, D. 1951. The metabolism of nitrate and nitrite in the
    sheep. 2. Hydrogen donators in nitrate reduction by rumen
    microorganisms in vitro. Biochem. J. 49:149-153.
Lewis, D. 1954. The reduction of sulfate in the rumen of the
    sheep. Biochem. J. 56:391-399.
Loosli, J. K., H. H. Williams, W. E. Thomas, F. H. Ferris,
    and L. A. Maynard. 1949. Synthesis of amino acids in
    the rumen. Science 110:144-145.
Macdonald, J. B., E. M. Madlener, and S. S. Socransky.
    1959. Observations of Spirillum sputigenum and its
    relationship to Selenomonas species with special re-
    ference to flagellation. J. Bacteriol. 77:559-565.
Maki, L. R. and E. M. Foster. 1957. Effect of roughage
    in the bovine ration on types of bacteria in the rumen.
    J. Dairy Sci. 40:905-913.
Mangan, J. L., A. T. Johns, and R. W. Bailey. 1959.
    Bloat in cattle. XIII. The effect of orally administered
    penicillin on the fermentation and foaming properties
    of rumen contents. N.Z.J. Agric. Sci. 2:342-354.
Masson, M. J. and A. T. Phillipson. 1951. The absorption
    of acetate, propionate and butyrate from the rumen of
    sheep. J. Physiol. 113:189-206.
McDonald, I. W. and R. J. Hall. 1957. The conversion of
    casein into microbial proteins in the rumen. Biochem. J.
    67:400-405.
McDougall, E. I. 1948. Studies on ruminant saliva. I. The
    composition and output of sheep's saliva. Biochem J. 43:
    99-109.
Moir, R. J. and M. J. Masson. 1952. An illustrated scheme
    for the microscopic identification of the rumen micro-
    organisms of sheep. J. Path. Bacteriol. 64:343-350.
Parthasarathy, D. and A. T. Phillipson. 1953. The movement
    of potassium, sodium chloride and water across the rumen
    epithelium of sheep. J. Physiol. 121:452-469.
Paynter, B. and S. R. Elsden. 1960. Personal communication.
Phillipson, A. T., M. J. Dobson, T. H. Blackburn, and M.
    Brown. 1962. The assimilation of ammonia nitrogen by
    bacteria of the rumen of sheep. Brit. J. Nutrit. 16:151-
    166.

Pittman, K. A. and M. P. Bryant. 1963. Nitrogen sources for growth of Bacteroides ruminicola. Bacteriol. Proc. p. 8.

Porter, J. W. G. 1961. Vitamin synthesis in the rumen. pp. 226-234. In D. Lewis (ed.), Digestive Physiology and Nutrition of the Ruminant. Butterworths, London.

Prescott, J. M., W. T. Williams, and R. S. Ragland. 1959. Influence of nitrogen source on growth of Streptococcus bovis. Proc. Soc. Exptl. Biol. Med. 102:490-492.

Provost, P. J. and R. N. Doetsch. 1960. Biological characteristics of an obligate anaerobic amylolytic coccus. J. Gen. Microbiol. 22:259-264.

Reiser, R. 1951. Hydrogenation of polyunsaturated fatty acids by the ruminant. Fed. Proc. 10:236.

Schmidt-Nielsen, B. and H. Osak. 1958. Renal response to changes in nitrogen metabolism in sheep. Am. J. Physiol. 193:657-661.

Sijpesteijn, A. K. 1948. Cellulose-decomposing bacteria from the rumen of cattle. Ph. D. Thesis, Leiden, Netherlands.

Sisson, S. and J. D. Grossmann. 1938. Anatomy of the Domestic Animals, W. B. Saunders Co., Philadelphia, Pa.

Smith, P. H. 1959. Studies on the methanogenic bacteria of the rumen. Ph. D. Thesis, University of California, Davis, California.

Smith, P. H. 1961. Studies on the methanogenic bacteria of domestic sludge. Bacteriol. Proc. p. 60.

Smith, P. H. and R. E. Hungate. 1958. Isolation and characterization of Methanobacterium ruminantium, n. sp. J. Bacteriol. 75:713-718.

Van Soest, P. 1963. Ruminant fat metabolism with particular reference to factors affecting low milk fat and feed efficiency. J. Dairy Sci. 46:204-216.

Veldkamp. H. 1960. Isolation and characteristics of Treponema zuelzerae nov. spec., an anaerobic, free-living spirochete. Antonie van Leewenhoek 26:103-125.

Walker, D. J. 1961. Isolation and characterization of a hemicellulose-fermenting bacterium from the sheep rumen. Austral. J. Agric. Res. 12:171-175.

Warner, A. C. I. 1955. Some aspects of the nitrogen metabolism of the microorganisms of the rumen with special reference to proteolysis. Ph. D. Thesis, U. of Aberdeen, Scotland.

Warner, A. C. I. 1962. Some factors influencing the rumen
    microbial population. J. Gen. Microbiol. 28:129-146.
Wasserman, R. H., H. W. Seeley, and J. K. Loosli. 1953.
    The physiology and nutrition of a rumen Lactobacillus.
    J. Animal Sci. 12:935-936.
Wegner, G. H. and E. M. Foster. 1960. Fatty acid re-
    quirements of certain rumen bacteria. J. Dairy Sci.
    43:566-568.
Wegner, G. H. and E. M. Foster. 1963. Incorporation of
    isobutyrate and valerate into cellular plasmalogen by
    Bacteroides succinogenes. J. Bacteriol. 85:53-61.
Weller, R. A., F. V. Gray and A. F. Pilgrim. 1958. The
    conversion of plant nitrogen to microbial nitrogen in the
    rumen of the sheep. Brit. J. Nutr. 12:421-429.
White, D. C., M. P. Bryant, and D. R. Caldwell. 1962.
    Cytochrome-linked fermentation in Bacteroides ruminicola.
    J. Bacteriol. 84:822-828.
Williams, P. P. and R. N. Doetsch. 1960. Microbial
    dissimilation of galactomannan. J. Gen. Microbiol. 22:
    635-644.
Wolin, M. J. 1960. A theoretical rumen fermentation balance.
    J. Dairy Sci. 43:1452-1459.

DISCUSSION

Chairman Heukelekian (Rutgers University): Thank you,
Dr. Bryant, for the information on rumen microbiology,
which should prove valuable to workers in the field of sewage
treatment and sewage sludge digestion. It seems to me you
have carried the search farther and deeper than we have in
many ways, especially in respect to hydrolytic organisms.
There are many similarities and differences between the
rumen and sludge digestion. I think the rumen could be compared with the reactor that Dr. McCarty was talking about
this morning. The optimum conditions seem to be similar
---temperature is one instance. The rumen has a natural
churning action which has to be provided mechanically in
the digester. With respect to the methane flora, it seems
that the rumen is even more restricted in its methane flora
than the sludge. But there are also differences in the complexity of the intermediates ---whether we have not looked
as diligently for other intermediate compounds or whether
these differences in the intermediate compounds are due
to differences in the raw material that we are dealing with,

I do not know. And with respect to hydrogen formation, although there is in sludge digestion some hydrogen under certain conditions, the rumen forms more of it.

Dr. Lindstrom (Penn. State University): I can see why methane fermentation is useful in a sludge digestion tank, but what is the physiological significance of this high methane activity to the ruminant? It is throwing away material that the animal wants, is it not?

Dr. Bryant: If we could stop methane production in the rumen and put the hydrogen into the volatile fatty acids, the combustible energy available to the animal could be increased by about ten per cent.

But the other interesting possibility in decreasing methane is that, in addition to the energy increase, theoretical fermentation balance calculations indicate that the proportion of acetate would be decreased and the propionate and butyrate would increase. Propionate is much more efficiently utilized for growth and for fat production in ruminants than is acetate. So there would be quite a material benefit if one could shunt the hydrogen from methane to propionic and butyric acids.

As to why methane is produced, I believe that one of the arguments is that the utilization of hydrogen in reduction of CO_2 is a better use of hydrogen in providing the energy for growth of microorganisms than some other reactions of hydrogen under anaerobic conditions.

Dr. Mc Carty (Stanford University): Is formic acid of any use to the cow?

Dr. Bryant: Not much is known about this. There is apparently, at some time, formic acid in the blood, but it is doubtful that it comes from the rumen because formate is so rapidly decomposed in the rumen that one usually can not detect it. Perhaps many of the times when it has been detected it has been generated during steam distillation.

Dr. Mc Carty: If formate is toxic to the cow, methane fermentation would be of some benefit, since it probably destroys the formate.

Dr. John Winter (Acad. Nat. Sciences, Philadelphia): Dr. Bryant, has anybody done any work on sterilizing the rumen? If so, what happens, or how fast does this complex community develop again, and from where?

Dr. Bryant: There have been some studies on bloat where the rumen was emptied, washed out with water, and the cows put on bloat-provoking pastures. It appeared that, on the very lush pasture, the flora comes back very rapidly; I think it required four or five days.

Some quantitative studies by Warner in Australia employing direct microscopic methods suggested there could be very great differences in sheep when the flora goes off due to starvation, for example, and then recovers.

It is very easy to keep the ciliate protozoa out of the rumen; whereas many of the groups of bacteria come in, even in isolated calves. As the calves are born, they are taken to an area where ruminants are not kept. As the calves flora developes the balance is somewhat different from normal. Some groups are very numerous but there are some intruders and some groups may be absent. After inoculating with rumen contents from mature animals the flora reverts to what one expects normally.

As to where the bacteria come from if they do not come from ruminants is uncertain. We do not know, except those suggestions that ruminococci and some others come from the alimentary canal of other animals.

Chairman Heukelekian: What is the retention time in the rumen?

Dr. Bryant: This subject is very important in rumen nutrition. The faster the rate of passage, usually the more propionate is formed and usually, there is a little greater feed efficiency. If hay is finely ground, retention time is decreased, resulting in lower digestion of cellulosic fractions, but the other compensating factors, such as increased propionate, will make the animal do as well, and quite often better, with less digestion of cellulose, so the rate of passage is quite important and the retention time, of course, would be too.

Chairman Heukelekian: Is it hours or days?

Dr. Bryant: Mean retention time varies greatly, depending on different fractions of the feed and various other factors, but for hay particles it may average about 1 to 3 days.

Dr. Zajic (Kerr-McGee Oil Ind.): I noticed that most of the microorganisms on which Dr. Bryant reported did not use amino acids, and that the work he reported was concentrated mostly on carbohydrate degradation. Do these microorganisms, or others, have proteolytic activity, and what is their overall contribution to the metabolism of the cow? I think that there must be an amino acid pool, although it may be very low.

Dr. Bryant: The protozoa are quite actively proteolytic as are the bacteria, but when one tries to isolate proteolytic bacteria that utilize the products as energy sources, in the way that Clostridium sporogenes would, they are not found in significant numbers in the rumen. When one looks at the strains that are proteolytic, one finds that they are spread over practically all of the species; but they are not very active, as Cl. sporogenes would be. But this seems consistent with the fact that, when rations with different levels of protein are fed, the potential of the proteolytic enzymes in the rumen remains about the same, suggesting that, perhaps, it is a case of many different organisms having proteolytic abilities.

People who have tried to study the catabolism of individual or pairs of amino acids have had difficulty in showing rapid ammonia production with a mixed flora or with pure cultures. Our recent studies with Bacteroides ruminicola showed that it will grow with ammonia or with some long chain peptides, but that it will not grow with free amino acids. This organism produces much ammonia from casein hydrolysates. This suggests that, perhaps, the main substances that get into the bacterial cell and from which ammonia is produced are peptides rather than free amino acids.

19

PHYSIOLOGY OF THE RUMEN PROTOZOA

J. Gutierrez and R. E. Davis
Animal Husbandry Research Division
USDA, Beltsville, Maryland

As a background before discussing the recent work on protozoa, we shall mention some of the known functions of the protozoa in the rumen and look at the various types. The protozoa of the rumen of cattle and sheep are usually placed in two groups; the isotrichs, which have rows of cilia over the entire cell, as in paramecium, and the oligotrichs, which have membranelles or tufts of cilia located at the anterior part of the body. The holotrichs include the two genera, Isotricha and Dasytricha, which readily digest soluble carbohydrates such as glucose and sucrose but do not attack cellulose. The oligotrichs include the genera Diplodinium, Entodinium and Ophryoscolex. Species of Entodinium, are smaller than most diplodinia and have only one row of membranelles located around the mouth. Ophryoscolex caudatus, one of the larger, more complex protozoa which inhabit the rumen, shows numerous spines and projections which give the cell a peculiar appearance. In all the rumen protozoa, reproduction is by transverse fission.

Some of the functions which are carried out by the protozoa living in the rumen are (1) the production of short-chain fatty acids, such as acetic and butyric which are absorbed, yielding energy to the host (Oxford, 1955). Amounts of acid produced per cell, obtained from manometric experiments, can be used in obtaining estimates of the total acid contribution of the protozoa for the host. This has been found to be about 20 per cent of the total fermentation acids available to the host. A second function of the protozoa is their aid in the digestion of

ingested substrates such as starch, cellulose , and bacteria.
Still another function of the protozoa is that the cells serve
as a source of protein for the host as they are digested.
More recently the protozoa have been shown to break down
proteinaceous materials in the feed and to metabolize long-
chain fatty acids, such as oleic and lauric (Gutierrez et al.,
1962, Williams et al., 1961). A proteinase for the rumen
oligotrich protozoa was suggested as early as 1936 (Schlottke,
1936), and Blackburn and Hobson (1960) have reported the
ingestion of stained casein particles and their subsequent
disappearance in some of the oligotrich protozoa. Warner
(1956) has suggested that the rumen protozoa are proteolytic
and that ammonia production appears to be the end product of
nitrogen metabolism. Recent studies with Ophryoscolex
have shown that washed suspensions of the protozoa in the
presence of antibiotics can attack protein-containing substrates such as cottonseed-, soybean-, and linseed-oil
meals (Williams et al., 1961). Species of Isotricha were
able also to metabolize trypticase, a pancreatic digest of
casein, when given the substrate in Warburg experiments.

Since crude protein sources were readily utilized by the
protozoa, tracer amino acids were used to determine if the
protozoa could metabolize a soluble, chemically defined
nitrogen source. One hour incubation periods with C^{14} -
labelled amino acids demonstrated (Table 1) that Ophryoscolex
readily concentrated DL-leucine, DL-alanine, and DL-valine
within the cells (Table 1, Williams et al., 1961). The
holotrich, Isotricha prostoma, also was able to incorporate
these three amino acids at a slightly higher rate than
Ophryoscolex.

Gruby and Delafond (1843) were the first to advance the
idea that the rumen protozoa served as a source of protein
for the host. They estimated that approximately 20 per cent
of the protein requirement of the host was furnished by the
protozoa. The biological value of the protozoan protein for
the host has been evaluated by McNaught et al. (1954), and
feeding trials with rats showed the protozoan protein had a
higher nutritive value than either bacterial or yeast protein.
Sufficient protozoan cells of Isotricha and Dasytricha were
collected, separated, washed, and counted in order to do a
micro-Kjeldahl determination of the total nitrogen content
per cell. Each determination was done in duplicate with
protozoa that were collected at different times. The values

TABLE 1: Incorporation of labelled amino acids and starch by Ophryoscolex caudatus

Amino Acid	Radioactivity in Counts per Min. per 100 µl		
	Initial Culture	Cells	Supernatant[a]
DL-valine-4-C ^{14}	12,146	1,074	38
DL-alanine-2-C^{14}	6,171	1,789	170
DL-leucine-2-C^{14}	6,790	813	18
Starch-C^{14}	6,822	207	21

[a] Radioactivity of the final wash water in which the protozoa were rinsed. The number of cells contained in 100 µl of the buffer solution was approx. 16,000.

of the total cell nitrogen varied between 1.12 and 1.18 µgm per cell for Dasytricha and 23.0 to 31.5 µgm per cell for mixed I. prostoma and I. intestinalis. Using the data of the cellular nitrogen content experiments, the protein contributed to the host by the holotrich protozoa can be calculated. With one isotrich per ml, there would be 2.5 mg of isotrich nitrogen or 15 mg of isotrich protein in a rumen containing 100 kg of contents. With one dasytrich per ml there would be 0.11 mg nitrogen or 0.66 mg dasytrich protein per 100 liters. With rumen protozoal counts of 3000 Isotricha and 5000 Dasytricha per ml, about 33 g of protein would be supplied to the host by the holotrich protozoa each day. No figures are available on the nitrogen content per cell of Diplodinium or Entodinium, but in cellular dimensions the latter approximates Isotricha and the former resembles Dasytricha. If each Diplodinium supplies as much protein as an Isotricha, and Entodinium as much as a Dasytricha, and using estimates of 3000 Diplodinium and 5000 Entodinium per ml of rumen contents, approximately 66 g of protein would be the contribution of the protozoa as a source of protein for the ruminant. (Gutierrez, 1955).

Paper chromatography of acid-hydrolyzed suspensions of Ophryoscolex and Isotricha have indicated the following list of amino acids are contained in the protozoal protein, which is made available to the host from the digestion of the protozoa. The amino acid composition for the two genera Isotricha and

Ophryoscolex were similar. Cysteine, aspartic and glutamic acids, serine, glycine, threonine, alanine, tyrosine, methionine, arginine, proline, valine, phenylalanine, leucine, and isoleucine were the amino acids found.

The nitrogenous end products from the metabolism of casein by Ophryoscolex were determined using a washed suspension of protozoa which had been deprived of substrate for four hours. By the use of the Conway technique, experiments with Ophryoscolex showed that 0.8 uM NH_3 were released from 6000 protozoa which were exposed to 6 mg of casein after an incubation period of 2 hr at 39C. The quantitative experiments on ammonia production from casein by counted numbers of Ophryoscolex show that, at least for some of the rumen protozoa, ammonia can be an important product of nitrogen metabolism.

The protozoa have been shown to contribute to the lipid metabolism of the rumen. Isolated steers faunated with individual species of ruminal ciliates, yielded 1.0 gram quantities of protozoa per 500 ml of filtered rumen liquor. These washed suspensions of protozoal species from the predominant groups of ruminal ciliates, the holotrichs represented by Isotricha prostoma and I. intestinalis, and the oligotrichs by Entodinium simplex showed a high affinity for C^{14}-labelled fatty acids of the C-18 to C-16 chain lengths. Since these are representative species, it is presumed the ability to metabolize long-chain fatty acids is a common characteristic among rumen ciliates. Lipid determinations indicated the holotrichs contained 7 to 9 per cent lipid dry weight compared to 6 per cent for the oligotrichs. Palmitic acid was prevalent in the lipid fractions of the ruminal ciliates. The holotrichs hydrogenated oleic acid to stearic acid and to a compound with a R_f value similar to linoleic. Unsaturation, saturation, and incorporation of C-16 to C-18 fatty acids by holotrichs were demonstrated, most of the activity taking place in the cellular matrix. Tributyrin incubated with suspensions of I. intestinalis stimulated volatile fatty acid production. Manometric experiments indicated that short-and long-chain fatty acids stimulated gas production more in holotrichs and less with oligotrich suspensions. From size comparison of different microbial species, the rumen ciliates appear to contribute significantly to the over-all microbial protoplasmic activity and, hence, to the degree of hydrogenation of fatty acids in rumen ingesta.

Since the rumen protozoa live in close association with immense numbers of bacteria, it was thought some of these might be ingested by the protozoa as a protein source. Recent studies have provided evidence that all the common genera of protozoa are bacteria feeders and that at times very large numbers of bacteria are contained within their endoplasms. Isotricha prostoma selectively ingests Gram-negative rods which have been classified tentatively as Butyrivibrio species (Gutierrez, 1958). The bacteria agglutinate at the mouth area and are gradually propelled inward, where a vacuole can be seen gradually to disintegrate. Entodinium (Fig. 1 and 2) and Diplodinium have been examined for bacterial feeding directly from the rumen contents of an animal fed a high starch diet. The bacteria isolated from crushed cells of these protozoa have been shown to have characteristics similar to Streptococcus bovis (Gutierrez, 1959).

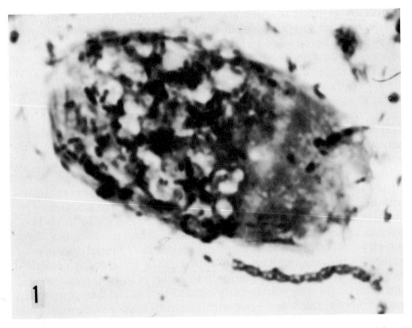

Fig. 1—Entodinium simplex showing ingested starch granules and bacteria. Gram stain. 1250.

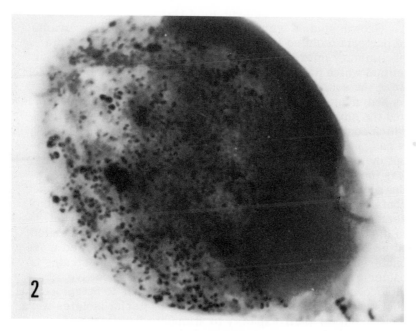

Fig. 2—Species of Entodinium with ingested bacteria. Gram stain. 1250.

Some of the protozoan requirements for growth have been
followed in in vitro culture work. Isotricha intestinalis has
been grown for short periods (three weeks) in a medium which
included rumen fluid, inorganic salts, ground alfalfa and
wheat, plus viable bacteria. When the bacteria were eliminated
from the culture, either by autoclaving or by the use of antibiotics, the protozoan culture would gradually diminish in
numbers and finally die out. Improved results in longevity
of the cultures have been obtained with the protozoan Epidinium
ecaudatum, which has been cultured for six months with known
bacteria, starch, and ground alfalfa (Gutierrez and Davis, 1962).
Sharp, in 1914, described the neuro-motor apparatus in the
ciliate and published his material using the name Diplodinium
ecaudatum for the protozoan. He recognized that the forms
both with and without caudal spines belonged to the same species.
Workers in New Zealand (Bailey, 1958) recently showed
Epidinium possesses significant amylase activity, and Oxford
(1958) demonstrated Epidinum swallows small clover starch

grains and has a requirement for CO_2.

Growth studies with Epidinium ecaudatum, using strains
of bacteria isolated from the protozoa, have yielded some
preliminary information. Rumen samples removed from an
animal which harbored Epidinium as the only large oligotrich
were the source of the protozoa. The ciliates were collected
by sedimentation in large test tubes and washed free of debris
and the smaller protozoa, using an inorganic salts solution
which contained NaCl, $CaCl_2$, $MgSO_4$, KH_2PO_4 and $NaHCO_3$.
A gas phase of 5 per cent CO_2 in nitrogen was used throughout the experiments. The washed suspension of Epidinium
was then ground in a tissue homogenizer and the contents of
the ruptured cells were inoculated into a series of agar tubes
containing starch feed extract medium. In a parallel control
series an equal amount of the last washing liquid adjacent
to the protozoa but containing no ciliates was also inoculated.
After 24 hr incubation, the experimental series showed more
bacterial colonies than the control series, and the strains of
bacteria isolated in this manner were a Gram-positive
diplococcus which had characteristics similar to Streptococcus
bovis, and a Gram-negative rod. The bacterial isolates were
then tested for their capacity to stimulate the growth of
Epidinium. Protozoa washed free of external bacteria and
debris were used to start cultures that were provided strains
of lactic acid-producing Streptococcus bovis originally isolated from Epidinium. In order to diminish the amount of
lactic acid produced by the food organisms, the daily addition
to the cultures of 0.1 ml of a standardized suspension of lactic
acid-utilizing Peptostreptococcus reduced the level of lactic
acid present, and aided in maintaining the pH of the cultures
between 6.5 and 6.8. The latter organism is a large Gram-
negative coccus with a strong dehydrogenase activity and its
use also permitted omission of reducing agents such as
cysteine hydrochloride from the medium.

Usually 80 to 100 epidinia were inoculated into 5 ml of
the culture medium which contained 0.02 per cent each of
ground rice starch and alfalfa. The 5 ml culture flasks
supported peak populations of 5000 to 6000 protozoa. The
cultures have been carried in the laboratory for six months,
and must be transferred every 24 hr, but show higher
populations if transferred and given fresh substrate twice
daily. Transfer is accomplished by removing half of the
supernatant with a fine capillary, replacing the old medium

with fresh salts solution, and adding new substrate. The
starch and alfalfa must be kept at low levels in order to
limit the growth of the bacteria. After initial inoculation
of the cultures with the rapidly growing S. bovis, no further
addition to the cultures was made. A check of the bacterial
populations in the cultures at three months demonstrated
S. bovis was able to maintain itself in numbers of approximately 500,000 per ml of the culture fluid. Attempts to grow
the protozoa without living bacteria have as yet not been
successful.

In Warburg experiments, Epidinium ecaudatum was shown
able to utilize some of the substrates which had been provided
in the culture medium. Rice starch and the protein-containing
substrates linseed-, cottonseed-, and soybean-oil meals were
metabolized by the protozoa. In order to identify the soluble
fermentation acids produced from starch by Epidinium, suspensions of the organisms were washed free of debris and the
final harvest of organisms divided into two equal amounts
after the addition of 0.5 mg per ml each of streptomycin and
penicillin. The control culture was killed at the beginning
of the experiment with 5 N H_2SO_4, and the second culture
was allowed to ferment 100 mg of rice starch for 5 hours
before the fermentation was also stopped with acid. The
soluble metabolic products produced by Epidinium include
butyric and acetic acids, carbon dioxide and hydrogen. In
the kinds of fermentation acids formed, Epidinium differs
from the rumen holotrichs, Isotricha and Dasytricha, which
produced mostly lactic acid and lesser amounts of acetic
and butyric acids.

Isotricha sp. contains 7 to 9 per cent lipid of the total
cellular dry weight. Preliminary results with silicic acid
columns and organic solvents indicate that approximately 40
per cent of this lipid is carbohydrate-containing phospholipid
(Moore and Doran, 1962). Sterol components are present in
the Isotricha lipid both in the sterol and the diglyceride (free
sterol) fractions. The cholesterol-like components present
mainly in the diglyceride fractions have been confirmed by
the Lieberman-Burchard and Zak methods for the detection of
cholesterol-containing substances. Entodinium simplex
lipid fractions also contain carbohydrate, phospholipid, and
cholesterol-like components. Other preliminary data indicate
that Isotricha species respond to sterols dissolved in paraffin
oil, particularly corticosterone, which stimulates CO_2 and

H_2 production to twice that of the endogenous controls in 80 min. Hexestrol stimulates less gas production with Isotricha species than corticosterone. Entodinium simplex is stimulated by either corticosterone or androstendione. Most of the sterol compounds tested manometrically did not stimulate gas production by the rumen ciliates.

LITERATURE CITED

Bailey, R.W. 1958. The carbohdrases of the cattle rumen ciliate Epidinium ecaudatum Crawley isolated from cows fed on red clover (Trifolium pratense L.) New Zealand J. Agric. Res. 1:825-833.

Blackburn, T.H. and P.N. Hobson.1960. Proteolysis in the sheep rumen by whole and fractionated rumen contents. J. Gen. Microbiol. 22:272-281.

Gruby, D. and O. Delafond. 1843. Récherches sur des animalcules se developant en grand nombre dans l'estomac et dans les intestines pendant la digestion des animaux herbivores et carnivores. Compt. Rend. Acad. Sci. (Paris) 17:1304-1308.

Gutierrez, J. 1955. Experiments on the culture and physiology of holotrichs from the bovine rumen. Biochem. J. 60: 516-522.

Gutierrez, J. 1958. Observations on bacterial feeding by the rumen ciliate Isotricha prostoma. J. Protozool. 5:122-126.

Gutierrez, J. and R. E. Davis. 1959. Bacterial ingestion by the rumen ciliates Entodinium and Diplodinium. J. Protozool. 6:222-226.

Gutierrez, J. and R. E. Davis. 1962. Culture and metabolism of the rumen ciliate Epidinium ecaudatum Crawley. Appl. Microbiol. 10:305-308.

Gutierrez, J., P. P. Williams, R. E. Davis, and E. J. Warwick. 1962. Lipid metabolism of rumen ciliates and bacteria. I. Uptake of fatty acids by Isotricha prostoma. Appl. Microbiol. 10:548-551.

McNaught, M.L., E.C. Owen, K. M. Henry, and S.K. Kon. 1954. The utilization of non-protein nitrogen in the bovine rumen. 8. The nutritive value of the proteins of preparations of dried rumen bacteria, rumen protozoa and brewer's yeast for rats. Biochem. J. 56:151-156.

Moore, J. H. and B. M. Doran. 1962. Lipid metabolism in the normal and vitamin B_{12} deficient chick embryo. Biochem. J. 84:506-513.

Oxford, A. E. 1955. The rumen ciliate protozoa: Their chemical composition, metabolism, requirements for maintenance and culture, and physiological significance for the host. Exptl. Parasitol. 4:569-605.

Oxford, A. E. 1958. Bloat in cattle. IX. Some observations on the culture of the cattle rumen ciliate Epidinium ecaudatum Crawley occurring in quantity in cows fed on red clover (Trifolium pratense L.) New Zealand J. Agric. Res. 1:809-824.

Schlottke, E. 1936. Untersuchungen über die Verdaungsfermente von Infusorien aus dem freien Wasser und aus dem Rinderpansen. Sitzlur. Naturforsch. Ges. Rostock 3F, 6:59-66.

Sharp, R. G. 1914. Diplodinium ecaudatum with an account of its neuromotor apparatus. Univ. Calif. (Berkeley) Publ. Zool. 13:43-122.

Warner, A. C. I. 1956. Proteolysis by rumen micro-organisms. J. Gen. Microbiol. 14:749-762.

Williams, P. P., R. E. Davis, R. N. Doetsch, and J. Gutierrez. 1961. Physiological studies of the rumen protozoan Ophryoscolex caudatus Eberlein. Appl. Microbiol. 9:405-409.

Zak, B., R. C. Dickerman, E. G. White, H. Burnett, and P. J. Cherney. 1954. Rapid estimation of free and total cholesterol. Am. J. Clin. Path. 24:1307-1315.

DISCUSSION

Chairman Heukelekian (Rutgers University): Thank you, Dr. Gutierrez, for the very striking slides of the protozoa and the wealth of information about the activities of these organisms and their function in the rumen. It seems to me, that rumen microbiologists are far ahead of us; that the function of the protozoan fauna in the rumen is better known than the function of the protozoan fauna in sludge digestion, or in other areas. Aside from the early work of Dr. Lackey on the identification of protozoa in sludge digestion tanks, I do not know of any subsequent work done to determine the function of protozoa in sludge digestion. This should open up a very fertile ground for research for some of us.

Dr. Edwin A. Boger (Univ. of Connecticut): Was the work on which you and the previous speaker reported done with beef cattle or dairy cattle? How do the two compare; and what about other ruminants?

Dr. Gutierrez: It has been done with both dairy cattle and beef cattle. I think there is not much difference regarding the protozoan aspect.

Dr. Alan Cassell (Univ. of N. Carolina): Have you noted whether the populations of the predator and prey organisms remain constant or do they fluctuate?

Dr. Gutierrez: They fluctuate considerably. Some research has been done with animals which have no protozoa; their bacterial populations are higher. When they are inoculated with protozoa, the bacteria decrease in numbers.

Mr. Leslie Reed (Chipman Chem. Co.): We are interested in the beta-oxidation of chemicals in animals and we believe that the bovine species are limited in this oxidation. Does the flora in the rumen contribute to beta-oxidation of chemicals, or anything else that may be taken in?

Dr. Gutierrez: I do not know of any work on that.

Dr. Bryant (U.S. Dept. of Agric.): Fatty acid metabolism in the rumen is being studied by many workers; so far, we know that very little beta-oxidation occurs in the rumen. There is a suggestion that a small amount of stearate may be converted to palmitate; however, there is no definite information. This is one instance in which the rumen is quite different from sewage sludge.

Chairman Heukelekian: How long do the ingested bacteria survive in the guts of the protozoa? The survival time could have some implications for water pollution.

Dr. Gutierrez. The digestive process is apparently rapid, because if one wants to isolate the bacteria alive it has to be done very rapidly. I usually get them out in about 15 minutes; if one waits an hour, one cannot get the bacteria out.

Mr. Robert Gerhold (Procter & Gamble): Did I understand it was possible to maintain cows in the absence of protozoa? If so, what effect does this have on the survival of the animals and their nutrition?

Dr. Gutierrez: They can get along very well without protozoa. We obtain calves at birth and maintain them in isolation and inoculate our calves with pure cultures. But the animals can do very well without protozoa.

20

MICROBIAL TRANSFORMATIONS OF
SOME ORGANIC SULFUR COMPOUNDS

Robert L. Starkey
Department of Agricultural Microbiology
Rutgers — The State University

Even a cursory examination of information on sulfur indicates that it is an important element of living things. It occurs in the cells of all organisms and it is one of the major elements. It occurs in abundance similar to that of phosphorous in higher plants and the soft tissues of animals. It is prominent in enzymes, particularly as hydrosulfide groups. It is involved in oxidation-reduction systems, particularly where there is inter-conversion between hydrosulfide and disulfide. It occurs in some vitamins and antibiotics, in most proteins, and in some storage products of microorganisms.

Sulfur is an interesting element from the microbiological standpoint because of its occurrence in diverse compounds. Its appearance in many chemical combinations is due, in part, to the fact that it has several different valence levels: in hydrogen sulfide, sulfur has a valence of 2, in sulfinic acids a valence of 4, and in sulfonates and sulfates a valence of 6. Sulfur, therefore, becomes oxidized and reduced.

Many oxidations and reductions of sulfur are brought about by microorganisms, and diverse organic and inorganic compounds of sulfur, as well as elemental sulfur itself, are susceptible to microbial attack. Among the susceptible organic sulfur compounds are those in which the sulfur occurs as hydrosulfide (R-SH), disulfide (R-S-S-R), ethereal sulfate (R-O-SO$_2$OH), sulfonate (R-SO$_2$OH), thiourea (S=C(NH$_2$)$_2$), and in ring structures.

Sulfur is a common constituent of proteins, occurring principally in the amino acids cyst(e)ine and methionine.

405

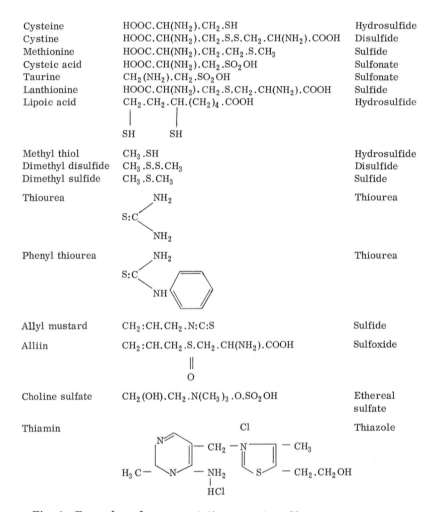

Fig. 1—Formulas of representative organic sulfur compounds of biological importance.

Biotin

Thiophene

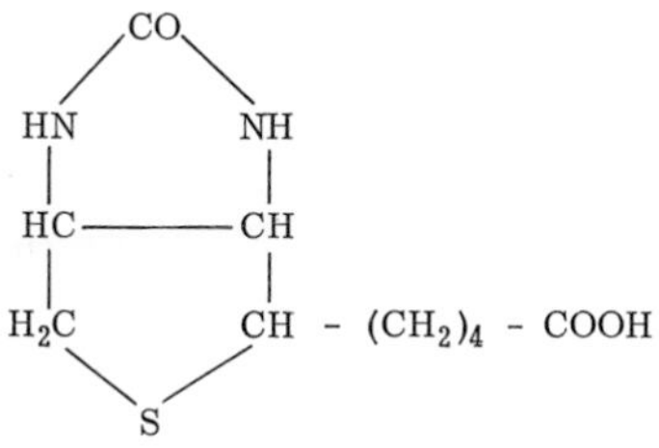

Penicillin G

Thiazole

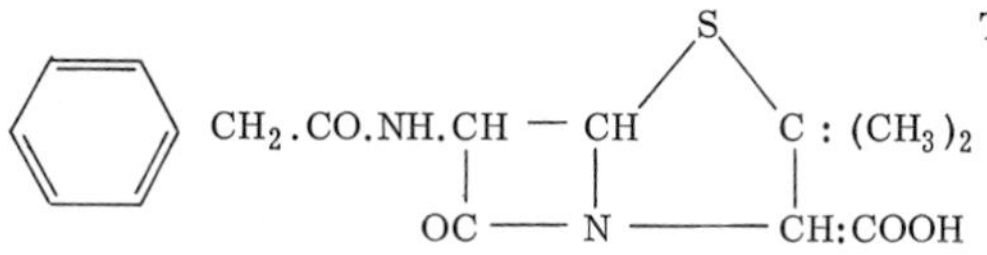

Gliotoxin

Disulfide

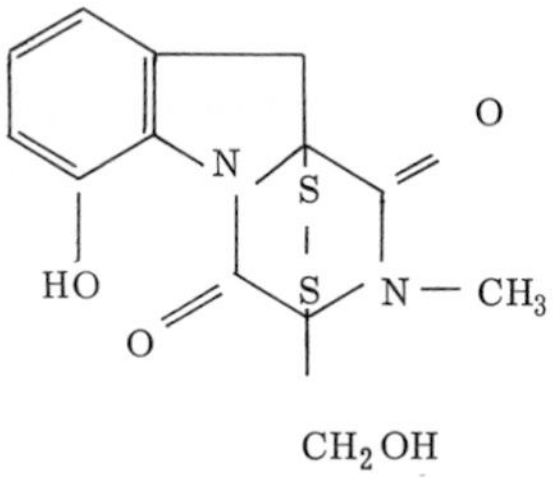

CH$_2$OH

Figure 1 (cont'd.)

Glutathione, the metabolically important diamide, contains cysteine. Coenzyme A is a mercaptan and the sulfhydryl is an active functional group. Some representative organic sulfur compounds are shown in Fig. 1. Alpha-lipoic acid and its disulfide are concerned with the oxidation of pyruvate and may be oxidized and reduced as are cysteine and cystine. Thiourea has been reported to be a constituent of some higher plants and filamentous fungi, particularly in diseased plant tissues. The sulfur in alliin and cycloalliin, which are contained in onion, occurs as sulfoxide. Allyl mustard oil is formed on the hydrolysis of glucosides contained in mustard and pepper. Choline sulfate occurs as a stored form of readily assimilable sulfur in higher plants, filamentous fungi, and algae (16, 35, 55). Nissen and Benson (35) reported that choline sulfate constituted 5 to 15 per cent of the soluble sulfur compounds of various plants.

According to Roberts et al. (41), cells of Escherichia coli had 95 per cent of the sulfur in the amino acids cyst (e)-ine and methionine. Approximately half the former and all the latter occurred in cell protein. The other half of the cystine was contained in glutathione. Findings of Rhodes et al. (1, 2, 40) indicate that the cell proteins of microorganisms contain considerably less methionine than lysine, but more methionine than tryptophan (Table 1). There were similar amounts of the amino acid in bacteria, filamentous fungi, and yeasts.

TABLE 1: Content of some amino acids in microbial cells*

Group	No. of strains	Amino acids	Ave. (% of protein)
Bacteria	86	Lysine	6.50 ± 1.97
		Methionine	1.75 ± 0.64
		Tryptophan	0.32 ± 0.11
Yeasts	271	Lysine	7.19 ± 1.07
		Methionine	1.15 ± 0.27
		Tryptophan	0.80 ± 0.23
Molds	135	Lysine	6.75 ± 1.49
		Methionine	1.25 ± 0.45
		Tryptophan	0.83 ± 0.28

* Cited from Rhodes et al., Ref. 40.

Cysteine, reduced glutathione, and probably other organic compounds with sulfhydryl groups react with elemental sulfur as follows to produce disulfides and hydrogen sulfide:

$$2\ R\text{-}SH + S° \longrightarrow R\text{-}S\text{-}S\text{-}R + H_2S$$

The reaction between cysteine and sulfur occurs at neutrality and even in the absence of enzymes. It is common to all cells since all have sulfhydryl groups. It was shown even for sulfur bacteria (59). The reduction of sulfur by cells is probably brought about also by other organic compounds or participation of enzymes because it was observed by Miller and McCallan (27, 28) that the amount of sulfur reduced by fungus spores was greater than that of ground spores and that the reaction with spores was more rapid than with glutathione.

Assimilation of organic sulfur compounds. The degree of utilization of organic sulfur compounds as sources of sulfur or nitrogen by microorganisms provides some evidences of the susceptibility of these compounds to microbial attack. Numerous studies have been made of the effects of various sulfur compounds on microbial growth. Typical of these studies are those of den Dooren de Jong (6), who tested the effects of 13 bacterial cultures on 11 sulfur compounds. Cystine supported slight to good growth of 5 cultures, and the following 3 compounds supported slight growth of 2 cultures: taurine, benzene sulfonic acid, and sulfanilic acid. The following compounds failed to support growth: thioacetic acid, thioglycollic acid, thiolactic acid, thioacetamide, thiourea, and diethyl thiourea. More of the sulfur compounds served as sources of nitrogen in media containing glucose than supported growth in the absence of other organic substances. Ten of the bacterial cultures derived nitrogen from cystine, thioacetamide, and sulfanilic acid, 9 from taurine and thiourea, and one from diethyl thiourea. Thioacetic acid, thioglycollic acid, and thiolactic acid failed to serve as sources of nitrogen. Of these compounds cystine was the most susceptible to attack, followed by taurine. All the other sulfur compounds resisted attack by the bacteria used.

DISSIMILATION OF SPECIFIC ORGANIC SULFUR COMPOUNDS

Considering the great diversity of organic sulfur compounds in plants and animals and their metabolic importance, it is surprising that there is relatively little information on the dissimilation of these compounds, on the microorganisms concerned in the transformations, and on the sulfur products formed.

Decomposition in soil. When organic sulfur compounds are exposed to the mixed microbial population of soil one finds marked differences in susceptibility of the compounds to microbial attack. Portions of several sulfur compounds were added to soil to make a concentration of 1 per cent, and determinations were made periodically for sulfate, on the assumption that, if the organic sulfur compounds decomposed aerobically, the sulfur would appear as sulfate (11). Based on this assumption, it would be concluded from Table 2 that cystine, taurine, and

sodium taurocholate decomposed fairly rapidly and that
thiamin, methionine, thiourea, and phenyl thiourea were
very resistant to decomposition. This conclusion, however,
is only partly valid. Other results indicate that, although
thiamin decomposes slowly, it disappears on prolonged incubation. Furthermore, methionine is not resistant to
decomposition. Sulfate formation is not a reliable index of
its susceptibility to microbial attack and, therefore, the
data are misleading for this compound. Schmidt et al. (47)
reported that most of the carbon of methionine added to soil
was recovered as carbon dioxide in 4 days. Thiourea, however, decomposes very slowly and, in addition, is toxic to
the soil population.

TABLE 2: Production of sulfate from some organic
sulfur compounds in perfused soil*

Compound	Sulfate-sulfur, %	
	2 weeks	6 weeks
Cystine	19	92
Taurine	67	100
Na-taurocholate	70	97
Thiamin	5	9
Methionine	1	1
Thiourea	1	1
Phenyl thiourea	0	0

* Cited from Frederick et al., Ref. 11.

Among additional sulfur compounds that decomposed very
slowly or failed to decompose with the formation of sulfate in
a period of several weeks are the following: sulfanilic acid,
sulfonamides, thiocresol, mercapto ethanol, and sulfon-
methane.

Ethereal sulfates. Sulfate is produced by hydrolysis of
aryl-, glucose-, and chondroitin-sulfates and possibly alkyl-
sulfates (42). The cleavage is brought about by sulfatases of
various bacteria and filamentous fungi and by animal and
plant tissues. A typical reaction is indicated below.

$$R \cdot O \cdot SO_2OH + H_2O \longrightarrow R \cdot OH + H_2SO_4$$

The substituent groups on the benzene ring and the position of
the group were found by Dodgson et al. (8) to affect the rate

of release of sulfate by the sulfatase of the bacterium
Alcaligenes metalcaligenes. The probability that the cleavage
occurs at the oxygen-sulfur bond and not at the radical-oxygen
bond was suggested. Chondroitin-sulfate is attacked by bacteria with release of sulfate, and the sulfatase action has
been demonstrated with bacterial extracts (26).

  Taurine and cysteic acid. The sulfonates, taurine and
cysteic acid, are natural constituents of tissues and waste
products of animals, and taurine has been found in plant
tissues. According to Garreau (15) the sulfur of taurine but
not of cysteic acid was transformed to sulfate by Aspergillus
niger. Others (52, 61) observed that both taurine and cysteic
acid served as sources of sulfur for certain fungi. Some of
the labeled sulfur of taurine injected into rats was excreted
as sulfate, but the conversion was ascribed to bacteria in
the digestive tract (48).

  In our laboratories, both bacteria and actinomycetes
obtained from soil by Stapley (57, 58) grew in culture media
with cysteic acid as the only organic compound. A bacterial
culture that grew in media with taurine as the only organic
constituent was also isolated. Dissimilation of both compounds
resulted first in release of the nitrogen as ammonia and then
of the sulfur as sulfite, which was oxidized to sulfate (Fig. 2).
With taurine there was rapid drop in pH because of the excess
of sulfate over neutralizing cations in the products. There
was evidence that the sulfur was released as sulfite, which
was oxidized to sulfate. The enzymes associated with the
t ransformations were adaptive.

  Thiourea. Thiourea at high concentrations has been reported to be toxic to nitrifying bacteria (17) and to soil
microorganisms as a whole (11). Jensen (17) obtained
several fungi from soil that used thiourea as a source of
nitrogen in a medium containing glucose, but growth with
thiourea as the source of nitrogen was invariably poorer
than it was with ammonium nitrogen. With thiourea as the
only source of sulfur, sulfate was produced slowly by
Aspergillus sp. and Penicillium sp.; 15 to 17 per cent of the
thiourea sulfur was recovered as sulfate in 50 days.

  Ergothioneine. Ergothioneine, the betaine of thiolhistidine,
is found in mammalian tissues and the fungus Claviceps
purpurea. The initial alteration by Alcaligenes faecalis,
according to Kelly and Appleman (22), is release of tri-
methylamine with formation of thioluracanic acid (Fig. 3).

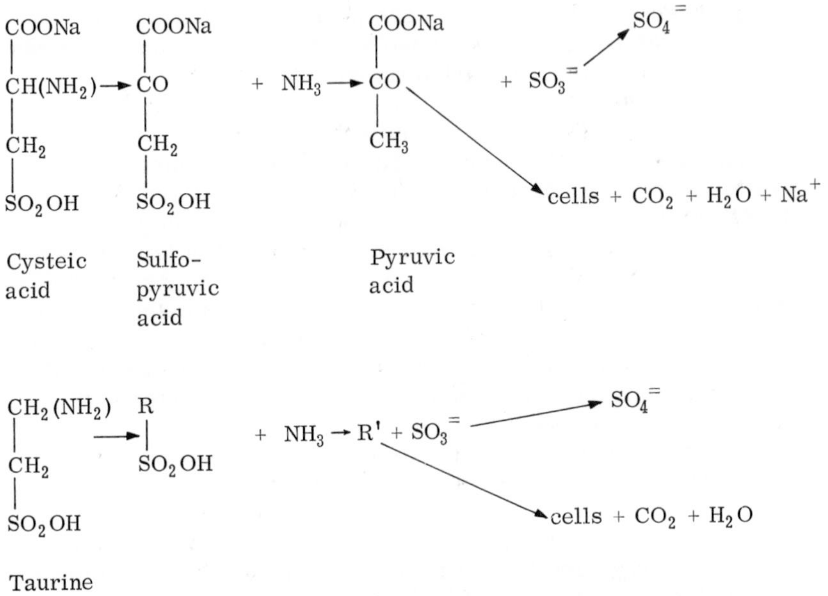

Fig. 2—Dissimilation reactions of cysteic acid and taurine.

Crude enxyme preparations and whole cells dissimilated thiolurocanic acid with production of H2S and unknown products.

Cyst(e)ine. The sulfur compounds whose dissimilation has received principal consideration are the amino acids cyst(e)ine and methionine, and the evidence indicates that there are several sulfur products of cyst(e)ine breakdown. Sulfide is a common sulfur product of its dissimilation. It was observed that hydrogen sulfide was produced from meat and other animal proteins well before the significance of bacteria in food spoilage was established. It is probable that much of the sulfide came from cyst(e)ine. One of the first reports of hydrogen sulfide production from the amino acid by fecal bacteria was that of Sasaki and Otsuka (46). Subsequently, the same transformation by diverse bacteria, including fluorescent bacteria (65), P. vulgaris (23, 66), E. coli, Streptococcus lactis aerogenes and Propionibacterium pentosaceum(7, 13), and other bacteria (4, 34), such as the anaerobes Clostridium sporogenes (66), C. tetanomorphum

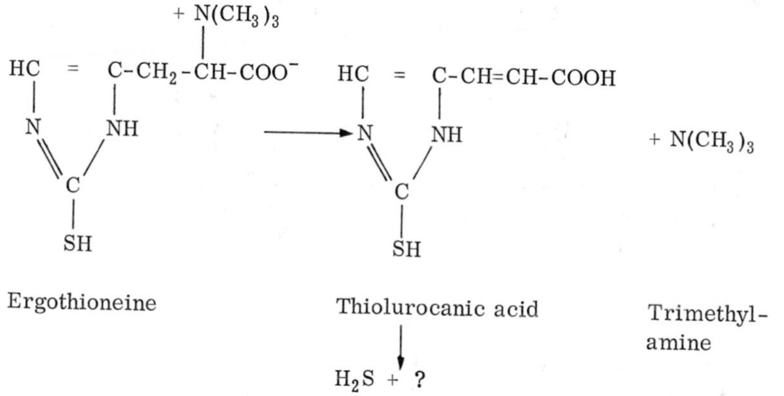

$$+ N(CH_3)_3$$

HC $=$ C-CH$_2$-CH-COO$^-$ HC $=$ C-CH=CH-COOH

N   NH $\longrightarrow$ N   NH $+ N(CH_3)_3$

C   C

SH   SH

Ergothioneine   Thiolurocanic acid   Trimethyl-
amine

$$H_2S + ?$$

Fig. 3—Dissimilation reaction of ergothioneine by Alcaligenes faecalis.

(70), and C. perfringens (14) was noted. Smythe (54) found
pyruvate, ammonia, and hydrogen sulfide as products of
cyst(e)ine breakdown. It was postulated that desulfuration
yielded amino acrylic acid, which decomposed spontaneously
to produce pyruvic acid. Desulfuration has been effected by
cell-free enzyme preparations of various bacteria, and the
enzyme is commonly referred to as cysteine desulfhydrase.
It appears to be an adaptive enzyme.

Sulfide is not the only sulfur product of cystine decomposition. Elemental sulfur was found by Barber and Burrows (3)
to be the only sulfur product of breakdown of the amino acid
by an aerobic bacterium named Achromobacter cystinovorum.

Sulfate is also a product of cyst(e)ine dissimilation by
various microorganisms, filamentous fungi in particular (15,
32, 36, 56). Sulfate formation from cyst(e)ine was demonstrated
by Kearney and Singer (19, 20, 21, 53) for washed cells and cell
extracts of Proteus vulgaris. According to a scheme prepared
by Shepherd (52), the course of transformation proceeds from
cysteine to the hypothetical compound cysteine sulfenic acid
to cysteine sulfinic acid to beta-sulphinyl pyruvic acid to
pyruvic acid and sulfite, and finally to sulfate. The terminal
reaction may be non-enzymatic, catalyzed by manganese.

In general, dissimilation of cysteine leads to formation of

hydrogen sulfide under anaerobic conditions; the other products, such as sulfate and elemental sulfur, are formed aerobically. This may not, however, occur invariably, because it was found by Tamiya (64) that E. coli decomposed cystine aerobically with production of H_2S and that this did not occur under anaerobic conditions except where nitrate was present. All of many strains of Pseudomonas aeruginosa tested by von Riesen (68) produced H_2S from cysteine under aerobic conditions. Hydrogen sulfide was produced also from the following related sulfur compounds by both dried and fresh-washed cells of the cultures: homocysteine, homocysteine lactone, and thiomalic acid.

From studies of the transformation of cysteine by the mixed population of soil, Freney (12) concluded that the sulfur became oxidized before being released from the carbon skeleton through the following series of compounds: cysteine, cystine, cystine disulfoxide, cysteine sulfinic acid, cysteic acid, and sulfate.

Studies of cyst(e)ine dissimilation in our laboratories were made with microorganisms isolated from cystine-enriched soil (9, 10, 24, 25, 60). Aerobic microorganisms were obtained that grew in mineral salts culture media in which cystine was the only organic compound. The microbial dissimilation yielded two different types of sulfur products.

One group of bacteria produced mixed sulfur products of which the two principal and primary ones were tetrathionate and elemental sulfur. Small amounts of sulfide, thiosulfate, trithionate, dithionate, sulfite, and sulfate were detected also, but these were probably secondary products. Under conditions of oxygen deficiency, elemental sulfur was the principal product, but in well-aerated media most of the cystine sulfur was transformed to tetrathionate. The pH of the media invariably rose during the dissimilation of cystine; in a typical experiment the reaction changed from initial pH 7.0 to pH 8.8. The dissimilations yielding tetrathionate or sulfur as the principal product are indicated by the following reactions:

$$10 \begin{bmatrix} NaOOC. CH(NH_2). CH_2.S \\ \\ \\ NaOOC. CH(NH_2). CH_2.S \end{bmatrix} + 65 \ O_2 \longrightarrow$$

$$4Na_2S_4O_6 + 4S° + 20(NH_4OH) + 6Na_2CO_3 + 54CO_2$$

$$20 \begin{bmatrix} NaOOC.CH(NH_2).CH_2.S \\ | \\ NaOOC.CH(NH_2).CH_2.S \end{bmatrix} + 115\ O_2 \longrightarrow$$

$$2Na_2S_4O_6 + 32S° + 40(NH_4OH) + 18\ Na_2CO_3 + 102CO_2$$

The course of the reactions is uncertain but it seems probable that the cystine sulfur was oxidized to different degrees before being released as inorganic products, and that the extent of oxidation varied with the environmental conditions.

It is possible that cystine and not cysteine was transformed, because the end products contained two or more atoms of sulfur. Some suggestion of the reactions involved are indicated by Szczepkowski (63), who observed that thiosulfate reacts with cysteine and cystine to produce cysteine sulfonic acid, cysteine thiousulfonic acid, and cystine dithiosulfonic acid. Furthermore, Swan (62) noted that cystine reacts with sulfite to give cysteine and cysteine-S-sulfonic acid. The sulfonates might be further transformed to tetrathionate, but the origin of the elemental sulfur is uncertain.

The second type of transformation of cystine was brought about by cultures of bacteria and filamentous fungi of the Fungi Imperfecti. Generally, sulfate was the principal and only product. The reaction becomes distinctly acid, dropping from an initial neutral reaction to pH 3.0 or even 2.0. Accordingly, it was necessary to control the reaction to promote continuous growth of the bacteria which do not grow at high acidity. The following reaction indicates the overall change:

$$2 \begin{bmatrix} NaOOC.CH(NH_2).CH_2.S \\ | \\ NaOOC.CH(NH_2).CH_2.S \end{bmatrix} + 17\ O_2 \longrightarrow$$

$$2Na_2SO_4 + 2(NH_4)_2SO_4 + 2H_2O + 12CO_2$$

It is unlikely that the cysteine sulfur was initially released as sulfide and then oxidized because, when a sulfide-trapping agent, cadmium phosphate, was included in the medium, the same sulfur products were formed and negligible amounts of sulfide were recovered. The cystine sulfur could have been transformed to sulfinic acid and thence to cysteic acid or taurine, and then to sulfite and sulfate, through the previously mentioned series of changes proposed by Shepherd. Since cysteic acid was more readily transformed by the cultures than taurine, it is probable that sulfite was released from the cysteic acid and the sulfite was then oxidized to sulfate.

When the reaction of the medium was held close to neutrality there was a mixture of sulfur products, predominantly tetrathionate and sulfur, suggesting a transformation like that brought about by the first-mentioned bacterial cultures.

One of the conclusions indicated by the studies of cysteine decomposition is that, although the sulfur in the cysteine is in a reduced state, the inorganic sulfur product need not be a highly reduced compound. Although sulfide may be the principal product under anaerobic conditions, other products that are completely oxidized, such as sulfate, or incompletely oxidized, such as a polythionic acid and elemental sulfur, are most common with aerobic dissimilation processes.

METHIONINE

The fate of the sulfur of methionine is different from that of the sulfur of cysteine. In fact, only one initial product has been consistently reported, namely, methyl thiol. It was reported that methyl thiol was a product of breakdown of some substances in animal proteins before methionine was discovered, but after the detection and characterization of methionine by Mueller (33) more definitive results were obtained.

As early as 1938, Onitake (39) reported that dried cell preparations of Escherichia coli and Proteus vulgaris liberated methyl thiol from methionine. Subsequently, Challenger and Charlton (5) observed that the fungus, Schizophyllum commune, also produced methyl thiol from methionine, and they reported that the fungus, Scopulariopsis brevicaulis, produced not only methyl thiol but also dimethyl disulfide and dimethyl sulfide from the amino acid. This was interpreted as evidence that the sulfur of methionine became methylated by the fungus, a transformation that should be examined further. Stahl and associates (56) found also that S. brevicaulis produced methyl thiol from methionine and that the fungi Microsporeum gypseum and Aspergillus niger formed the same product. Woods and Clifton (70) noted formation of mercaptan from Clostridium tetanomorphum and Uchida (67) reported production of methyl thiol by resting cells of Shigella flexneri.

Furthermore, enzymes were obtained from several bacteria

that dissimilated methionine with production of methyl thiol, alpha-amino butyric acid, and ammonia. This was noted for a soil bacterium by Mitsuhashi (29), and Mitsuhashi and Matsuo (30). Similar results were reported by Ohigashi et al. (37, 38) with enzyme material from E. coli; by Wiesendanger and Nisman (69) with an enzyme from C. sporogenes; and by Miwatani et al. (31) with an enzyme of a Pseudomonas sp. obtained from soil.

Whereas most of the culture studies were carried out in media that contained substrate material additional to methionine, Kallio and Larson (18) obtained a Pseudomonas species from soil that grew on methionine. Cell-free enzyme preparations transformed the methionine to methyl thiol, dimethyl disulfide, alpha-keto butyric acid, and ammonia. The enzyme was specific for the L-isomer, but the presence of D-methionine racemase converted the L- to the D-form. It was reported that the enzyme failed to attack keto methionine and it was presumed, therefore, that deamination did not precede demethiolation. In this respect the enzyme preparation differed from enzymes obtained by Mitsuhashi (29, 30) and in our laboratories, both of which formed methyl thiol from both methionine and keto methionine.

Our results (43, 44, 45, 49, 50, 51, 60) have been obtained with cultures of aerobic microorganisms isolated from methionine-enriched soil. A few of these could grow on methionine, whereas most of the isolated cultures and many obtained from culture collections decomposed the amino acid only when they were cultivated in media containing organic substrates in addition to methionine.

Methionine dissimilation by bacteria. The few of our cultures that could grow in a simple mineral salts medium that contained methionine as the only organic substance were all similar, Gram-negative, non-sporulating bacteria. During development of these bacteria on methionine in a solution medium, the sulfur content of the medium decreased proportionally with the methionine, so that when the methionine had all disappeared the medium contained practically no sulfur. Balances to account for the sulfur showed that two volatile sulfur products, methyl thiol and dimethyl disulfide, were formed, and that these were the only products. One of the bacterial cultures produced methyl thiol as the principal product and small quantities of dimethyl disulfide, whereas another bacterial culture produced dimethyl disulfide as the principal product and a small amount of methyl thiol. In both cases, however, methyl thiol was produced first and dimethyl disulfide was its oxidation product. Also, when methionine was added to soil, the mixed microbial population converted the methionine sulfur to the same volatile products. Washed cells of the culture that produced dimethyl disulfide as the principal sulfur product converted methyl thiol to dimethyl disulfide more rapidly than did the culture that produced methyl thiol as the principal product. The fact that dimethyl sulfide was produced from neither methionine nor dimethyl disulfide suggests that the cultures were unable to effect methylations such as those reported by Challenger and Charlton (5) for the fungus S. brevicaulis.

The deamination reaction yielded the keto acid which was demethiolated to methyl thiol and alpha-keto butyric acid, and deamination preceded demethiolation. Whereas deamination appeared to be constitutive, demethiolation was mediated by an induced system. Washed cells demethiolated alpha-keto methionine more rapidly than methionine, and demethiolated alpha-hydroxy methionine and ethionine also. Cystathionine was attacked, but more slowly than the other compounds.

The deaminated product of methionine, alpha-keto methionine, might be expected to undergo demethiolation anaerobically, since the methiol group is substituted by hydrogen. Nevertheless, in the absence of oxygen there was no demethiolation of the keto acid, nor of methionine. Unlike these results, those of Miwatani et al.(31) and Kallio and Larson (18) showed that enzymes of Pseudomonas sp. demethiolated methionine anaerobically.

Over the range of pH 5.5 to 9.0, reaction had little effect on either deamination or demethiolation.

The fact that the bacteria grew on methionine implies that the carbon chain was oxidized, yielding energy for cell development, and this was found to be the case.

Methionine decomposition by fungi. Since it had been noted that diverse microorganisms could attack methionine in a medium containing utilizable organic substrate (co-transformation), some of the conditions for their dissimilation of the amino acid were determined. Attention was concentrated on Aspergillus sp., one of many fungi isolated from methionine-enriched soil, which attacked methionine in media containing other organic compounds such as glucose. The results are probably representative for a large group of other filamentous fungi, bacteria, and actinomycetes.

When the fungus was grown in a methionine (5 per cent) glucose (2 per cent) mineral salts medium, results were similar to those with the bacterial cultures, in that the methionine was stripped of the nitrogen and sulfur, the nitrogen being recovered as ammonia and the sulfur as methyl thiol and dimethyl disulfide. There was no sulfate. The amount of methionine decomposed was greater the larger the amount of supplemental substrate.

The fungus cultures differed from the bacteria in that they failed to develop in a mineral salts medium with methionine as the only organic material. Nevertheless, in a similar medium containing any of several hexoses or disaccharides, the cultures grew well and decomposed methionine. Methionine and alpha-amino butyric acid served as sources of nitrogen for growth, but neither supported growth.

As with the bacteria, the fungus deaminated the amino acid to form alpha-keto methionine which was demethiolated to alpha-keto butyric acid. Both transformations required free oxygen.

Whereas the bacterial cultures completely oxidized alpha-keto butyrate and, therefore, could grow on methionine, the fungus showed no ability to decarboxylate alpha-keto butyric acid nor to grow on it. This, then, explains the lack of ability of the fungus to grow in a medium containing methionine as the only organic material. Nevertheless, under suitable conditions the fungus could attack methionine and both deaminate and demethiolate it, yielding the products alpha-amino butyric acid, ammonium, and methyl thiol or its oxidized product, dimethyl disulfide.

Methionine-transforming fungus enzyme. Cell-free fungus extract was obtained that both deaminated and demethiolated methionine and, irrespective of the purification procedure, the product had both deaminase and demethiolase activity. It is considered likely, therefore, that the same enzyme effects both transformations. It was concluded, also, by Wiesendanger and Nisman(demercapto deaminase, 69), Miwatani et al. (methioninase, 31), and Kallio and Larson (demethiomethylase, 18), that deamination and demethiolation of methionine were catalyzed by a single enzyme.

The fungus itself attacked both the D- and L-methionine, but the activity of the enzyme preparations differed in that only the D-stereoisomer of methionine was deaminated and

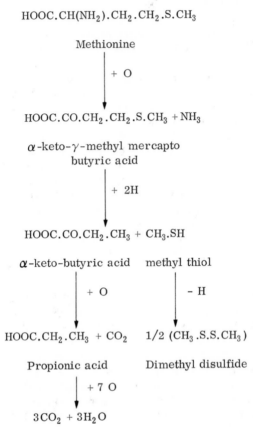

Fig. 4—Course of events in dissimilation of methionine by some bacteria and filamentous fungi.

demethiolated. Both the fungus and the purified fungus enzyme demethiolated also alpha-hydroxy methionine, alpha-keto methionine, and ethionine, but gamma-methyl mercapto butyric acid and methionol were not demethiolated.

Summary of methionine dissimilation. The dissimilation of methionine by the cultures of bacteria and fungi according to results of our studies are summarized in Fig. 4. Initial deamination results in formation of alpha-keto-gamma-methyl mercapto butyric acid which is demethiolated with release of methyl thiol and alpha-keto butyric acid. The fungus oxidizes methyl thiol to dimethyl disulfide, but is unable to

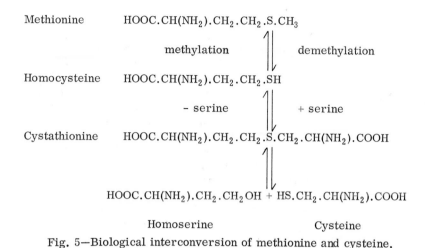

Fig. 5—Biological interconversion of methionine and cysteine.

transform the keto butyric acid further. The bacterium oxidizes alpha-keto butyric acid and, therefore, grows in a medium with methionine as the only organic substrate.

INTERCONVERSION OF CYSTEINE AND METHIONINE

Interconversion of methionine and cysteine has been established for certain microorganisms and animal tissue cells by the changes shown in Fig. 5. Methionine is converted to homocysteine by demethylation, and homocysteine is transformed to cystathionine by combination with serine. Finally, cleavage of cystathionine produces cysteine and homoserine. The reverse process results in formation of methionine from cysteine.

In view of this interconversion it seemed likely, when our studies on decomposition of cysteine and methionine were initiated, that the products of both amino acids might be the same, at least for some microorganisms. Accordingly, if cysteine was the compound dissimilated, methionine would be converted first to cysteine and then it would undergo the typical cysteine breakdown. There was no evidence of this type of transformation. Although the microorganisms may be able to meet their requirements for each amino acid from the other, the dissimilation reactions proceed without any change to the other amino acid.

CONCLUDING REMARKS

These studies with organic sulfur compounds are but the beginning of investigations that are needed to obtain an under-standing of the dissimilation of organic sulfur compounds by microorganisms. There are many sulfur compounds in each of several groups that deserve consideration. These include disulfides and hydrosulfides and the odoriferous thiols. There are also numerous thioureas, sulfinates, sulfonates, ethereal sulfates, and compounds in which the sulfur is in rings, as in thiazoles and thiophenes. Representatives of all of these groups occur in plants and animals, and there are additional compounds of industrial importance, as raw materials, products, and waste materials. One of these is the group of alkyl aryl sulfonates, the synthetic detergents that are currently attracting widespread attention because of their resistance to microbial attack.

ACKNOWLEDGEMENT

Paper of the Journal Series, New Jersey Agricultural Experiment Station, Rutgers-The State University, Department of Agricultural Microbiology.

This manuscript was prepared in part under National Science Foundation Grant G-18536 and U.S. Public Health Research Grant WP-6.

LITERATURE CITED

1.   Anderson, R.F. and R. W. Jackson. 1958. Essential amino acids in microbial proteins. Appl. Microbiol. 6:369-373.
2.   Anderson, R.F., R.A.   Rhodes, G.E.N. Nelson, M.C. Shekleton, A. Barreto Jr., and M. Arnold. 1958. Lysine, methionine, and tryptophan content of microorganisms. 1. Bacteria. J. Bacteriol. 76:131-135.
3.   Barber, H.H. and R.B. Burrows. 1936. Production of free sulfur from L-cystine by a soil bacterium. Biochem. J. 30:599-603.
4.   Bürger, M. 1914. Über Schwefelwasserstoffbildung aus Zystin durch Bakterien. Arch. Hyg. 82:201-211.
5.   Challenger, F. and P. T. Charlton. 1947. Studies on biological methylation. 10. The fission of the mono-and di-sulfide links by molds. J. Chem. Soc., p. 424-429.
6.   den Dooren de Jong, L.E. 1926. Bijdrage tot kennis van het mineralisatieproces. Dissertation, Delft, 200 pages.

7. Desnuelle, P. and C. Fromageot. 1939. La décomposition anaérobie de la cystéine par Bacterium coli. 1 Existence d'une cystéinase, ferment d'adaptation. Enzymologia 6:80-87.

8. Dodgson, K. S., B. Spencer, and K. Williams. 1956. Studies on sulfatases. 13. The hydrolysis of substituted phenyl sulfates by the arylsulfatase of Alcaligenes metalcaligenes. Biochem. J. 64:216-221.

9. Frederick, L. B. 1950. Transformations of organic sulfur compounds by soil microorganisms with particular consideration of cystine. Ph. D. Thesis, Rutgers University, New Brunswick, N.J. 147 pages.

10. Frederick, L. B. and R. L. Starkey. 1950. Transformations of cystine sulfur by soil microorganisms. Bact. Proc., p. 137-138.

11. Frederick, L. B., R. L. Starkey, and W. Segal. 1957. Decomposability of some organic sulfur compounds in soil. Soil Sci. Soc. Am. Proc. 21:287-292.

12. Freney, J. R. 1960. The oxidation of cysteine to sulfate in soil. Australian J. Biol. Sci. 13:387-392.

13. Fromageot, C. and P. Desnuelle. 1942. La décomposition anaérobie de l'homocysteine par différents systèmes biologiques; existence d'une homocystéine désulfurase. Compt. rend. 214:647-648.

14. Fuchs, A. R. and G. J. Bonde. 1957. The availability of sulfur for Clostridium perfringens and an examination of hydrogen sulfide production. J. Gen. Microbiol. 16:330-340.

15. Garreau, Y. 1941. Recherches sur la formation d'acide sulfurique, à partir de quelques dérivés organique du soufre, sur l'influence de Aspergillus niger. Compt. rend. biol. 135:508-510.

16. Harada, T. and B. Spencer. 1960. Choline sulfate in fungi. J. Gen. Microbiol. 22:520-527.

17. Jensen, H. L. 1957. Biological transformation of thiourea. Arch. Mikrobiol. 28:145-152.

18. Kallio, R. E. and A. D. Larson. 1955. Methionine degradation by a species of Pseudomonas. Symposium on Amino Acid Metabolism. McElroy, W. D. and H. B. Glass, ed., Johns Hopkins Press, Baltimore. Pages 616-631.

19. Kearney, E. B. and T. P. Singer. 1952. Intermediary metabolism of cysteinesulfinic acid in cell-free extracts of Proteus vulgaris. Biochim. Biophys. Acta 8:698-699.

20. Kearney, E. B. and T. P. Singer. 1953. The oxidation of cysteine-sulfinic and cysteic acids in Proteus vulgaris.

Biochim. Biophys. Acta 11:270-275.
21.   Kearney, E. B. and T. P. Singer. 1953. Enzymic transformations of L-cysteinesulfinic acid. Biochim. Biophys. Acta 11:276-289.
22.   Kelly, B. and M.B. Appleman. 1961. Degradation of ergothioneine by cell-free extracts of Alcaligenes faecalis. J. Bacteriol. 81:715-720.
23.   Kondo, M. 1923. Über die Bildung des Mercaptans aus L-cystin durch Bakterien. Biochem. Z. 136:198-202.
24.   Manker, R. A. 1953. Transformations of the sulfur of L-cystine by microorganisms. Ph.D. Thesis, Rutgers University, New Brunswick, N.J. 130 pages.
25.   Manaker, R. A. and R. L. Starkey. 1952. Sulfur products of microbial decomposition of cystine. Bact. Proc. p. 156-157.
26.   Martinez, R. J., J. B. Wolfe, and H. I. Nakada. 1959. Degradation of chondroitin sulfate by Proteus vulgaris. J. Bacteriol. 78:217-224.
27.   McCallan, S.E.A. and L. P. Miller. 1957. Equimolar formation of carbon dioxide and hydrogen sulfide when fungus tissue reduces sulfur. Contrib. Boyce Thompson Inst. 18: 497-506.
28.   Miller, L. P., S.E.A. McCallan, and R. M. Weed. 1953. Quantitative studies on the role of hydrogen sulfide formation in the toxic action of sulfur to fungus spores. Contrib. Boyce Thompson Inst. 17:151-171.
29.   Mitsuhashi, S. 1949. Decomposition of thioether derivatives by bacteria. 1. Methylmercaptan formation and the properties of the responsible enzyme. Japan. J. Exp. Med. 20:211-222.
30.   Mitsuhashi, S. and Y. Matsuo. 1950. Decomposition of thioether derivatives by bacteria. 2. a-keto acid as a product in the enzymatic cleavage of thioether derivatives. Japan. J. Exp. Med. 20:641-646.
31.   Miwatani, T., Y. Omukai, and D. Nakada. 1954. Enzymatic cleavage of methionine and homocysteine by bacteria. Med. J. Osaka Univ. 5:347-352.
32.   Mothes, K. 1939. Über den Schwefelstoffwechsel der Pflanzen. 2. Planta 29:67-109.
33.   Mueller, H. 1923. A new sulfur-containing amino acid isolated from the hydrolytic products of protein. J. Biol. Chem. 56:157-169.
34.   Myers, J. T. 1920. The production of hydrogen sulfide

by bacteria. J. Bacteriol. 5:231-252.
35.   Nissen, P. and A. A. Benson. 1961. Choline sulfate in higher plants. Science 134:1759.
36.   Obata, Y. and Y. Ishikawa. 1959. Biochemical studies on sulfur-containing amino acid. 2. Sulfate formation from L-cystine by molds. J. Biochem. (Tokyo) 46:293-295.
37.   Ohigashi, K., A. Tsunetoshi, and K. Ichihara. 1951. The role of pyridoxal in methylmercaptan formation, partial purification, and resolution of methioninase. Med. J. Osaka Univ. 2:111-117.
38.   Ohigashi, K., A. Tsunetoshi, M. Uchida, and K. Ichihara. 1952. Studies on cysteinase. J. Biochem. (Tokyo) 39:211-224.
39.   Onitake, J. 1938. On the formation of methyl mercaptan from L-cystine and L-methionine by bacteria. J. Osaka Med. Assoc. 37:263-270.
40.   Rhodes, R. A., H. H. Hall, R. F. Anderson, G. E. N. Nelson, M. C. Shekleton, and R. W. Jackson. 1961. Lysine, methionine, and tryptophan content of microorganisms. 3. Molds. Appl. Microbiol. 9:181-184.
41.   Roberts, R. B., P. H. Abelson, D. B. Cowie, E. T. Bolton, and R. J. Britten. 1955. Studies of biosynthesis in Escherichia coli. Carnegie Inst. Washington Publ. 607, Washington, D. C., 521 pages.
42.   Roy, A. B. 1960. The synthesis and hydrolysis of sulfate esters. Advances in Enzymol. 22:205-235.
43.   Ruiz-Herrera, J. 1963. Microbial degradation of methionine. Ph.D. Thesis, Rutgers University, New Brunswick, N.J. 196 pages.
44.   Ruiz-Herrera, J. and R. L. Starkey. 1961. Decomposition of methionine by certain filamentous fungi. Bact. Proc. p. 188.
45.   Ruiz-Herrera, J. and R. L. Starkey. 1962. Deamination and demethiolation of methionine by fungus enzymes. Bact. Proc. p. 120.
46.   Sasaki, T. and I. Otsuka. 1912. Experimentelle Untersuchungen über die Schwefelwasserstoffentwicklung der Bakterien aus Cystin und sonstigen Schwefelverbindungen. Biochem. Z. 39:208-215.
47.   Schmidt, E. L., H. D. Putnam, and E. A. Paul. 1960. Behavior of free amino acids in soil. Soil Sci. Soc. Amer. Proc. 24:107-109.
48.   Schram, E. and R. Crokaert. 1957. Études sur le

métabolism de la taurine chez le rat. Arch. Intern. physiol. et biochem. 65:165-166.

49.   Segal, W. 1952. Transformation of methionine by microorganisms. Ph.D. Thesis, Rutgers University, New Brunswick N.J. 151 pages.

50.   Segal, W. and R. L. Starkey. 1950. Transformation of methionine sulfur by bacteria isolated from soil. Bact. Proc. p. 137.

51.   Segal, W. and R. L. Starkey. 1952. Sulfur products of microbial decomposition of methionine. Bact. Proc. p. 156

52.   Shepherd, C. J. 1956. Pathways of cysteine synthesis in Aspergillus nidulans. J. Gen. Microbiol. 15:29-38.

53.   Singer, T. P. and E. B. Kearney. 1953. Studies on coenzyme III. 1. L-cysteinesulfinic dehydrogenase and its prosthetic group. Biochim. Biophys. Acta 11:290-299.

54.   Smythe, C. V. 1942. The utilization of cysteine and cystine by rat liver with the production of hydrogen sulfide. J. Biol. Chem. 142:387-400.

55.   Spencer, B. and T. Harada. 1960. The role of choline sulfate in the sulfur metabolism of fungi. Biochem. J. 77: 305-315.

56.   Stahl, W. H., B. McQue, G. R. Mandels, and R.G.H. Siu. 1949. Studies on the microbiological degradation of wool. 1. Sulfur metabolism. Arch. Biochem. 20:422-432.

57.   Stapley, E. O. 1959. Transformation of cysteic acid and taurine by soil microorganisms. Ph.D. Thesis, Rutgers University, New Brunswick, N.J. 102 pages.

58.   Stapley, E.O. and R. L. Starkey. 1959. Transformations of cysteic acid and taurine by soil microorganisms. Bact. Proc. p. 125.

59.   Starkey, R. L. 1937. Formation of sulfide by some sulfur bacteria. J. Bacteriol. 33:545-571.

60.   Starkey, R. L., W. Segal, and R. A. Manaker. 1953. Sulfur products of decomposition of methionine and cystine by microorganisms. Proc. 6th Internat'l microbiol. Cong. Rome, 256-257.

61.   Steinberg, R. A. 1941. Sulfur and trace-element nutrition of Aspergillus niger. J. Agr. Res. 63:109-127.

62.   Swan, J. M. 1957. Thiols, disulfides and thiosulfates: some new reactions and possibilities in peptide and protein chemistry. Nature 180:643-645.

63.   Szczepkowski, T. W. 1958. Reactions of thiosulfate with cysteine. Nature 182:934-935.

64.   Tamiya, N. 1951. Aerobic decomposition of cystine by
Escherichia coli. 1, 2. J. Chem. Soc. Japan, Pure Chem.
Sect. 72:118-121; 121-124 (Chem. Abs. 46:4049, 1952).
65.   Tanner, F. W. 1917. Studies on the bacterial metabolism of sulfur. 1. Formation of hydrogen sulfide from certain
sulfur compounds under aerobic conditions. J. Bacteriol.
2:585-593.
66.   Tarr, H. L. A. 1933. The anaerobic decomposition of
1-cystine by washed cells of Proteus vulgaris. Biochem. J.
27:759-763.
67.   Uchida, S. 1957. Amino acid metabolism of Shigella
flexneri . 2. Degradation of cysteine and methionine by resting
cells. Okayama-Igakkai-Zasshi 69:619-625 (Chem. Abs. 52:
5545, 1958).
68.   von Riesen, V. L. 1963. Hydrogen sulfide production by
Pseudomonas aeruginosa. 2. Qualitative substrate study.
J. Bacteriol. 85:248-249.
69.   Wiesendanger, S. and B. Nisman. 1953. La L-méthionine
démercapto désaminase: un novel enzyme à pyridoxal-phosphate.
Compt. rend. 237:764-765.
70.   Woods, D. D. and C. C. Clifton. 1937. Studies in the
metabolism of the strict anaerobes (genus Clostridium). 6.
Hydrogen production and amino-acid utilization by Clostridium
tetanomorphum. Biochem. J. 31:1774-1788.

DISCUSSION

Dr. Mulder (Landbouwhoogeschool, Wageningen): Is there
an effect of hydrogen sulfide production on the trace element
supply of microorganisms? Some years ago we studied the
effect of the production of hydrogen sulfide by bacteria on the
copper supply of Aspergillus, and found that the bacteria could
reduce copper availability. Can one get copper deficiency in
Aspergillus when using methionine as a sulfur source when
copper sulfide is formed?

Dr. Starkey: With methionine as a sulfur source for
Aspergillus there is no evidence that sulfide is produced. The
only sulfur product of methionine dissimilation, that I know of,
is methyl thiol. Dissimilation of methionine results in the
formation, initially, of methyl thiol which may be oxidized to
dimethyldisulfide, but sulfide is not a product.

Sulfide is produced by many organisms. The sulfate-
reducing bacteria produce and accumulate large quantities of
it. Although the metals occur in solution in only very low

concentrations in the presence of sulfide, some microorganisms obtain enough to meet their requirements. Desulfovibrio has cytochrome, which contains iron, and it obtains the iron even when there is high concentration of hydrogen sulfide in the medium. The same may apply to copper. The evidence we have obtained indicates that sulfide is not commonly produced from organic sulfur compounds by fungi and other aerobic microorganisms.

Dr. Green (Wallerstein Co.): We know that yeasts, at least under anaerobic conditions, have an avid appetite for methionine and we know they produce H_2S in a rather complex medium. You did not mention any of the yeasts in connection with sulfur dissimilation. Have you any comments on yeasts?

Dr. Starkey: No evidence has come to my attention of dissimilation of methionine by yeasts. Many microorganisms incorporate methionine. Once incorporated, many things can happen, such as interconversion of methionine and cysteine and dissimilation of cysteine. This recalls Beijerinck's work, in which sulfide was formed from sulfate. He concluded that sulfate was incorporated and that the small amount of sulfide that was found in the medium resulted from breakdown of transformed sulfur compounds. Some yeasts reduce sulfate to sulfide apparently without incorporation.

It seems unlikely that sulfide is a direct product of dissimilation of methionine. Formation of a small amount of sulfide in a medium containing methionine does not necessarily indicate that the methionine is desulfurated with the formation of sulfide.

Mr. Morris Smith (Toms River Chemical): One of the curves presented showed a comparison of transformation in the presence of air and in oxygen. Is it implied that oxygen tension could be a limiting factor in this particular system, and is any generalization possible?

Dr. Starkey: I believe you refer to experiments in which a heavy cell suspension was used in static medium. Under these condtions oxygen availability might be the limiting factor that resulted in the effects that were observed. More oxygen would have been available from pure oxygen than from air.

Mr. Smith: Is there any threshold tension of oxygen below which the system will not go?

Dr. Starkey: Determinations for amounts of dissolved oxygen were not made. We were attempting to ascertain whether or not demethiolation and deamination occurred in the absence of free oxygen. It was found that there was little deamination and desulfuration when impure nitrogen was used, but that there was none when the nitrogen was purified to eliminate all oxygen.

21

PROTEOLYSIS AND PROTEOLYTIC ORGANISMS

Samuel R. Green
Wallerstein Company
Division of Baxter Laboratories
Staten Island, N. Y.

In today's scientific society, considerable speculation and research is focused on the development of a closed, recycling, and regenerating biological system suitable for "long-term" space flight. One of the ideals of this closed ecological system would be a microbial population capable of utilizing carbon dioxide, other waste gases, liquid and solid wastes (urine and feces) and generating therefrom a food supplement. Since protein, 14 amino acids (aspartic acid, glutamic acid, cystine, serine, glycine, lysine, threonine, arginine, alanine, tyrosine, hydroxyproline, valine, phenylalanine and isoleucine), and ammonia have been found in human feces (1, 2), proteolytic microorganisms and their enzyme systems would play an important role in the production and synthesis of a suitable, high-quality protein food supplement.

In the sewage disposal plants of our cities and towns, there is, likewise, the need for the synthesis of microbial protein as well as the need for the degradation of protein, protein fragments and amino acids to assist in the lowering of the biolochemical oxygen demand (BOD) of the sewage. In this connection, Heukelekian and Balmat (3) have indicated that amino acids are a significant component of the nitrogen fraction of domestic sewage; the metabolism thereof by biological processes being, therefore, an important phase of biological utilization of wastes (3). Although domestic sewage contains amino acids, Placak and Ruchhoft (4) and Wuhrmann

Dr. Green is presently an independent consultant,
1188 Tice Place, Westfield, New Jersey

(5, 6) noted that 90 per cent of the amino acids were removed in biological treatment. Subrahmanyam, et al. (7), concurred with Wuhrmann's observations, reporting that although raw sewage in India contained almost all the essential amino acids, activated sludge treatment produced an effluent practically devoid of amino acids.

Since, as noted above, organic nitrogen can be metabolized by microorganisms, the proteolytic microorganisms and their enzyme systems capable of functioning in either the closed ecological system or in the sewage disposal system will be reviewed in this paper. Our concern with protein is further instigated and stimulated by the belief that, while life might possibly subsist without polysaccharides and perhaps even without fat, no cell would be likely to exist in the absence of protein since these substances provide the essential catalytically active surfaces without which metabolism cannot proceed.

Regarding the proteolytic microorganisms generally associated with sewage treatment, Gaub (8), in an early extensive bacteriological study, reported that the Imhoff effluent contained the greatest number of gelatin-liquefying and albumin-digesting microorganisms (approximately 50 per cent of the total population), smaller numbers being present in the raw sewage, screen effluent, sprinkler effluent, and final settling tank effluent. Among the proteolytic microorganisms identified were Aerobacter cloacae, Bacillus subtilis, Achromobacter delicatulum, and Bacillus mesentericus.

The presence of Penicillium, as one of the principal fungi in the slimy film of a sewage stone filter bed, was reported by various investigators at the New Jersey Agricultural Experiment Station (9, 10). In this connection, Tomlinson (11) isolated four fungi occurring at the surface of percolating filters. These were designated as Fusarium aquaeductum, Oospora, Phonia, and Sepedonium; Oospora and Sepedonium being found in many filters treating domestic sewage. It is of interest that Sepedonium cannot utilize the nitrogen of ammonia, nitrate, lysine or asparagine for growth, but does possess the enzyme system capable of assimilating peptone. Accordingly, Tomlinson observed that "it appears that Sepedonium depends on the complex nitrogenous materials present in sewage for its nutrition". This work was confirmed by Painter (12) in a study of the nutrition of four fungi associated with sewage purification. It was noted that Fusarium aquae-

ductum, Trichosporon cutaneum and a Geotrichum produced
best growth when the nitrogen source was amino acids derived from casein.

McKinney and Horwood (13), isolated eleven microorganisms from activated sludge, which were capable of
forming a floc similar to activated sludge in aerated laboratory substrates. The cultural characteristics of six of
the identified bacteria, shown in Table 1, indicate that
Bacillus cereus and Nocardia actinomorpha liquefied gelatin
and that B. cereus and a Flavobacterium peptonized the
casein in milk. While B. cereus was unable to oxidize the
organic matter of a synthetic sewage to carbon dioxide and
water, N. actinomorpha provided for an 88 per cent BOD
removal as compared to 76 to 78 per cent BOD removal in a
synthetic sewage for Paracolobactrum aerogenoides,
Escherichia intermedia and the Flavobacterium; the sewage-
seeded sludge control mixture of microorganisms producing
a 94 to 99 per cent BOD removal.

TABLE 1: Cultural characteristics of floc-forming
bacteria isolated from activated sludge

Culture	Substrate Metabolized				
	Gelatin	Casein	Glucose	Lactose	Starch
Zooglea ramigera	–	–	–	–	–
Paracolobactrum aerogenoides	–	–	+	+	–
Escherichia intermedium	–	–	+	+	–
Bacillus cereus	+	+	+	–	+
Nocardia actinomorpha	+	–	–	–	–
Flavobacterium	–	Sl.+	–	–	–

(Data from McKinney and Horwood, 1952)

In a very extensive study of the types and physiological
characteristics of bacteria encountered in intermittent sand
filters, Calaway, Carroll and Long (14) amassed data covering
the metabolic reactions of thirteen microorganisms. Ten
of these microorganisms were capable of liquefying gelatin

and nine peptonized casein (Tables 2 and 3). All six of the species of the <u>Bacillus</u> genus were capable of liquefying gelatin, whereas only four peptonized milk and only two could utilize ammonium phosphate as a source of nitrogen. The adequacy of gelatin, casein and ammonium nitrogen for the growth of species of <u>Alcaligenes</u>, <u>Flavobacterium</u>, <u>Nocardia</u> and <u>Streptomyces</u> is shown in Table 3.

TABLE 2: Cultural characteristics of bacteria
found in intermittent sand filters

Culture	Substrate Metabolized				
	Gelatin	Casein	$NH_4H_2PO_4$	Lactose	Glucose
B. alvei	+	+	−	−	+
B. cereus	+	+	−	−	+
B. circulans	+	+	−	−	+
B. megatherium	+	−	+	−	+
B. pumilus	+	−	−	−	+
B. subtilis	+	+	+	−	+

(Data from Calaway, et al., 1952)

TABLE 3: Cultural characteristics of bacteria
found in intermittent sand filters

Culture	Substrate Metabolized				
	Gelatin	Casein	$NH_4H_2PO_4$	Lactose	Glucose
Al. bookeri	+	+	−	−	−
Al. faecalis	−	+	−	−	−
Fl. aquatile	+	−	−	−	−
Fl. balustinum	+	+	−	−	+
Fl. devorans	+	−	−	−	−
Nocardia sp.	−	+	+	+	−
Streptomyces sp.	−	+			

(Data from Calaway, et al., 1952)

The studies of Ringer and Drake (15) indicated that the
normal habitat of Pseudomonas aeruginosa is human feces
and sewage and that this microorganism can be isolated from
raw and clarified sewage, including the primary and final
clarifiers, but not from sludge. P. aeruginosa produced
acid from glucose, galactose, mannose, arabinose and
xylose only when the culture was actively aerated.

The same species, P. aeruginosa, was isolated by
Jasewicz and Porges (16) from actively assimilating dairy
waste sluge. A study of the various bacterial species found
by these investigators in dairy waste sluge (Table 4) would
reveal the ubiquity of many microorganisms in sewage and
industrial wastes. Thus, for example, Bacillus cereus,

TABLE 4: Cultural characteristics of bacteria isolated from
actively assimilating dairy waste sludge

Culture	Substrate Metabolized			
	Casein	Lactose	Glucose	Gelatin [a]
Bacillus brevis	+	−	+	+
B. cereus	+	−	+	+
B. firmus	+	+	+	Slow +
B. laterosporus	+	−	+	Slow +
B. lentus	−	+	+	−
B. pasteurii	−	−	−	Slow +
Bacterium healii	+	−	+	+
Bacterium linens	+	−	−	+

[a] Liquification as listed in Bergey's Manual

(Data from Jasewicz and Porges, 1956)

Bacillus circulans, Flavobacterium aquatile and Alcaligenes
faecalis isolated from dairy wastes were also found by
Calaway, et al. (14), in intermittent sand filters. In the
same connection, Bacillus cereus was found among the floc-
forming bacteria by McKinney and Horwood (13). It is of
interest that the aforementioned bacteria can liquefy gelatin
or peptonize casein or both. The fact that 74 per cent of
the total bacteria enumerated during the assimilative phase
were members of the genera Bacillus and Bacterium (in

contrast with a count of only 8 per cent for these same genera
in the endogenous period of sludge digestion) was the basis for
the speculation by Jasewicz and Porges (16) that Bacillus and
Bacterium species are responsible for the high purification
rate and the ability of the sludge to remove and store oxygen-
demanding substances. In this connection, Bacterium linens
(gelatin liquefying, casein peptonizing microorganism) accounted for 40 per cent of the total bacteria found in aerated
dairy waste during active assimilation. In addition, Bacillus
cereus (also capable of metabolizing gelatin and casein) was
present in large numbers.

Another bacillus, Bacillus endorhythmos, a rapid gelatin
liquefier, was isolated from digested sludge by Keefer et
al. (17). Raw sewage sludge was liquefied and gasified by
this facultative anaerobe, Bacillus endorhythmos, whereas
no gas was produced from sterilized sludge. The investigators
speculated that B. endorhythmos functions in sludge in
synergism with gas-producing bacteria.

Wattie (18) classified the zooglea-forming bacteria isolated
from activated sludge and trickling filters into nine groups.
Five of the nine groups were found to liquefy gelatin. Culture
86 (from one of the gelatin liquefying groups) "produced turbid
growth and floc throughout" in an aerated synthetic sewage
containing 300 mg per 1 peptone.

While this reviewer could further tabulate the reported
isolation of still other proteolytic bacteria, streptomyces,
fungi, etc., or record still other papers confirming the
observations of earlier investigators, it would appear desirable at this time to launch into an examination of the
enzyme systems elaborated by the microorganisms capable
of hydrolyzing or synthesizing peptides or proteins.

Regarding the enzyme reaction equilibrium of hydrolysis
vs. synthesis of peptides and proteins, the equilibrium of
these reactions decidedly favors the formation of hydrolysis
products. Theoretically, of course, increasing the concentration of amino acids would shift the equilibrium in favor
of synthesis, whereas the removal of the synthetic product
should permit more to be formed.

At the onset, those who have worked with enzymes, or
those who have perused the literature are aware of the fact
that bacterial and mold proteases, like the animal enzymes,
encompass enzyme systems which are active at acidic,
alkaline, and neutral pH. On the other hand, the classification

of microbial proteinases according to the formal system
suitable for animal proteases, either endopeptidases (proteinases which act only on inner peptide bonds of proteins or
specially substituted peptides) or exopeptidases (peptidases
which act only on the peptide bonds adjacent to the terminal
amino acids) apparently is not totally valid since no microbial
enzymes have been clearly shown to be active only on proteins;
in fact several crystalline microbial enzymes have been
shown to hydrolyze both proteins and many oligopeptides
(19, 20). Thus, in contrast to the animal proteases, all of
the well-characterized microbial proteases have been found
to possess wide ranges of side-chain specificity, i. e.,
Streptomyces griseus protease has an extremely broad substrate specificity, being capable of hydrolyzing not only the
internal peptide bonds of proteins, but also the terminal
peptide bonds of oligopeptides, including dipeptides and
tripeptides. In this connection, Streptomyces griseus
protease exhibits the substrate specificities of such proteases
and peptidases as trypsin, chymotrypsin, pepsin, carbo-
xypeptidase, and aminopeptidase. Streptomyces griseus
protease has been reported to hydrolyze 87 per cent of the
total peptide bonds in egg albumin and 75 per cent of the
total peptide bonds of casein, such activity being twice that
of Bacillus subtilis protease and four times that of trypsin.

Regarding the synthesis of protein and the incorporation
of amino acids into microbial protein, it is evident that
these mechanisms require a source of energy which is usually
supplied by the metabolism of utilizable carbohydrates. However, even in the presence of fermentable carbohydrate,
microorganisms vary widely in their synthetic abilities towards proteins. Some, such as the wild type of Escherichia
coli, can rapidly synthesize all amino acids if they are
supplied with ammonia and carbon. The other extreme is
illustrated by Leuconostoc mesenteroides , strain P-60,
which requires 17 amino acids for the intracellular enzymic
synthesis of protein. Unfortunately, although evidence regarding true microbial in vivo protein synthesis via amino
acids has been obtained in few specific instances, there are
too many questions still unresolved to offer a dogmatic
statement regarding the course of protein synthesis in a
dynamic heterogeneous substrate such as sewage which also
contains numerous and fluctuating types and numbers of
microbes. Thus, for example, while there is still doubt

that microbial ribosomes alone are responsible for peptide
bond formation and synthesis of soluble protein, difficulties
in translating in vitro incorporation of amino acids into
ribosomes to the synthesis of protein in vivo further indicate
that the understanding of protein synthesis as a whole is still
in its infancy. Thus for example, amino acid incorporation
into ribosomes in vitro represents about 1 per cent of the
synthesis of protein in vivo. Similarly, how deoxyribonucleic
acid is involved in the synthesis of bacterial enzymes is not
as yet completely clear; much concerning the induction and
repression action on enzyme synthesis remains a mystery.
At the present time, it is difficult to state dogmatically that
there is necessarily one correct series of reactions or one
path of protein biosynthesis, especially since there are some,
let us say, minority reports which tend to throw some doubt
on the absolute necessity for activating enzymes or soluble
ribonucleic acid in synthetic systems, or which indicate the
possibility of alternative mechanisms involving lipid materials.

Understandably, much more knowledge is at hand regarding the hydrolysis of proteins and peptides. Recent
advances in the purification and crystallization of microbial
proteolytic enzymes have provided useful information concerning these reactions. In this connection, reference can
be made to the presence of two kinds of extracellular proteases
elaborated by Bacillus subtilis; one a neutral protease,
optimum activity at pH 7.0, and the other an alkaline protease,
optimum pH 10.5 (21). Crystalline proteases have been
obtained from B. subtilis, B. amyloliquefaciens, B. natto
and B. mesentericus (22, 23, 24, 25). Purified or crystalline
proteases have also been isolated from liquors of Streptococcus,
Pseudomonas fluorescens, Pseudomonas aeruginosa,
Pseudomonas myxogenes, Clostridium and Streptomyces
(26, 27, 28, 29, 30).

Aspergillus proteases, as well as those obtained from
B. subtilis have been produced on a commercial scale.
Actually the aspergilli have been reported as capable of
producing three kinds of proteolytic enzymes having optimum
activity at acidic, neutral and alkaline pH (31).

CONCLUSIONS

The superabundantly varied microbial flora present in
wastes and sewage strikingly illustrates the tremendous
range of the nutritional requirements of microorganisms.

This encompasses the autotrophic microorganisms (requiring only water, carbon dioxide and appropriate inorganic salts) to the heterotrophic bacteria which can assimilate carbon dioxide to only a limited extent but which require organic compounds for growth. The nutritional requirements of the heterotrophic microorganisms may be as simple as those of Escherichia coli, which can effectively utilize inorganic salts (ammonia) and glucose, to Sepedonium, which cannot utilize the nitrogen of ammonia, nitrate, lysine, or asparagine for growth but requires peptone as a source of nitrogen.

Understandably, the total enzyme complex of the heterotrophic organism which is necessary to oxidize or synthesize the aforementioned range of nitrogen compounds will vary from microorganism to microorganism. Although the work of many investigators has been cited in this connection, there is clearly much more work to be done before the mechanism of protein synthesis is understood. With the crystallization of many proteases, information is accumulating at an accelerated pace such that the understanding of the sequence of synthesis and hydrolysis of nitrogenous compounds may be at hand in the near future.

LITERATURE CITED

1.   Spector, W. S., ed. 1956. Handbook of Biological Data, W. B. Saunders Co., Philadelphia, p. 242.
2.   Ingram, W. T. 1958. ASTIA Document No. AD 162 277, Contract AF 18 (603) - 71. Air Force Research and Development Command, U.S. Air Force, Washington, D. C.
3.   Heukelekian, H. and J. L. Balmat. 1959. Sew. Ind. Wastes, 31:413-423.
4.   Placak, O. R. and C. C. Ruchhoft. 1947. Sew. Works J. 19:423-440.
5.   Wuhrmann, K. 1949. Verhandl. intern. Ver. theoret. angew. Limnol. 10:580-6; Biol. Abstrs. 27:677 (1953).
6.   Wuhrmann, K. 1954. Sew. Ind. Wastes, 26:1-27.
7.   Subrahmanyam, P. V. R. , C.A. Sastry, A. V.S. P. Rao, and S. C. Pillai. 1960. J. Water Poll. Contr. Fed. 32:344-350.
8.   Gaub, W. H., Jr. 1924. N. J. Agric. Exptl. Sta. Bull. 394, pp. 3-24.
9.   Haenseler, C. M., W. D. Moore and J. G. Gaines. 1923. N. J. Agric. Exptl. Sta. Bull. 390, pp. 39-48.

10. Rudolfs, W. and H. A. Trajkovich. 1924. N. J. Agric. Exptl. Sta. Bull. 403, pp. 84-88.

11. Tomlinson, T. G. 1942. J. Soc. Chem. Ind. 61:53-58.

12. Painter, H. A. 1954. J. Gen. Microbiol. 10:177-190.

13. McKinney, R. E. and M. P. Horwood. 1952. Sew. Ind. Wastes, 24:117-123.

14. Calaway, W. T., W. R. Carroll and S. K. Long. 1952. Sew. Ind. Wastes, 24:642-653.

15. Ringen, L. M. and C. H. Drake. 1952. J. Bacteriol. 64:841-845.

16. Jasewicz, L. and N. Porges. 1956. Sew. Ind. Wastes. 28:1130-1136.

17. Keefer, C. E., T. C. Buck, Jr., and H. Hatch. 1954. Sew. Ind. Wastes 26:164-170.

18. Wattie, E. 1943. Sew. Works Journal 15:476-490.

19. Hagihara, B., M. Nakai, H. Matsubara, T. Komaki, T. Yonetani, and K. Okuniki. 1958. J. Biochem. (Tokyo), 45:305-311.

20. Nomoto, M., Y. Narahashi, and J. Murakami. 1959. Symposia on Enzyme Chem. Japan, 11, 103.

21. Hagihara, B., M. Nakai, H. Matsubara, T. Komaki, T. Yonetani and K. Okunuki. 1958. J. Biochem. (Tokyo), 45:305-311.

22. Güntelberg, A. V. and M. Ottesen. 1952. Nature 170, 802.

23. Fukumoto, J. and H. Negoro. 1951. Proc. Japan Acad. 27:441-444.

24. Miyake, S. and J. Shimizu. 1953. Sci. Repts. Hyogo Univ. Agr. Ser. Agr. Chem. Ed. 1:11-14.

25. Miyake, S., Y. Hamaguchi, and K. Takahashi. 1954. J. Japanese Biochem. Soc. 26, 105.

26. Elliot, S. D. 1950. J. Exptl. Med. 92:201-218.

27. Virtanen, A. I. and U. Kokkola. 1950. Acta Chem. Scand. 4:64-71.

28. Morihara, K. 1957. Bull. Agric. Chem. Soc. Japan 21:11-17.

29. Maschmann, E. 1937. Biochem. Z., 294:1-33.

30. Simon, S. 1955. Acta Microbiol. Acad. Sci. Hung. 3:53-65.

31. Motsushima, K. 1958. J. Ferm. Technol. 36:414-419.

32. Castaneda-Agulló, M. 1956. J. Gen. Physiol. 39:369-375.

33. Fukumoto, J., T. Yamamoto, D. Tsuru, and K. Ichikawa

1957. Proc. Intern. Symp. Enzyme Chem. Tokyo and
Kyoto 479-482.
34. Haines, R. B. 1931. Biochem. J., 25:1851-1859.
35. Tomlinson, T. G. 1942. J. Soc. Chem. Ind. 61:53-58.
36. Tomlinson, T. G. 1950. J. Inst. Sewage Purif. Part
4, 338-355.

DISCUSSION

Dr. D. Pramer (Rutgers Univ.): When an organism
provided with ammonium nitrogen fails to grow, but will grow
when given organic nitrogen in the form of casein hydrolysate
or peptone, can one conclude that it cannot utilize ammonium
nitrogen as a source of nitrogen and that it has a requirement
of organic nitrogen for growth? Is it not likely that, in the
case where the organism develops only when given an organic
nitrogen supplement, that it can use ammonium nitrogen
obtained by deamination but it also has a specific requirement
for the amino acid present in the complex supplement?

Dr. Green: Whether the microorganism has to incorporate
actively a specific amino acid into its amino acid pool, or
whether the microorganism breaks down the amino acid to
ammonia and then incorporates it into the protoplasm, we
do not know. It seems implausible, at times, to think that
the amino acid is not broken down to ammonia but, of course,
it can be incorporated into the amino acid pool. We have no
data in this connection. All we can do is report what we
found in the literature. We have done no work with nitrogen
in that connection.

22

RESEARCH IN AQUATIC MICROBIOLOGY: TRENDS AND NEEDS

H. Heukelekian and Norman C. Dondero
Department of Environmental Science
Rutgers — The State University

For the purposes of this discussion, the field of aquatic microbiology is considered to be the study of microorganisms, and the chemical transformations caused by these organisms, in bodies of water or in circumstances which might affect the quality of the water.

Types of water reasonably include seas, estuaries, rivers, springs, lakes, and ground waters, but there are, in addition to these naturally occurring bodies of water such artificially created counterparts as reservoirs, wells, water mains, sewers, waste-water treatment plants, oxidation lagoons, cooling towers, and other means by which man diverts water for his more convenient use. These natural and artificial situations have some common, basic, biological, physical and chemical characteristics, and some differences, which, although they may be extreme, appear from limited information, more quantitative than qualitative.

Man's increasing use of water for domestic, industrial, agricultural, and recreational purposes poses problems: on the one hand, for instance, the problem of the nuisances attendant on pollution and eutrophication which result when the assimilation capacity of natural waters for wastes is exceeded; on the other hand, the problem of the disturbance of natural equilibria that results when natural waters are diverted to artificial uses, for instance the fouling of surfaces of pipes, condensers, and cooling towers, the solution or deposition through biological agencies of iron or manganese, and corrosion.

An increase in industrial and agricultural activity has
intensified the reuse of water, and much, if not all, reused
water may be regarded, in a technical sense, as polluted,
in that one use of water is likely to alter it detrimentally for
a subsequent use. Just how important is this effect of water
reuse on individuals, industry, and the water environment
can be illustrated by the following examples.

Gloyna et al. (1963) estimated that in 1963, of 180 million
people in the United States, 70 million were using water from
sources already used once for domestic sewage and industrial
waste disposal, and that the expected future concentration of
population in urban centers would probably tend to increase
the practice of reuse of receiving waters.

Scott (1963) quoted estimates made by Picton that, in the
United States in 1970, total water use will amount to more
than 4×10^{11} gallons per day. This figure includes reused
sewage effluents and brackish waters as well as fresh waters,
and total use includes industrial and agricultural as well as
domestic uses.

After use, this water (except for evaporation losses) will
again mingle with that of lakes and rivers, and some will also
enter the ground water. To comprehend the magnitude of these
figures, let us compare Picton's estimate of 1970 total daily
use in the United States of 4×10^{11} gallons with Leopold's
(1962) estimate of the average daily total river runoff in the
United States of 1.4×10^{11} gallons. Because some river
water will escape to the sea, a simple calculation that the
water will be used twice yields a figure that is too conservative.
Further comparison of the water-use figure with Leopold's
data for the discharge of major rivers reveals that the future
daily water requirement will be about seven times the combined
average daily discharge of the Amazon, Mississippi, St.
Lawrence, and Columbia Rivers, which drain a total area of
4.2×10^6 square miles.

Large metropolitan areas consume a large volume of water
and produce large amounts of sewage. The city of New York,
for example, uses approximately 1.2×10^9 gallons of drinking
water per day. This amount plus ground water and water from
industrial wells reaches the sewers to give a total sewage flow
of about 1.3×10^9 gallons per day (W.N. Torpey, personal
communication). The daily sewage flow for the Metropolitan
Sanitary District of Greater Chicago attains approximately the
same value (A. J. Kaplovsky, personal communication).

With an increasing pollution of both fresh and salt water
as industrialization and agriculture expand, and with the increase in demand for more water for utilitarian and recreational purposes as populations rapidly increase, it becomes
more and more necessary to think in terms water "manage -
ment". Management, in this sense, has two aspects: (1)
the preservation of desired qualities by the prevention of
degradation, and (2) the production of the desired qualities
from substandard water. The biological factor, and particularly the microbiological factor, enters into the series of
causes and effects which affect the quality of water and its
uses. For water management to achieve the highest degree
of success, a clear understanding of the scientific principles
involved is a first consideration.

In this discussion, our attention will focus principally
upon the bacteria, although, by implication, the protozoa,
fungi, and actinomycetes, are included. Marine microbiology
and epidemiology are not specifically included. We shall
also deal with some of the general but less-explored areas.
Although there has been a long-standing interest in the microbiology of fresh waters and sewage, research interest has been
largely directed to the necessities of public health and of
waste water treatment, leaving other important areas in these
general fields much less well explored.

In limnology, hydrobiology and chemistry have received
the lion's share of the attention, and most of the microbiology
has centered on the algae, dealing primarily with productivity,
distribution, and taxonomy. In recent years, however, emphasis on the nutrition and physiology of the algae (Provasoli, 1958)
has greatly increased. The water bacteria, themselves, have
received relatively little more than tacit recognition, although
the chemical conversions which they mediate, at least in part,
have been better studied.

Similarly, in waste treatment the greatest interest hitherto
has been in conversions of organic matter in general, with
some attention to the specific types of compounds entering and
resulting from the treatment processes. Except in the most
recent years, in comparison with the emphasis placed on
manipulatory variables, such as temperature, detention time,
and loading, little attention has been given to the intermediate
conversions and the organisms concerned. These considerations have led to progress in technology and will continue to
do so. Progress in this area, however, is not an end in itself,

but rather an invitation to impose further stresses on the
technology of purification processes. In water management
there is considerable empiricism to be overcome.

It is generally acknowledged that many of the processes
that operate in waste water treatment are similar to those
that operate in the self-purification of streams and lakes.
The conditions imposed by nature in natural bodies of water
are, however, much more varied and subtle than those that
man is able consciously to impose in artificial waste treatment.
The study of the effects of waste pollution in nature can
nevertheless be expected to reveal principles which may be
applied with advantage to waste water treatment and water
management. Conversely, because of their manipulative and
control features, waste treatment practices can help us
understand, in a limited way, some natural situations. Thus,
the subjects of the microbial ecology of pure waters, of
polluted waters, and of waste water treatment are complementary parts of a whole study area, or they represent at
least, broadly overlapping areas.

One of the largest and, perhaps, most obvious deficiencies
in our knowledge concerns the composition of the bacterial
plankton, the bacterial periphyton, and the benthic bacteria,
and the specific biochemical roles of the species concerned.
Similarly, we know little of the species active in waste water
treatment, or of their roles and the environmental conditions
which dictate the establishment of species. Some habitats--
activated sludge, sewage filter slime, the stream periphyton,
beach flora, among others — especially deserve more investigation. Some of the microorganisms that inhabit these
niches are microscopically identifiable but not many of them
are, as yet, readily cultivated and little of value is, thus,
known about them.

Slide studies (Henrici, 1933; Henrici and Johnson, 1935),
and the work of Taylor (1940, 1942) and of others, provide
morphological and statistical evidence that strongly suggest
the existence of an autochthonous (perhaps more literally in
this case, autolimnetic) flora of lakes and ponds. Conventional culture media may not be sufficiently productive
to support many species of this flora simultaneously. Fuller
knowledge of the nutrition and physiology of these organisms
would undoubtedly allow some of them to be used as indicators
of the biochemical state of the environment, but the first
steps along these lines will have to be some form of culti-

vation. In their own right also, many of these bacteria offer intriguing possibilities for the study of morphogenesis.

A subject of not only long-standing but considerable recent interest is the ability of microbial populations to adapt to changing conditions. The concept of the adaptation of a population is, according to modern views, a complicated one, involving not only adjustments at the species level in response to chemical or physical changes in the environment, but also reactions at cellular and molecular levels. There are still questions about the survival of microorganisms in water. In a series of papers beginning in 1959, Carlucci and Pramer reopened the subject of the fate of Escherichia coli in sea water and showed that the situation was complex. Burke and Baird (1931; Burke, 1934) showed that some bacteria could survive on transfer from saline to fresh water and vice versa. Pengra and Wilson (1958) reported that Aerobacter aerogenes is able to fix atmospheric nitrogen. Hedrick et al.(1960) and Noble (1960) noted that Lake Michigan water was toxic for enteric bacteria.

In view of the exceptional adaptability and physiological potential of the organisms of the coliform group, it would seem that it is time to assess more definitely their physiology in relation to the survival and activity of these organisms apart from the intestinal tract, especially in water.

McKinney et al. (1958) have shown that one of the factors in the disappearance of Salmonella typhosa in anaerobic digesters is the inability to compete successfully with other microorganisms for combined tryptophan. This finding supplies a positive, specific explanation in place of hypothetical explanation of inability to compete for food, destruction by bacteriophage, or other factors.

The ability of a mixed population of microorganisms to adjust to shifting environmental conditions was demonstrated by Jasewicz and Porges (1956), who showed that the species composition of an activated sludge in the assimilation phase was quite different from the sludge in the endogenous phase. Somewhat in contrast to this, although the experimental material was not exactly comparable, were findings which implied that the species composition was constant, and that activated sludges could make intracellular adjustments without population shifts when the nutrients which were being fed were changed. McKinney et al. (1956) extended the concept of simultaneous enzyme adaptation to activated sludge, and Gaudy (1962; Gaudy

et al. 1963) reported enzyme induction and repression in
activated sludge.

Nutritional conditions are obviously of great importance
as determining factors in respect to what species will prevail
at a given time. Similarly, certain species may modify the
environment in the nutritional sense, as for example in the
benthic environment and in anaerobic sludge digestion certain
bacteria convert insoluble organic matter into compounds
available for the methane-forming bacteria.

The more general use of isotope tracer techniques is
desirable. The use, for instance, of radioisotopes as tracers
in the study of rumen metabolism should have its counterpart
in the study of benthic decomposition of organic matter and
in the anaerobic digestion of sewage sludges. Methodology in
the study of the rumen has, in fact, made strides worthy of
emulation in aquatic microbiology. Work with radioactive
phosphorus (e.g., Hayes and Phillips, 1958) indicates that the
bacterial flora of waters turns over nutrients rapidly and is
of great importance in the nutrient cycles of waters.

The positions of phosphorus, carbon, and nitrogen as
essential elements are well understood in the development
of microbial populations, especially of algae. It seems, however, that certain specific organic molecules can act as
limiting growth factors in the aquatic environment. Provasoli
(1958) has reviewed the effects of thiamine, biotin, and
vitamin B_{12}. In the interplay of production and demand of
these substances in natural habitats and waste treatment processes, the fates of species are determined (Collier, 1958).
Vitamin B_{12} is produced under certain conditions in significant quantities in water (Burkholder and Burkholder 1956,
1958), activated sludge (Hoover, et al. 1951), and anaerobic
sludge digesters (Neujahr, 1955).

The general level of nutrients in artificial culture media
routinely used in the laboratory is very high(biochemical
oxygen demand equal to about 2000 to 7000 mg per liter) in
contrast with sewage (about 100 to 300 mg per liter BOD) and
unpolluted natural waters, which have comparatively little
or no oxygen demand. The cellular economy and physiology
of microorganisms able to survive and reproduce at the extremely low nutrient levels in water would be of interest.
Gaudy's studies of enzyme induction and repression were made
on bacteria grown in media much more concentrated than
sewage, but possibly the induction and repression would not

be typical of less well-nourished bacteria. Amberg (Washington Pollution Control Commission, et al. 1958) showed
that the existence of a current is necessary for Sphaerotilus
to thrive in competition with the mixed population of microorganisms present in streams and artificial channels, and
that the current is the agency which brings the required
quantity of food, although the concentration may be very low.
It has also been known for some time that submerged surfaces
concentrate nutrients from the water and that these surfaces
are physical substrates for attachment of the periphyton
(ZoBell and Anderson, 1936; Heukelekian and Heller, 1940).

It has been an old belief that the bacteria in water are
starving and debilitated organisms (e.g. Ward, 1897; Fuller
and Johnson, 1899). Taylor's (1940; 1942) data indicated
that on the other hand, in addition to the declining bacteria,
there may indeed be an autochthonous flora of lakes and ponds
which, in the aggregate, appears to be different in composition
from that washed in from the soil. The general lack of response
of water bacteria to conventional media and the usual microbiological techniques may explain why workers have been more
inclined to deal with the more active heterotrophs of sewage
and water. As might be expected, there also is some evidence
that the predominant species in sewage differ from those of
lakes. Allen (1944) obtained the highest plate counts from
sewage on nutrient agar, whereas others have reported the
highest plate counts from lake water on sodium caseinate agar
(Fred et al. 1924; Henrici, 1938).

Regarding both laboratory and field studies, culture media
and methods require improvement -- culture media to give
improved yields and greater variety of water organisms; and
methods to improve the ease of sample collection, preservation
of samples, and of culturing the organisms. No doubt the few
studies of bacterial distribution in lakes and rivers is a reflection of the extreme expense and difficulty of sampling and
examination, particularly since, in order to have much ecological significance, long-term programs are desirable.

In contrast to the broader programs mentioned above, there
are also benefits to be gained from the studies of particular
genera or species, in that studies of this type, which are more
manageable, can lead to more concentrated and perhaps more
intelligible results.

The genus Vibrio is challenging because of its ubiquity and
continuous range of types, from free-living aquatic forms to

pathogens.   The genus Pseudomonas is similar in this respect.

The ecology of the Azotobacter-Beijerinckia groups in water should be revealing in regard to the nitrogen economy and to the oxidation of organic material. We are unaware of extensive work on the association of nitrogen-fixing bacteria with aquatic plants, although ZoBell (1946) mentions instances of Azotobacter on the surface of the large marine algae. Microscopic examination of fresh water filamentous algae often reveals myriads of bacteria growing in close contact with the surfaces of the algal cells.

The genus Bacillus possesses properties which would seemingly fit its members for survival and attack on organic matter in water and sewage.   Jasewicz and Porges (1956) working on dairy waste treatment, found a remarkably e- phemeral appearance of Bacillus sp. in the assimilative stage of their activated sludge and a decline in the endogenous phase. The role of these bacteria in polluted waters should be an important one; if it is not, then the reason why it is not should be important.

An intriguing and potentially important member of the microflora of soil and sewage was reported by Stolp and Starr (1963). They studied a small vibrio which attached to sus- ceptible, living bacterial cells and caused their lysis. On agar plates covered with a lawn of susceptible bacteria, the capability of the predator, Bdellovibrio bacteriovorus, of lysing the prey cells was manifested by cleared plaques simi- lar to those produced by bacteriophage. The degree of activity in nature and its ecological importance is, as yet, unknown.

To add another, but by no means final, example to the list in spite of the work of Barker and many others, there remains much to be done on the methane-forming bacteria, on their physiology and on their place in water, sewage, and soil.

In concluding, we do not wish to imply that all the areas of potentially fruitful activity have been noted in this discussion. One has but to turn to the old volumes of the Centralblatt to find suggestions and unanswered questions associated with aquatic microbiology.   One might find, for example, that the reports on the spirilla seem to have radically declined in number since nutrient gelatin was abandoned as a routine medium for the examination of water. The utilization of new techniques and new concepts on old questions, however, need not be the sole incentive for the encouragement of aquatic microbiology. With the constant and increasing introduction of complex synthetic chemicals and radioactive materials to the aquatic environment from air, soil, and industry, and with the knowledge that bacteria are primary agents in the turnover of metabolizable materials in water, and in the mobilization, concentration, and precipitation of certain minerals, microbial ecology and, particularly aquatic ecology has an extremely practical side. At this point it is obvious that when basic scientific principles can be derived, the differences between the so-called academic and the applied phases of the science are not very great.

ACKNOWLEDGMENT

Paper of the Journal Series, New Jersey Agricultural Experiment Station, Rutgers, the State University of New Jersey, Department of Environmental Science, New Brunswick, New Jersey. This paper contains some modifications from a paper, Trends and Needs of Research in Aquatic Microbiology, submitted to the Congress, Global Aspects of Applied Microbiology, Stockholm, 1963.

LITERATURE CITED

Allen, L. 1944. The bacteriology of activated sludge. J. Hyg. 43:424-431.

Burke, V. and L. Baird. 1931. Fate of fresh water bacteria in the sea. J. Bact. 21:287-298.

Burke, V. 1934. Interchange of bacteria between the fresh water and the sea. J. Bact. 27:201-205.

Burkholder, P. and L. Burkholder. 1956. Vitamin B_{12} in suspended solids and marsh muds collected along the coast of Georgia. Limnol. and Oceanogr. 1:202-208.

Burkholder, P. and L. Burkholder. 1958. Studies on B. vitamins in relation to productivity of the Bahia Fosforescente, Puerto Rico. Bull. Mar. Sci. Gulf and Caribbean, 8:201-223.

Carlucci, A. and D. Pramer. 1959. Factors affecting the survival of bacteria in sea water. Appl. Microbiol. 7:388-392.

Carlucci, A. and D. Pramer. 1960. An evaluation of factors affecting the survival of Escherichia coli in sea water. I. Experimental procedures. Appl. Microbiol. 8:243-247.

Carlucci, A. and D. Pramer. 1960. An evaluation of factors affecting the survival of Escherichia coli in sea water. II.

Salinity, pH, and nutrients. Appl. Microbiol. 8:247-250.

Carlucci, A. and D. Pramer, 1960. An evaluation of factors affecting the survival of Escherichia coli in sea water. III. Antibiotics. Appl. Microbiol. 8:251-254.

Carlucci, A. and D. Pramer. 1960. An evaluation of factors affecting the survival of Escherichia coli in sea water. IV. Bacteriophages. Appl. Microbiol. 8:254-256.

Carlucci, A., P. Scarpino and D. Pramer. 1961. Evaluation of factors affecting survival of Escherichia coli in sea water. V. Studies with heat- and filter-sterilized sea water. Appl. Microbiol. 9:400-404.

Collier, A. 1958. Some biochemical aspects of red tides and related oceanographic problems. Limnol. and Oceanogr. 3:33-39.

Fred, E., F. Wilson and A. Davenport. 1924. Distribution and significance of bacteria in Lake Mendota. Ecology. 5: 322-339.

Fuller, G. and G. Johnson. 1899. On the differentiation of water bacteria. Jour. Exp. Med. 4:609-628.

Gaudy, A. 1962. Studies on induction and repression in activated sludge systems. Appl. Microbiol. 10:264-271.

Gaudy, A., E. Gaudy and K. Komolrit. 1963. Multicomponent substrate utilization by natural populations and a pure culture of Escherichia coli. Appl. Microbiol. 11:157-162.

Gloyna, E., J. Wolff, J. Geyer and A. Wolman. 1960. A report upon the present and prospective means for improved reuse of water. pp. 1-54. Committee print No. 30. Select Committee on National Water Resources, U.S. Senate. United States Govt. Printing Office, Washington, D.C.

Hayes, F. and J. Phillips. 1958. Lake water and sediment. IV. Radiophosphorus equilibrium with mud, plants, and bacteria under oxidized and reduced conditions. Limnol. and Oceanogr. 3:459-475.

Hedrick, L., R. Meyer, M. Kossoy and M. Sutherland. 1960. Viability of E. coli and related pathogens when stored in filtered Lake Michigan water. Bact. Proc. 1960. A 24, p. 35.

Henrici, A. 1933. Studies of freshwater bacteria. I. A. direct microscopic technique. J. Bact. 25:277-287.

Henrici, A. 1938. Studies of freshwater bacteria. IV Seasonal fluctuations of lake bacteria in relation to plankton production. J. Bact. 35:127-139.

Henrici, A. and D. Johnson. 1935. Studies of freshwater

bacteria. II. Stalked bacteria, a new order of schizomycetes. J. Bact. 30:61-95.

Heukelekian, J. and A. Heller. 1940. Relation between food concentration and surface for bacterial growth. J. Bact. 40:547-558.

Hoover, A., L. Jasewicz and N. Porges. 1951. Vitamin B_{12} in activated sewage sludge. Science 114:213.

Jasewicz, L. and N. Porges. 1956. Biochemical oxidation of dairy wastes. VI. Isolation and study of sludge microorganisms. Sew. and Ind. Wastes. 28:1130-1136.

Leopold, L. 1962. Rivers. American Scientist 50:511-537.

McKinney, R., H. Tomlinson and R. Wilcox. 1956. Metabolism of aromatic compounds by activated sludge. Sew. and Ind. Wastes. 28:547-557.

McKinney, R., H. Langley and H. Tomlinson. 1958. Survival of Salmonella typhosa during anaerobic digestion. I. Experimental methods and high-rate digester studies. Sew. and Ind. Wastes. 30:1469-1477.

Neujahr, H. 1955. On vitamins in sewage sludge II. Formation of vitamin B_{12}, folic acid, and folinic acid factors in municipal sludge. Acta Chem. Scand. 9:622-630.

Pengra, R. and P. Wilson. 1958. Physiology of nitrogen fixation by Aerobacter aerogenes. J. Bact. 75:21-25.

Provasoli, L. 1958. Nutrition and ecology of protozoa and algae. Ann. Rev. Microbiol. 12:279-308.

Scott, G. 1963. The consulting engineer's role in water resources. Proc. 2nd Ann. San. Eng. Conf. Vanderbilt Univ. Nashville, Tenn. pp. 6-13.

Stolp, H. and M. Starr. 1963. Bdellovibrio bacteriovorus gen. et sp. n., a predatory, ectoparasitic, and bacteriolytic microorganism. Antonie van Leeuwenhoek 29:217-248.

Taylor, C. 1940. Bacteriology of fresh water. I. Distribution of bacteria in English lakes. J. Hyg. 40:616-640.

Taylor, C. 1942. Bacteriology of fresh water. III. The types of bacteria present in lakes and streams and their relationship to the bacterial flora of soil. J. Hyg. 42:284-296.

Ward, H. M. 1897. Fifth report to the Royal Society Water Research Committee. Proc. Roy. Soc. London 61:415-423.

Washington Pollution Control Commission and Crown Zellerbach Corp. 1958. Columbia River Study 1956-1958 Progress Report. Crown Zellerbach Corp. Camas Mill Div. pp. 1-61.

ZoBell, C. and D. Anderson. 1936. Observations on the
    multiplication of bacteria in different volumes of stored
    sea water and the influence of oxygen tension and solid
    surfaces. Biol. Bull. 71:324-342.
ZoBell, C. 1946. Marine Microbiology. 240 pp. Chronica
    Botanica Co., Waltham, Mass.